**Interactive
Practice Book** *ei*

Teacher's Annotated Edition

Hampton-Brown

EDGE

Reading, Writing & Language

NATIONAL GEOGRAPHIC LEARNING | CENGAGE Learning

Acknowledgments

Grateful acknowledgment is given to the authors, artists, photographers, museums, publishers, and agents for permission to reprint copyrighted material. Every effort has been made to secure the appropriate permission. If any omissions have been made or if corrections are required, please contact the Publisher.

Photographic Credits

Cover: Ancient Eye, Arches National Park, Utah, USA, Marsel van Oosten. Photograph © Marsel van Oosten/ squiver.com.

Acknowledgments continue on page Ack 1.

For product information and technology asistance, contact us at
Cengage Learning Customer & Sales Support, 1-800-354-9706

For permission to use material from this text or product, submit all requests online at **www.cengage.com/permissions**
Further permissions questions can be emailed to
permissionrequest@cengage.com

National Geographic Learning | Cengage Learning
1 Lower Ragsdale Drive
Building 1, Suite 200
Monterey, CA 93940

Cengage Learning is a leading provider of customized learning solutions with office locations around the globe, including Singapore, the United Kingdom, Australia, Mexico, Brazil, and Japan. Locate your local office at **www.cengage.com/global**.

Visit National Geographic Learning online at **ngl.cengage.com**
Visit our corporate website at **www.cengage.com**

Printed in the USA.
RR Donnelley, Menasha, WI

ISBN: 978-12854-43454 (Practice Book)
ISBN: 978-12854-43492 (Practice Book Teacher's Annotated Edition)

Printed in the United States of America
13 14 15 16 17 18 19 20 21 22
10 9 8 7 6 5 4 3 2 1

▶ **The Moustache; Who We Really Are**

    Prepare to Read: Key Vocabulary **6**

    Before Reading: *The Moustache* **8**

        Literary Analysis: *Analyze Conflict*
        Focus Strategy: *Make and Confirm Predictions*

       ▶ **Interact with the Text:** *Who We Really Are* **11**

        Literary Analysis: *Analyze Structure: News Feature*
        Focus Strategy: *Preview and Set a Purpose*

    Reflect and Assess **15**

        Writing: *Write About Literature*

    Integrate the Language Arts **16**

        Literary Analysis: *Analyze Setting*
        Vocabulary Study: *Prefixes*

▶ **Two Kinds; Novel Musician**

    Prepare to Read: Key Vocabulary **18**

    Before Reading: *Two Kinds* **20**

        Literary Analysis: *Analyze Protagonist and Antagonist*
        Focus Strategy: *Clarify Ideas*

       ▶ **Interact with the Text:** *Novel Musician* **23**

        Literary Analysis: *Analyze Structure: Profile*
        Focus Strategy: *Clarify Ideas*

    Reflect and Assess **27**

        Writing: *Write About Literature*

    Integrate the Language Arts **28**

        Literary Analysis: *Analyze Characters and Plot*
        Vocabulary Study: *Suffixes*

▶ **Skins; Nicole**

    Prepare to Read: Key Vocabulary **30**

    Before Reading: *Skins* **32**

        Literary Analysis: *Analyze Character and Theme*
        Focus Strategy: *Clarify Vocabulary*

       ▶ **Interact with the Text:** *Nicole* **35**

        Literary Analysis: *Determine Viewpoint*
        Focus Strategy: *Clarify Vocabulary*

    Reflect and Assess **39**

        Writing: *Write About Literature*

    Integrate the Language Arts **40**

        Literary Analysis: *Characters (Static and Dynamic)*
        Vocabulary Study: *Greek and Latin Roots*

▶ **Yes**

    Close Reading **42**

        Literary Analysis: *Analyze Character and Plot*
        Writing: *Write About Characters and Conflicts*

▶ **Unit Review**

    Key Vocabulary **46**

Unit 2

▶ **La Vida Robot; Reading, Writing, and...Recreation?**

    Prepare to Read: Key Vocabulary **48**

    Before Reading: *La Vida Robot* **50**

        Literary Analysis: *Analyze Nonfiction Text Features*
        Focus Strategy: *Identify Main Ideas and Details*

        ▶ **Interact with the Text:** *Reading, Writing, and...Recreation?* **54**

        Literary Analysis: *Analyze Development of Ideas*
        Focus Strategy: *Relate Main Ideas and Details*

    Reflect and Assess **57**

        Writing: *Write About Literature*

    Integrate the Language Arts **58**

        Literary Analysis: *Analogy and Allusion*
        Vocabulary Study: *Context Clues (Definitions)*

▶ **My Left Foot; Success Is a Mind-Set**

    Prepare to Read: Key Vocabulary **60**

    Before Reading: *My Left Foot* **62**

        Literary Analysis: *Analyze Development of Ideas*
        Focus Strategy: *Summarize*

        ▶ **Interact with the Text:** *Success Is a Mind-Set* **66**

        Literary Analysis: *Relate Ideas*
        Focus Strategy: *Summarize*

    Reflect and Assess **71**

        Writing: *Write About Literature*

    Integrate the Language Arts **72**

        Literary Analysis: *Author's Purpose, Text Structure, and Point of View*
        Vocabulary Study: *Context Clues (Multiple-Meaning Words)*

▶ **The Freedom Writers Diary; Strength, Courage, and Wisdom**

    Prepare to Read: Key Vocabulary **74**

    Before Reading: *The Freedom Writers Diary* **76**

        Literary Analysis: *Relate Ideas*
        Focus Strategy: *Determine What's Important*

        ▶ **Interact with the Text:** *Strength, Courage, and Wisdom* **79**

        Literary Analysis: *Analyze Style: Word Choice*
        Focus Strategy: *Determine What's Important*

    Reflect and Assess **81**

        Writing: *Write About Literature*

    Integrate the Language Arts **82**

        Literary Analysis: *Analyze Point of View*
        Vocabulary Study: *Context Clues: Examples*

▶ **The Cruelest Journey**

    Close Reading **84**

        Literary Analysis: *Analyze Nonfiction Text Features; Analyze Development of Ideas;*
        Relate Ideas
        Writing: *Write About Viewpoint*

▶ **Unit Review**

    Key Vocabulary **90**

▶ **Amigo Brothers; Lean on Me**

    Prepare to Read: Key Vocabulary **92**

    Before Reading: *Amigo Brothers* **94**

        Literary Analysis: *Analyze Style: Language*
        Focus Strategy: *Make Inferences*

      ▶ **Interact with the Text:** *Lean on Me* **98**

        Literary Analysis: *Analyze Structure: Rhyme Scheme*
        Focus Strategy: *Make Inferences*

    Reflect and Assess **101**

        Writing: *Write About Literature*

    Integrate the Language Arts **102**

        Literary Analysis: *Word Choice in Description*
        Vocabulary Study: *Word Families*

▶ **My Brother's Keeper; What Price Loyalty?**

    Prepare to Read: Key Vocabulary **104**

    Before Reading: *My Brother's Keeper* **106**

        Literary Analysis: *Analyze Style: Sentence Structure*
        Focus Strategy: *Make Inferences*

      ▶ **Interact with the Text:** *What Price Loyalty?* **110**

        Literary Analysis: *Determine Viewpoint*
        Focus Strategy: *Make Inferences*

    Reflect and Assess **113**

        Writing: *Write About Literature*

    Integrate the Language Arts **114**

        Literary Analysis: *Analyze Style and Theme*
        Vocabulary Study: *Word Families*

▶ **The Hand of Fatima; Old Ways, New World**

    Prepare to Read: Key Vocabulary **116**

    Before Reading: *The Hand of Fatima* **118**

        Literary Analysis: *Analyze Viewpoint*
        Focus Strategy: *Make Inferences*

      ▶ **Interact with the Text:** *Old Ways, New World* **121**

        Literary Analysis: *Determine Viewpoint*
        Focus Strategy: *Make Inferences*

    Reflect and Assess **125**

        Writing: *Write About Literature*

    Integrate the Language Arts **126**

        Literary Analysis: *Symbolism*
        Vocabulary Study: *Word Families*

▶ **Anthem**

    Close Reading **128**

        Literary Analysis: *Analyze Style: Language; Analyze Style: Sentence Structure*
        Writing: *Write About Style*

▶ **Unit Review**

    Key Vocabulary **134**

Unit 4

▶ **Face Facts: The Science of Facial Expressions; Silent Language**

Prepare to Read: Key Vocabulary **136**

Before Reading: *Face Facts: The Science of Facial Expressions* **138**
  Literary Analysis: *Analyze Text Structure: Cause and Effect*
  Focus Strategy: *Self-Question*

▶ **Interact with the Text:** *Silent Language* **141**
  Literary Analysis: *Analyze Text Structure: Problem and Solution*
  Focus Strategy: *Self-Question*

Reflect and Assess **147**
  Writing: *Write About Literature*

Integrate the Language Arts **148**
  Literary Analysis: *Literary Paradox*
  Vocabulary Study: *Multiple-Meaning Words*

▶ **They Speak for Success; Breaking the Ice**

Prepare to Read: Key Vocabulary **150**

Before Reading: *They Speak for Success* **152**
  Literary Analysis: *Analyze Text Structure: Main Idea and Details*
  Focus Strategy: *Find Question-Answer Relationships*

▶ **Interact with the Text:** *Breaking the Ice* **155**
  Literary Analysis: *Analyze Humor*
  Focus Strategy: *Find Question-Answer Relationships*

Reflect and Assess **159**
  Writing: *Write About Literature*

Integrate the Language Arts **160**
  Literary Analysis: *Flashback*
  Vocabulary Study: *Jargon*

▶ **My English; How I Learned English**

Prepare to Read: Key Vocabulary **162**

Before Reading: *My English* **164**
  Literary Analysis: *Analyze Text Structure: Chronological Order*
  Focus Strategy: *Question the Author*

▶ **Interact with the Text:** *How I Learned English* **168**
  Literary Analysis: *Analyze Text Structure: Free Verse*
  Focus Strategy: *Question the Author*

Reflect and Assess **171**
  Writing: *Write About Literature*

Integrate the Language Arts **172**
  Literary Analysis: *Multiple Levels of Meaning*
  Vocabulary Study: *Content-Area Words*

▶ **Txtng: The Gr8 Db8**

Close Reading **174**
  Literary Analysis: *Analyze Text Structure*
  Writing: *Write About Text Structure*

▶ **Unit Review**

Key Vocabulary **180**

▶ **Say It with Flowers; The Journey**

    Prepare to Read: Key Vocabulary 182

    Before Reading: *Say It with Flowers* 184

        Literary Analysis: *Analyze Structure: Plot*
        Focus Strategy: *Make Connections*

      ▶ **Interact with the Text:** *The Journey* 188

        Literary Analysis: *Analyze Language: Metaphor and Extended Metaphor*
        Focus Strategy: *Make Connections*

    Reflect and Assess 191

        Writing: *Write About Literature*

    Integrate the Language Arts 192

        Literary Analysis: *Compare Characters' Motivations*
        Vocabulary Study: *Synonyms*

▶ **Just Lather, That's All; The Woman Who Was Death**

    Prepare to Read: Key Vocabulary 194

    Before Reading: *Just Lather, That's All* 196

        Literary Analysis: *Analyze Structure: Suspense*
        Focus Strategy: *Make Connections*

      ▶ **Interact with the Text:** *The Woman Who Was Death* 199

        Literary Analysis: *Analyze World Literature: Myth*
        Focus Strategy: *Make Connections*

    Reflect and Assess 203

        Writing: *Write About Literature*

    Integrate the Language Arts 204

        Literary Analysis: *Understand Irony*
        Vocabulary Study: *Synonyms and Antonyms in Analogies*

▶ **Be-ers and Doers; My Moment of Truth**

    Prepare to Read: Key Vocabulary 206

    Before Reading: *Be-ers and Doers* 208

        Literary Analysis: *Analyze Structure: Foreshadowing*
        Focus Strategy: *Make Connections*

      ▶ **Interact with the Text:** *My Moment of Truth* 211

        Literary Analysis: *Determine Author's Purpose*
        Focus Strategy: *Make Connections*

    Reflect and Assess 215

        Writing: *Write About Literature*

    Integrate the Language Arts 216

        Literary Analysis: *Dialect*
        Vocabulary Study: *Synonyms and Antonyms in Analogies*

▶ **Black Boy**

    Close Reading 218

        Literary Analysis: *Determine Author's Purpose; Analyze Text Structure*
        Writing: *Write About Text Structure*

▶ **Unit Review**

    Key Vocabulary 224

Unit 6

▶ **Too Young to Drive?; Rules of the Road**

    Prepare to Read: Key Vocabulary **226**

    Before Reading: *Too Young to Drive?* **228**

        Literary Analysis: *Evaluate Argument*
        Focus Strategy: *Draw Conclusions*

    ▶ **Interact with the Text:** *Rules of the Road* **231**

        Literary Analysis: *Analyze Development of Ideas*
        Focus Strategy: *Draw Conclusions*

    Reflect and Assess **237**

        Writing: *Write About Literature*

    Integrate the Language Arts **238**

        Literary Analysis: *Bias*
        Vocabulary Study: *Denotation and Connotation*

▶ **Piracy Bites!; Doonesbury on Downloading**

    Prepare to Read: Key Vocabulary **240**

    Before Reading: *Piracy Bites!* **242**

        Literary Analysis: *Evaluate Argument*
        Focus Strategy: *Compare Evidence Across Texts*

    ▶ **Interact with the Text:** *Doonesbury on Downloading* **245**

        Literary Analysis: *Analyze Central Idea*
        Focus Strategy: *Compare Evidence Across Texts*

    Reflect and Assess **251**

        Writing: *Write About Literature*

    Integrate the Language Arts **252**

        Literary Analysis: *Faulty Persuasive Techniques*
        Vocabulary Study: *Connotation*

▶ **Long Walk to Freedom; We Hold These Truths**

    Prepare to Read: Key Vocabulary **254**

    Before Reading: *Long Walk to Freedom* **256**

        Literary Analysis: *Analyze Argument: Word Choice*
        Focus Strategy: *Form Generalizations*

    ▶ **Interact with the Text:** *We Hold These Truths* **259**

        Literary Analysis: *Relate Arguments*
        Focus Strategy: *Evaluate Generalizations*

    Reflect and Assess **263**

        Writing: *Write About Literature*

    Integrate the Language Arts **264**

        Literary Analysis: *Rhetorical Devices*
        Vocabulary Study: *Denotation and Connotation*

▶ **What to the Slave Is the Fourth of July?**

    Close Reading **266**

        Literary Analysis: *Analyze and Evaluate Argument; Analyze Text Structure*
        Writing: *Write About Argument*

▶ **Unit Review**

    Key Vocabulary **272**

▶ **The Jewels of the Shrine; Remembered**

    Prepare to Read: Key Vocabulary 274

    Before Reading: *The Jewels of the Shrine* 276

        Literary Analysis: *Analyze Structure: Script*
        Focus Strategy: *Identify Emotional Responses*

        ▶ **Interact with the Text:** *Remembered* 279

        Literary Analysis: *Analyze Word Choice*
        Focus Strategy: *Identify Emotional Responses*

    Reflect and Assess 283

        Writing: *Write About Literature*

    Integrate the Language Arts 284

        Literary Analysis: *Dialogue, Character Traits, and Character Foils*
        Vocabulary Study: *Idioms*

▶ **Romeo and Juliet; West Side Story**

    Prepare to Read: Key Vocabulary 286

    Before Reading: *Romeo and Juliet* 288

        Literary Analysis: *Analyze Structure: Blank Verse*
        Focus Strategy: *Form Mental Images*

        ▶ **Interact with the Text:** *West Side Story* 291

        Literary Analysis: *Relate Story to Its Source*
        Focus Strategy: *Form Mental Images*

    Reflect and Assess 295

        Writing: *Write About Literature*

    Integrate the Language Arts 296

        Literary Analysis: *Parody*
        Vocabulary Study: *Figurative Language (Simile)*

▶ **Poems for the Earth; I Was Born Today/Touching the Earth**

    Prepare to Read: Key Vocabulary 298

    Before Reading: *Poems for the Earth* 300

        Literary Analysis: *Analyze Representations: Poetry and Art*
        Focus Strategy: *Form Sensory Images*

        ▶ **Interact with the Text:** *I Was Born Today/Touching the Earth* 303

        Literary Analysis: *Analyze Structure and Style*
        Focus Strategy: *Form Sensory Images*

    Reflect and Assess 307

        Writing: *Write About Literature*

    Integrate the Language Arts 308

        Literary Analysis: *Rhythm and Line Length*
        Vocabulary Study: *Figurative Language (Metaphor)*

▶ **Wild Geese/Like You**

    Close Reading 310

        Literary Analysis: *Analyze Structure and Style; Analyze Representations in Poetry and Art*
        Writing: *Write About Structure and Style*

▶ **Unit Review**

    Key Vocabulary 314

Prepare to Read

▶ The Moustache
▶ Who We Really Are

Key Vocabulary

A. How well do you know these words? Circle a rating for each word. Check your understanding of each word by circling *yes* or *no.* Then answer the questions using complete sentences. If you are unsure of a word's meaning, refer to the Vocabulary Glossary, page 926, in your student text.

Rating Scale

1	I have never seen this word before.
2	I am not sure of the word's meaning.
3	I know this word and can teach the word's meaning to someone else.

Key Word	Check Your Understanding	Deepen Your Understanding
❶ **characterize** (**kair**-ik-tu-rīz) *verb* **Rating:** 1 2 3	Danger and suspense **characterize** action movies. (Yes) No	How would you characterize a person who gets good grades? *Possible response:* A person who gets good grades is usually responsible, smart, and organized.
❷ **intensity** (in-**ten**-su-tē) *noun* **Rating:** 1 2 3	Professional athletes rarely show **intensity.** Yes (No)	What are the qualities of a person who shows intensity? *Possible response:* A person who shows intensity shows a lot of energy and strong emotion.
❸ **lucid** (**lü**-sid) *adjective* **Rating:** 1 2 3	Throwing spaghetti on the floor instead of eating it demonstrates **lucid** behavior. Yes (No)	What are some examples of lucid behavior? *Possible response:* Lucid behavior consists of clear speech and sensible actions.
❹ **obscure** (ob-**skyur**) *verb* **Rating:** 1 2 3	Celebrities sometimes **obscure** their faces with enormous sunglasses to hide their appearance. (Yes) No	What types of things can obscure a view? *Possible response:* Tall buildings, lack of light, and Fog can obscure a view.

Key Word	Check Your Understanding	Deepen Your Understanding
5 **pathetic** (pu-**the**-tik) *adjective* **Rating:** 1 2 3	A lost and frightened dog is a **pathetic** sight. (Yes) No	What characteristics might a pathetic person have? _____ *Possible response:* A pathetic person can have sad eyes and a frowning face. _____ _____
6 **perspective** (pur-**spek**-tiv) *noun* **Rating:** 1 2 3	Being open and listening is one way to understand someone else's **perspective.** (Yes) No	How can a person express his or her perspective? _____ *Possible response:* A person can express his or her perspective by sharing opinions with others. _____ _____
7 **pretense** (**prē**-tens) *noun* **Rating:** 1 2 3	Faking happiness is nothing but a **pretense.** (Yes) No	What is an example of a pretense? *Possible response:* A pretense is acting happy when you are sad and angry. _____ _____
8 **stigmatize** (**stig**-mah-tīz) *verb* **Rating:** 1 2 3	It is thoughtful to **stigmatize** someone you admire. Yes (No)	What is one example of how people stigmatize one another? *Possible response:* People stigmatize one another by labeling others as lazy when they are just struggling to understand. _____

B. Use one of the Key Vocabulary words to write about a time when a friend's actions surprised you.

Answers will vary. _____

_____

LITERARY ANALYSIS: Analyze Conflict

In most stories, the main character faces a **conflict,** or struggle.

1. In an **external conflict**, a character struggles with something or someone outside of himself or herself.
2. In an **internal conflict**, the character struggles with something inside of himself or herself.

A. Read the passage below. Write Mike's internal conflict and external conflict in the chart.

> ### Look Into the Text
>
> I had to go to Lawnrest [Nursing Home] alone that afternoon. But first of all I had to stand inspection. My mother lined me up against the wall. . . . She frowned and started the routine.
> "That hair," she said. . . .
> I sighed. I have discovered that it's better to sigh than argue.
> "And that moustache." She shook her head. "I still say a seventeen-year-old has no business wearing a moustache."
> "It's an experiment," I said. . . .
> "It's costing you money, Mike," she said.
> "I know, I know."

Mike's Internal Conflict	Mike's External Conflict
Mike does not want to argue with his mom.	Mike's mom tells him she does not like his moustache and hair.

B. Mike faces an internal conflict and an external conflict. How do you think he will resolve each conflict?

Possible responses: Internal—Mike will keep quiet and not argue. External—Mike will cut his hair and shave his moustache.

FOCUS STRATEGY: Make and Confirm Predictions

How to MAKE AND CONFIRM PREDICTIONS

Focus Strategy

1. **Look for Clues** Notice clues about the characters.

2. **Predict** Imagine what the characters would do if they were real.

3. **Check It Out** Read on to see if you are right. Look for evidence in the text to confirm your prediction.

A. Read the passage. Use the strategies above to make a prediction as you read. Then answer the questions below.

Look Into the Text

> Frankly, I wasn't too crazy about visiting a nursing home. They reminded me of hospitals and hospitals turn me off. I mean, the smell of ether makes me nauseous, and I feel faint at the sight of blood. And as I approached Lawnrest—which is a terrible cemetery kind of name, to being with—I was sorry I hadn't avoided the trip. <u>Then I felt guilty about it. I'm loaded with guilt complexes.</u> Like driving like a madman after promising my father to be careful. <u>Like sitting in the parking lot, looking at the nursing home with dread and thinking how I'd rather be with Cindy.</u>

---

1. What do you predict Mike will do next? Why?

   Possible response: I predict that Mike will go inside the nursing home to visit his grandmother. I think he feels too guilty not to go.

2. Which strategy did you use to make your prediction?

   Possible response: Strategy 1; I noticed clues about Mike's character.

B. Underline the sentences in the passage that gave clues about Mike's character. Then read "The Moustache" to see if you can confirm, or need to change, your prediction.

Selection Review The Moustache

EQ **When Do You Really Know Someone?**
Watch for the moment when people show you who they are.

A. In "The Moustache," Mike faces conflicts that lead him to learn things he never knew about his grandmother. Decide whether the conflicts are internal or external, then write each conflict's resolution in the chart.

Conflict-Resolution Chart

Mike's Conflict	How Mike Resolves the Conflict
External: Mike's mom thinks his moustache makes him look too old. Internal: Mike does not like nursing homes, but feels guilty about not visiting his grandmother. Internal: Mike's grandmother mistakes Mike for her late husband; Mike doesn't know how to tell his grandmother who he really is.	At first, Mike ignores her; eventually he shaves off his moustache. Mike visits his grandmother in the nursing home. Mike pretends to be his grandfather, because Mike begins to see his grandmother as a real person.

B. Use the information in the chart to answer the questions.

1. Why does Mike go along with his grandmother when she doesn't recognize him?

Possible response: At first, Mike feels guilty hearing personal details of her life. Then he begins to see her as a person.

2. How does Mike's perspective of his grandmother change by the end of the story? Use **perspective** in your answer.

Possible response: Mike's new perspective of his grandmother is that she is a real person with fears, dreams, and regrets just like anyone else.

3. Look back at the prediction you made about Mike on page 11. Did it happen? What evidence in the text confirms your prediction?

Possible response: Mike does go to the nursing home to visit his grandmother. Evidence: Mike remembers all the birthday presents his grandmother gave him.

Connect Across Texts

In "The Moustache," Mike gains a new understanding about himself and others. Read this news feature about others who want to be seen for who they really are.

JOSHUNDA SANDERS

Who We Really Are

Tamisha started her life with huge obstacles to overcome. She was exposed to drugs **in utero** and so sick that doctors didn't expect her to live. But when she was 4 days old, she went straight into **foster care**, where her foster mother nursed her back to health. Most people have heard stories about foster youth who are placed in one home after another, but Tamisha stayed in the same home her whole life. When she was 4 years old, her foster mother **adopted her**.

Today, she is a **giddy** 17-year-old with perfectly manicured nails. She loves to tell the story of how people used to call her the "miracle baby." But her expression turns more serious when she talks about people's perceptions of her. People always have questions, she says: "Don't you miss your family? Why not a black home? Why is your family white?"

Nationally, there are half a million youths in foster care. Many of them are **stigmatized** as hardened troublemakers. That attitude may keep some adults from adopting youths from foster care, and some foster youths see adoption as an undesirable option. But being adopted was "the best thing that could ever happen to me," Tamisha wrote in a 2004 exhibition at the Zeum children's museum. (The last names of the artists featured in the show were withheld at their request.)

That's what she tells prospective adoptive parents at seminars in San Mateo, California, where she now lives. By sharing her **perspective** on what it's like to be a former foster child through a videotape she made with Fostering Art—a local program that teaches foster youth about photography—Tamisha hopes to change some of the negative attitudes toward foster youth.

"Just looking at the video we made . . . even me, coming from foster care and being adopted, it still touched me and it does every time," Tamisha said.

Fostering Art is an arts-based project that works with A Home Within, a nonprofit organization that has been

Key Vocabulary
stigmatize v., to label or mark as bad
• **perspective** n., point of view

In Other Words
in utero before she was born
foster care a temporary, safe home
adopted her legally became her mother
giddy happy and carefree

Interact with the Text

1. Preview/Set a Purpose
You can set a purpose for reading by asking a question. Write a question that gives you a personal reason to continue reading the news feature.

Possible response: How does creating art help foster youth?

2. News Feature
News features focus on real people—their feelings, opinions, and problems. Highlight the text that describes Tamisha's feelings and opinions. What do they tell you about Tamisha?

Possible response:
Tamisha has positive feelings about her adoption and wants to share those feelings with others.

3. Preview/Set a Purpose

Remember that photos and captions give you information about a selection. Circle the photo and caption. What would the selection have been like without them?

Possible response:

The photo and caption

provide interest by

showing foster youths'

artwork. I might never

have understood how

important the program

is to foster youth.

In a photography workshop hosted by *National Geographic* magazine in San Francisco, teens from Fostering Art and other high school students showed their unique perspective on self and place.

offering free **therapy** to foster youth for ten years. When A Home Within's founder, Toni Heineman, started the program, she was working with **a caseload** of young people who had been shuffled from therapist to therapist. It was taking a toll on them. Because "often, there's not a single person who is not being paid to care for them," Heineman created the Children's Psychotherapy Project that matched therapists who agreed to volunteer their services with one youth for as long as therapy would take. The project was so successful that the program has been duplicated in fourteen other cities nationwide.

In 2004, A Home Within started Fostering Art as another outlet for foster youth to express their feelings about the world they live in. "There will be some horrible story in *Newsweek* and then everyone is thinking about foster kids for a while," Heineman said, "but it's hard over time to understand

In Other Words
therapy counseling
a caseload several cases

what it's like to be raised by someone else's parents."

Fostering Art helps foster youth empower themselves. At the same time it educates the community about the day-to-day realities of foster care that are rarely seen. "Very often, we just don't think about who foster kids are," she said. "And if you can show people foster kids through art, they can stop and look at it, and it stays with them longer."

Plus, young people often asked her for a mental health approach that wasn't just "50 minutes sitting in a room talking to someone," Heineman added.

On a mustard yellow wall at Zeum, two white pages explain Fostering Art's mission: "We're special and unique. We are: foster kids . . . intelligent . . . human beings . . . not the people who become outcasts of the world, hoodlums or drug dealers . . . people with a deeper understanding of the world because we've been through things many people haven't."

The exhibition provides a window into their world with photographs and a multimedia display that includes a videotape of the group as they read their poetry and thoughts about home, life, and who they are.

Each photographer has a sunken box containing their portraits and **artifacts**. Tamisha's box includes a picture of her smiling at the center, her braces still on. On the left side of the installation there's a cluster of photographs from her childhood; on the right, pictures of her now, with her family and friends.

"We're invisible to the media and

Educational Achievement of Youth

■ General Population
■ Foster Youth

BA Degree or More: 24.4% / 10.8%
Some College: 51.7% / 43.7%
High School Completion: 80.4% / 86.1%

Source: Casey Family Programs and the U.S. Census Bureau

In Other Words
artifacts objects people make

4. Interpret
Highlight the sentences that tell you the goal of the Fostering Art program. Why do you think the name of the program is "Fostering Art"?

Possible response:

The name refers to the
youths the program
helps and explains how
it helps them.

5. Preview/Set a Purpose
Remember that looking at graphs and other text features is one way to preview a reading. Circle the part of the graph that tells you the percentage of foster youth that attend some college. Then write a question that gives you a personal reason to read on.

Possible response: Why
do fewer foster youths
complete college?

6. News Feature

Reread this part of the article. What characteristics of a news feature does this part include?

This part combines

facts about Delpheanea

with her feelings and

opinions.

just about everybody else out there," writes Delpheanea, 16. No matter, she does well for herself and lists, beside her picture, a long group of positive accomplishments. She gets good grades, she's engaged, and she's only been late to class twice this year. And she also has, if she does say so herself, a beautiful smile.

"This group is a gateway to freedom, a way to express yourself without someone judging," another sheet reads. "Our hope for the show is to be a messenger, to tell people about ourselves and what we do, to tell our stories. We hope you will get to know who we really are." ❖

Selection Review Who We Really Are

A. Is reading a news feature more interesting than reading a news story? Why or why not?

Possible responses: Yes, because I like reading about people's feelings and opinions; No, because I think facts are more interesting than opinions.

B. Answer the questions.

1. You previewed the title, photos, captions, and graph. Write a sentence explaining how one of these text features gave you a personal reason to read the news feature.

Possible response: The graph gave me a personal reason to read because I was curious about why many foster youths do not complete college.

2. List two facts or other information that you learned about foster youth. Why are these facts important?

Possible response: 1. More foster youths complete high school than the general population. There are half a million foster children and teenagers. 2. These facts are important to know so that we can create more programs to help foster youth or inform the public.

Reflect and Assess

The Moustache
Who We Really Are

WRITING: Write About Literature

A. Plan your writing. Which group is treated better: the elderly or foster teens? List examples from both selections in the chart about how each group is treated. *Answers will vary.*

The Elderly	Foster Teens
Mike's mom visits his grandmother almost every day.	Tamisha's foster mother nursed her back to health after Tamisha was born.

B. Which group do you think is treated better? Make a judgment and tell what you think in a paragraph. Use examples from both selections to support your judgment.

Students should support their answers with examples from both selections.

_____

_____

_____

_____

_____

_____

_____

_____

_____

Integrate the Language Arts

LITERARY ANALYSIS: Analyze Setting

A story's **setting** is the time and place in which events happen. Setting often affects the plot of a story and affects the conflicts the characters face.

A. Look through "The Moustache." List the setting details in the chart. *Answers will vary.*

Time	Place
the afternoon	

B. Imagine each of the new settings below. How might each of the following changes affect the plot of "The Moustache"? *Answers will vary. Possible responses are shown.*

1. The story takes place late at night.

When Mike arrives at Lawnrest at night, his grandmother is asleep. Instead of speaking with his grandmother, Mike speaks with one of the nurses about her illness.

2. A tornado occurs while Mike is visiting his grandmother.

Mike is trapped at Lawnrest with his grandmother. They are both scared, but he helps her relax by asking questions about her past.

3. The story is set in the house of Mike's grandmother.

Mike might not struggle with the decision to visit her, because she would not live in the dreaded nursing home.

C. Think of your favorite movie. Write a description of the setting. How might the conflict and plot of the movie be different if the setting changed?

Answers will vary.

_____

_____

_____

_____

VOCABULARY STUDY: Prefixes

A **prefix** is a word part that comes at the beginning of a word and changes the word's meaning. *Answers will vary. Possible responses are shown.*

A. Remember that *pre-* means "before." Use each word in a sentence to show that you understand its meaning.

preview _After I saw the preview of the movie, I couldn't wait for the movie's release._

preheat _When I bake cookies, I always preheat the oven so it reaches the correct temperature._

premature _My cousin was born premature because my aunt went into labor a month early._

predetermine _I waited for my friends outside the donut shop at noon, which was our predetermined meeting time._

B. The chart below shows some common prefixes and their meanings. Complete the chart by listing words you've heard that begin with each prefix. Use a dictionary if you need to.

Prefix	Meaning	Words I've Used
de-	opposite	deactivate
il-	not	illegal
re-	again	review
semi-	half	semiannual
trans-	across	transportation

C. Three common prefixes are *un-*, *dis-*, and *non-*. Write a word that begins with each prefix. Then use the word in a sentence.

1. _nonsense; The baby spoke a nonsense language that sounded like gibberish to me._

2. _disappear; When spring arrives, the snow will disappear._

3. _unnecessary; The sunny weather made our umbrellas and raincoats unnecessary._

Prepare to Read

▶ **Two Kinds**
▶ **Novel Musician**

Key Vocabulary

A. How well do you know these words? Circle a rating for each word. Check your understanding of each word by choosing the correct synonym or antonym. Then provide examples. If you are unsure of a word's meaning, refer to the Vocabulary Glossary, page 926, in your student text.

Rating Scale

1	I have never seen this word before.
2	I am not sure of the word's meaning.
3	I know this word and can teach the word's meaning to someone else.

Key Word	Check Your Understanding	Deepen Your Understanding
❶ accusation (ak-yū-**zā**-shun) *noun* **Rating:** 1 2 3	If you believe an **accusation**, you are believing a _____. lie (**slur**)	Example: *Possible response:* blaming a person for a mistake
❷ ambitious (am-**bi**-shus) *adjective* **Rating:** 1 2 3	The opposite of **ambitious** is _____. (**lazy**) forgetful	Example: *Possible response:* studying hard to reach the top of my class
❸ assert (uh-**surt**) *verb* **Rating:** 1 2 3	When people **assert** their opinions, they _____ them. (**say**) create	Example: *Possible response:* persuading another person that I am right
❹ discordant (dis-**kord**-nt) *adjective* **Rating:** 1 2 3	If you hear **discordant** sounds, you hear _____ sounds. (**harsh**) beautiful	Example: *Possible response:* car horns honking during a traffic jam

Key Word	Check Your Understanding	Deepen Your Understanding
5 expectation (ek-spek-**tā**-shun) *noun* Rating: 1 2 3	When people have an **expectation,** they have a _____ that something will happen. (**belief**)　　fear	Example: *Possible response:* anticipating that the trees will bloom in the spring _____ _____ _____
6 inevitable (in-**ev**-e-tuh-bul) *adjective* Rating: 1 2 3	The opposite of **inevitable** is _____. certain　　(**avoidable**)	Example: *Possible response:* taking tests and writing papers _____ _____ _____
7 prodigy (**prah**-du-jē) *noun* Rating: 1 2 3	If someone is a **prodigy,** he or she is a _____. (**talent**)　　disappointment	Example: *Possible response:* playing a musical instrument at a very young age _____ _____ _____
8 reproach (ri-**prōch**) *noun* Rating: 1 2 3	If you experience **reproach,** you experience _____. (**criticism**)　　praise	Example: *Possible response:* getting in trouble for being late to class _____ _____ _____

B. Use one of the Key Vocabulary words to describe a time you discovered something surprising about a friend.

*Answers will vary.*_____

_____

LITERARY ANALYSIS: Analyze Protagonist and Antagonist

The **protagonist** is the main character. The **antagonist** is the opposing character. Conflict occurs when the two characters want different things.

A. Read the passage below. Identify the protagonist and the antagonist and write what each character wants in the chart. Then answer the question.

Look Into the Text

Three days after watching *The Ed Sullivan Show*, my mother told me what my schedule would be for piano lessons and piano practice. She had talked to Mr. Chong, who lived on the first floor of our apartment building. Mr. Chong was a retired piano teacher and my mother had traded housecleaning services for weekly lessons and a piano for me to practice on every day, two hours a day, from four until six.

When my mother told me this, I felt as though I had been sent to hell. I whined and then kicked my foot a little when I couldn't stand it anymore.

"Why don't you like me the way I am? I'm not a genius! I can't play the piano. And even if I could, I wouldn't go on TV if you paid me a million dollars!" I cried.

Types of Characters	Who Is She?	What Does She Want?
Protagonist	The narrator (the daughter)	She wants to be left alone and accepted for who she is.
Antagonist	The narrator's mother	She wants her daughter to take piano lessons and practice two hours every day.

B. What is the conflict between the protagonist and the antagonist?

The narrator, or protagonist, wants to be accepted for who she is and not made to play the piano. Her mother, the antagonist, opposes her by wanting her to practice two hours every day.

FOCUS STRATEGY: Clarify Ideas

HOW TO CLARIFY IDEAS

1. **Note Confusion** Stop reading if something is unclear.

2. **Reread** Go back. Reread slowly to see if you missed something important.

3. **Read On** Keep reading. The answer may come later.

4. **Relate to Personal Experience** Link ideas by using what you already know.

A. Read the passage. Use the strategies above to clarify the ideas. Answer the questions below.

> **Look Into the Text**
>
> And after seeing my mother's disappointed face once again, something inside of me began to die. I hated the tests, the raised hopes and failed expectations. Before going to bed that night, I looked in the mirror above the bathroom sink and when I saw only my face staring back—and that it would always be this ordinary face—I began to cry. Such a sad, ugly girl! I made high-pitched noises like a crazed animal, trying to scratch out the face in the mirror.

1. Why is the narrator crying and behaving "like a crazed animal"?

   She is behaving that way because she is discouraged about being ordinary. The narrator is upset to think that she can never fulfill her mother's expectations.

2. Which strategy did you use to answer question 1? How did the strategy help you clarify ideas?

   Possible response: Rereading helped me clarify ideas, because reading the passage again more slowly made me realize I missed the part where the narrator says she is ordinary.

B. Choose one of the strategies you did not use. Explain how you could have used this strategy to clarify ideas.

   Possible response: I could have related the passage to a time I felt so upset that I felt "like a crazed animal."

Selection Review Two Kinds

When Do You Really Know Someone?
Consider that there might be more to someone than you think.

A. In "Two Kinds," the narrator finds out that she doesn't know her mother as well as she first thought. Write in the chart how Jing-Mei thinks her mother will react, then compare it to how she actually reacts.

T Chart

What Jing-Mei Thinks Will Happen	What Actually Happens
Jing-Mei thinks her mother will yell at her after the talent show. Jing-Mei thinks her mother will not want her to play the piano anymore. As an adult, Jing-Mei thinks her mother is still angry about the piano lessons.	Her mother says nothing. Her mother tries to force Jing-Mei to continue practicing. Her mother offers her the piano as a gift.

B. Use the information in the chart to answer the questions.

1. What do the characters discover about each other?

The mother discovers that her daughter does not want to be a prodigy. In the end, Jing-Mei finds out that her mother has forgiven her.

2. How does the mother's expectation of her daughter affect Jing-Mei? Use **expectation** in your answer.

Possible response: Her mother's expectation makes Jing-Mei feel as if she is not good enough, and it makes her angry. She does not feel accepted by her mother.

3. Would Jing-Mei's mother have accepted her if Jing-Mei had tried harder? Why or why not?

Possible responses: No, Jing-Mei's mother would never have been satisfied; Yes, if she had at least tried, she may have been proud of her.

"Two Kinds" reflects the serious side of author Amy Tan.
This profile shows another side of her that may surprise you.

Novel Musician
What You Don't Know About Amy Tan

by Sharon Wootton, *The Herald* (Washington)

Interact with the Text

1. Interpret
Look at the photo. Read the title and "Connect Across Texts." What do you predict this selection will be about?

Possible response:

Amy Tan writes novels,

but she is also part

of a band. I think the

selection will describe

her role in the band.

2. Clarify Ideas

Underline the words or phrases that tell you who and what this article is about. Write the subject matter in your own words.

Possible response: The article is about Amy Tan and her work with the band the Rock Bottom Remainders.

3. Profile

Profiles include fun, lively facts. Mark an *X* next to an interesting fact about Amy Tan's childhood. Why do you think the author included this fact?

Possible response: This fact shows that music was part of Tan's life from a young age.

4. Interpret

What does this article tell you about Tan?

Possible response: Tan can be silly and does not take music very seriously. She sings to have fun.

Most people know Amy Tan as the award-winning writer of *The Joy Luck Club* and *The Kitchen God's Wife.* <u>What they don't know is that she sometimes **moonlights** as the leading vocalist for the Rock Bottom **Remainders**—a garage band made up of famous writers who secretly dream of being rock stars.</u> Once a year, the band goes on tour across the United States to create a few laughs and to raise money for literacy-based charities.

Wearing colorful wigs and costumes is of the fun when Amy Tan sings with th Rock Bottom Remainders.

Amy Tan, Rock Star?

Best-selling horror novelist Stephen King and Tan "scare up" some creativity.

*X*Tan's musical "career" started at age 5, when she practiced piano an hour a day. She was given an IQ test at age 6 and her parents were told that she was smart enough to be a doctor.

"Since my mother believed that the most important organ of the body was the brain, she decided I was going to be a neurosurgeon [and] then a concert pianist. There was, after all, no sense in taking all these lessons if you weren't going to make something of it."

In Other Words
moonlights works a second job
Remainders leftover things

Cultural Background
Literacy-based charities are organizations that help people learn to read and write. The Rock Bottom Remainders raise money for America Scores, a program that combines academic and athletics activities for children.

Two Kinds of Storytelling

The author sees the connection between music and creativity in terms of storytelling. "When I was practicing piano, what I always saw when I played the pieces were stories in my head," Tan said.

"The rock 'n' roll songs I like best are the ones with a definite story, often quite stupid stories, like the ones I'll be singing." (She's best known for her **off-key rendition** of Nancy Sinatra's classic, "These Boots Are Made for Walkin'.") "They're very dramatic, almost hysterical, and at best quite funny to watch."

Don't Quit Your Day Job

None of these literary giants is likely to quit writing to pursue a musical career, but they all enjoy **jamming** as part of the Rock Bottom Remainders.

Author Name	Literary Achievement	Musical Contribution
Amy Tan	author of *The Joy Luck Club* and *The Kitchen God's Wife*	vocals
Dave Barry	nationally syndicated humor columnist	guitar and vocals
Stephen King	author of highly successful horror novels, including *Carrie*, *The Shining*, and *The Dark Tower* series	guitar and vocals
Scott Turow	attorney and author of best-selling legal thrillers, such as *Presumed Innocent* and *Ordinary Heroes*	vocals
James McBride	author of *The Color of Water*	saxophone

In Other Words
off-key rendition version that does not hit the right musical notes
jamming playing music for fun

5. Interpret

Does Tan's attitude about music surprise you? Why or why not?

Possible responses: Yes, her attitude surprised me because she seems so serious in her writing; No, she doesn't surprise me because she writes stories about music that are humorous.

"I will sing **my heart out** [and] with absolute seriousness that my career depends on it and everybody should have a good time. Mostly people think it's pretty hilarious. . . . Everyone [in the band] is so great about their lack of musical talent," Tan said. "We're a joke but we're actually not bad to dance to. My recommendation is for people to put on their '60s and '70s clothes and come and dance." ❖

In Other Words
my heart out with great enthusiasm

Selection Review Novel Musician

A. How do the quotations contribute to the profile's humorous tone?

The quotations from Tan show that she is not afraid to be silly and loves to make people laugh. Her words give the profile a silly angle.

B. Answer the questions.

    1. Answer the 5W questions about the profile.

        1. Who? Amy Tan and the Rock Bottom Remainders

        2. What? singing career

        3. When? tours once a year

        4. Where? tours all across the United States

        5. Why? to have fun and to raise money

    2. What did you learn about Tan that you might not have learned in a news story that contained only facts about her?

        Possible response: I learned that Tan has a great sense of humor and that she wants people to come out to dance and enjoy the band's music.

Reflect and Assess

WRITING: Write About Literature

A. Plan your writing. Complete the chart below with details from both selections that show reasons for and against children being required to take music lessons. Then form an opinion. *Answers will vary.*

	Two Kinds	Novel Musician
For Music Lessons	Some children, like Waverly, may discover that they are very talented.	
Against Music Lessons		

B. Should children be required to learn a musical instrument? Write an opinion statement. Support your opinion with examples from both texts.

Students should support their answers with examples from both selections.

_____

_____

_____

_____

_____

_____

_____

_____

_____

Integrate the Language Arts

LITERARY ANALYSIS: Analyze Characters and Plot

A story's **plot** usually has both **conflict** and **resolution**. Conflict is a struggle between opposing forces, and resolution is the way that conflict ends. The interactions of characters can complicate the plot and lead to the climax, or the turning point of the story.

A. How do the interactions between Jing-Mei and her mother complicate the plot? Complete the chart below with the complications.

Climax
Jing-Mei and her mother have a terrible argument.

Complication
Jing-Mei embarrasses her mother at the talent show.

Complication
Jing-Mei doesn't bother to correct her mistakes.

Complication
Jing-Mei's mother says Jing-Mei is ungrateful.

Conflict
Jing-Mei's mother wants Jing-Mei to become a musical prodigy.

Exposition
Jing-Mei, her mother, Chinatown, San Francisco

Resolution
Jing-Mei quits playing the piano, and Jing-Mei's mother never mentions their argument again.

B. Answer the questions below.

1. How do the complications between Jing-Mei and her mother lead to the climax? Write the climax in the diagram above.

Jing-Mei and her mother want different things. Jing-Mei wants to be accepted; her mother wants her to be

a prodigy.

2. What is the resolution of the story's conflict? Plot it on the diagram above.

C. Imagine a different resolution to the story's conflict. Write a new ending.

Answers will vary.

VOCABULARY STUDY: Suffixes

A **suffix** is a word part that comes at the end of a word. It changes the word's part of speech or meaning. Sometimes letters are added or dropped to make the new word.

A. The suffix *-tion* changes a verb into a noun. Complete the chart below by adding the suffix *-tion* to the word. Then write a sentence using the noun. You can use a dictionary to check your spelling.

Verb	Suffix	Noun	Sentence
explain	-tion	explanation	I asked my teacher for an explanation of the diagram in my science textbook.
act	-tion	action	*Possible response:* He sprang into action when the child started to fall out of his chair.
quote	-tion	quotation	*Possible response:* I included many famous quotations from historical people in my social studies paper.
converse	-tion	conversation	*Possible response:* During lunch, I had an interesting conversation with my friend.

B. The chart below shows some words that contain suffixes. Draw a slash to separate the root word, or base word, from the suffix in the first column. Then indicate the parts of speech for each.

Word with Suffix	Part of Speech	
	Root Word	Root Word + Suffix
joy/ful	noun	adjective
establishment	verb	noun
disappearance	verb	noun
dangerous	noun	adjective
fearless	noun	adjective

C. Write sentences using the words in the first column of the chart above.
Answers will vary. Possible responses are shown.

1. We felt joyful when we heard that our grandparents were coming for a visit.

2. Most business establishments in the city are located downtown.

3. The dog's disappearance is not surprising because the gate was left open.

4. It is dangerous to jump into the ocean if you do not know how to swim.

5. The firefighter showed fearless behavior every time he entered a burning building.

Prepare to Read

▶ **Skins**
▶ **Nicole**

Key Vocabulary

A. How well do you know these words? Circle a rating for each word. Check your understanding of each word by circling *yes* or *no*. Then complete the sentences. If you are unsure of a word's meaning, refer to the Vocabulary Glossary, page 926, in your student text.

Rating Scale	
1	I have never seen this word before.
2	I am not sure of the word's meaning.
3	I know this word and can teach the word's meaning to someone else.

Key Word	Check Your Understanding	Deepen Your Understanding
❶ authenticity (aw-then-**ti**-su-tē) *noun* **Rating:** 1 2 3	A certificate can show the **authenticity** of a painting. **(Yes)** No	Things that should be checked for authenticity include *Possible response:* a famous person's autograph, or signature _____ _____ .
❷ compel (kum-**pel**) *verb* **Rating:** 1 2 3	If you **compel** a person to do something, you discourage him or her. Yes **(No)**	Some things that compel me to work hard are _____ *Possible response:* success and self-respect _____ _____ _____ .
❸ discriminate (dis-**kri**-mu-nāt) *verb* **Rating:** 1 2 3	If you **discriminate,** you treat everyone equally. Yes **(No)**	If people discriminate against a group, they _____ *Possible response:* do not give the group the same opportunities as others _____ _____ .
❹ eliminate (i-**li**-mu-nāt) *verb* **Rating:** 1 2 3	Many scientists work hard to **eliminate** diseases. **(Yes)** No	Police officers work to eliminate _____ *Possible response:* crime _____ _____ _____ .

Key Word	Check Your Understanding	Deepen Your Understanding
5 potential (pu-**ten**-shul) *noun* **Rating:** 1 2 3	With hard work, an Olympic athlete has the **potential** to win a medal. (Yes) No	I have the potential to *Possible response:* be a good writer _____ .
6 predominate (pri-**dah**-mu-nāt) *verb* **Rating:** 1 2 3	To **predominate** in a conversation is to sit quietly and not speak. Yes (No)	Characteristics that predominate in my family are _____ *Possible response:* stubbornness and generosity _____ .
7 racism (**rā**-si-zum) *noun* **Rating:** 1 2 3	Teaching others about different cultures and customs can help to eliminate **racism.** (Yes) No	One thing I can do to eliminate racism is to _____ *Possible response:* try to get to know people of all ethnicities and cultures _____ .
8 tension (**ten**-shun) *noun* **Rating:** 1 2 3	Mid-term and final exams cause **tension** for many students. (Yes) No	I eliminate tension by *Possible response:* exercising and spending time with friends _____ .

B. Write about a time in your life when you felt discriminated against. How did it make you feel? Use at least two of the Key Vocabulary words.

Answers will vary. _____

_____

Before Reading Skins

LITERARY ANALYSIS: Character and Theme

Characters in a story often learn a life lesson from a conflict they experience. This lesson, or message, is called the **theme** of the story.

A. Read the passage below. Find the clues about Mitchell Sabattis. Write the clues in the chart.

> **Look Into the Text**
>
> ### Skins
>
>   The first day I saw Jimmy T. Black, I thought he was a real Indian. Realer than me. I thought that even before I heard him tell the group of kids hanging around him that his middle initial stood for "Thorpe." Jim Thorpe was . . . the world's greatest [Native American] athlete. . . . [My] father was an Indian . . . [and my] mom is Swedish and as blonde as Brunhilde. Despite the hair coloring that I comb in every week or so, I know my classmates still see the old Mitchell Sabattis, would-be Native American. I tan up real dark in the summer, but during the winter my skin gets as pale as something you might find under a rock.

Type of Clue	Mitchell Sabattis
Character's thoughts and words	He thinks about how he is only half Native American, how he colors his hair, and how he turns pale in the winter.
Character's problem or conflict	A new student seems to be completely Native American; Mitchell is always trying to be more Native American.
Character's secret wishes	He wants to look more Native American.

B. What life lesson do you think Mitchell Sabattis will learn because of the conflict he experiences?

Possible response: Mitchell Sabattis may learn that hair and skin color do not make a person real or better.

FOCUS STRATEGY: Clarify Vocabulary

HOW TO CLARIFY VOCABULARY

1. **Look for Familiar Word Parts**

2. **Make Connections** Look for clues in the sentence to help you find the word's meaning.

3. **Compare Words** Look for similar word parts, or how the words are used in a sentence.

A. Read the passage. Use the strategies above to clarify vocabulary as you read. Then answer the questions below.

Look Into the Text

> Even if I did have a blonde mother, I'd always been the only kid in Long Pond School who really (identified) himself as Indian. And I certainly wasn't the only one with (Indian) ancestry. There's plenty of (Native blood) in the mountains, but a lot of it is kept hidden. In the past, it was better not to be Indian. And it's not hard for people who are Indian to hide that fact.

1. Underline the word *ancestry* in the passage. Circle the words from the passage that help you find the meaning of *ancestry*.

2. List two more words that share a word part with *ancestry*.

   Possible responses: ancestor, ancestral

B. Write a definition for *ancestry* using the information you gathered.

   Possible response: where a family comes from, a person's heritage or relatives from earlier generations

Selection Review Skins

 When Do You Really Know Someone?
Look beyond the stereotype.

A. In "Skins," you found out that people's ideas about each other can change the more they get to know one another.

Character Description Map

Character	Character's Feelings and Ideas	How Character's Feelings and Ideas Change
Mitchell	admires Jimmy T for not hiding his heritage; thinks Randolph will be like people he sees on TV	tells Jimmy T to be himself; learns that stereotypes are wrong
Jimmy T	hates Randolph; seems as if he is avoiding Mitchell because he is not true to his heritage	admits that he is not Native American and that Randolph might be right
Randolph	dislikes Jimmy T and calls him a "faker"; encourages Mitchell to be himself	supports Jimmy T even if there is tension between them; wants Mitchell to help him

1. What life lessons do Mitchell and Jimmy T learn from Randolph?

   Mitchell and Jimmy T learn that it is important to acknowledge your heritage and for people to be who they really are.

2. How does seeing Mr. and Mrs. Black help Mitchell understand Jimmy T and the tension Jimmy T must live with? Use **tension** in your answer.

   Possible response: Mitchell sees that Jimmy's parents cause a lot of tension in Jimmy's life and that this is why he pretends to be Native American. Jimmy T wants to be someone else.

3. How might Mitchell and Randolph treat Jimmy T differently in the future now that they know the truth about him?

   Possible response: Mitchell and Randolph might be able to encourage Jimmy T to be proud of who he is and not try to be someone he is not.

Nicole

Rebecca Carroll and Nicole

Connect Across Texts

In "Skins," three teenagers find out what makes people who they are. In this oral history, Nicole discusses how she wants people to see her.

My mother is white and my father is black.

I don't consider myself **biracial**, or black, or white. I consider myself Nicole, although when we visit my white grandparents' house and there are other family members around like my cousin, it is he who is seen as the "good" child. He is pure white. I am **the black sheep** of the family, just like my mother is the black sheep of her family for dating my father. In society, I am made to feel like a black sheep for precisely that reason of my white mother and my black father getting together and having me, which was considered wrong at the time and still is in some people's minds. I am the **walking representative** of that wrongness.

We all have the ability and the resources to be individuals, but when I walk down the street I am clearly identified as a black person and am **discriminated** against accordingly. I don't blame my parents and I don't blame people for their ignorance. Nobody has done anything wrong here, but it's like having to work at a job I didn't apply for. I alone have to come up with the added strength to deal with **racism**, and that isn't something I bargained for when I came into this world. I don't draw from the loving union my parents had when they got together to make me; I draw from the love I have for and within myself. Basically, I'm the one who is going to be

Key Vocabulary

- **discriminate** *v.*, to treat differently because of prejudice
- **racism** *n.*, ill treatment of people on the basis of ancestry

In Other Words

biracial of two races
the black sheep a person who doesn't fit in or who is considered an outcast
walking representative living example

Interact with the Text

1. Determine Viewpoint

This personal narrative gives Nicole's viewpoint. Circle two qualities of a personal narrative on this page. How do these qualities help you understand Nicole's viewpoint?

Possible response: Nicole writes about herself. By reading her personal thoughts and feelings, I can understand her viewpoint.

2. Clarify Vocabulary

Underline words and phrases that help you understand the word *draw*. Rewrite the sentence replacing *draw* with a synonym or phrase.

Possible response: I don't take strength from the loving union my parents had when they got together to make me.

here in the end. I'm the one who is going to have to defend myself. I can tell my mother when I am discriminated against or whatever, but I'm the one who has to **look it square in the face**.

I think when people act stupid they are holding themselves back and ultimately losing out. I'm the one winning in a situation where someone is acting stupid toward me. I have the advantage because when we **throw down**, in the final analysis I'm the one with the knowledge and the sense of self. The racist is the one who will forever have in his or her mind that I am bad and that they are good, which is a lie. It's just not true. Period. End of story. I get so tired of people believing in their heart of hearts that they can win or achieve anything by making someone feel inferior. I think that's how I have developed my defense mechanisms against racism; I just got so tired of hearing the rude remarks and having teachers and counselors tell me that there wasn't anything I could do about it. Because there most certainly is.

When I was younger, my teachers would tell me not to beat up these kids who were saying racist things to me because then they would win twice:

© Stephan Daigle/Corbis

▲ **Critical Viewing: Effect** Compare this image with Nicole's description of herself. How does the image make you feel?

In Other Words
look it square in the face deal with it
throw down have a conflict

I would look like twice the animal they were telling me I was. What made me mad was that I didn't think they were winning at all, never mind once or twice, and I felt **compelled** to do them the favor of making that completely clear. My teachers would tell me just to walk away, that I would come off more powerful if I just walked away, which, **in retrospect**, I suppose was true, but it took me a long time to truly believe that. It's all well and good in theory, but it doesn't exactly **eliminate** the feeling of having a knife twisted around in your gut. Now, as I've grown older, I find that it is really important to just be focused and to stay as positive as I can. I do still get angry, though. I have a real temper. Emotions and theory don't really go hand in hand, so it

> I find that it is **really important** to just **be focused** and to **stay as positive** as I can.

can be very difficult for me sometimes. But I have learned from my mistakes.

On the census checkoff lists that offer little boxes next to black, white, or other, I refuse to check just one box. I check them all off because I am all of those things. My mother told me that when I was born and she was filling out my birth certificate, the nurse asked her to write in *mulatto*, which my mother did not do. I think the word is incredibly negative and **degrading**. It sounds like a sickness. The part of me that is black-identified doesn't fit into a category or a box. Society has such awful ideas about black people, and I don't want society to decide for me what it means to be black. When I think of being black, I think of kings and queens and history and beauty and **authenticity**.

You can call me black if you want to, you can call me *mulatto*, you can call me biracial, you can call me whatever you please, but I'll still be Nicole. Are you going to remember me as "that black girl"? No, you're going to

Key Vocabulary
compel *v.*, to urge forcefully, to cause to do
● **eliminate** *v.*, to remove, to get rid of
authenticity *n.*, realness, genuineness

In Other Words
in retrospect in thinking about the past
mulatto person of both white and African American ancestry (in Spanish)
degrading insulting

Interact with the Text

3. Determine Viewpoint
Underline the sentences on page 36 that show that Nicole and her teachers feel differently about racism. Write their opposing opinions in your own words.

Possible response:

Nicole believes she can

do something about

people's racist attitudes.

Her teachers tell her

she cannot.

4. Clarify Vocabulary
Underline the words and phrases on page 37 that are examples of the word *category*. Write a definition in your own words.

Category means

"group."

5. Determine Viewpoint

Underline Nicole's reaction to people who have trouble accepting interracial relationships or biracial children. How does she feel?

Possible response:

Nicole wants people to call her by her name and nothing else. She does not care how others feel about her.

remember me as Nicole if you've taken the time to learn my name. And those who haven't taken the time, I don't care to be remembered by. It's Nicole today, it'll be Nicole tomorrow, and it'll be Nicole when I die. <u>I don't care if you have something against black people, or if you have a problem with **interracial relationships**, or if you don't like biracial kids. I don't care.</u> But if you are talking to me, <u>call me by my name.</u> ❖

In Other Words

interracial relationships friendships between people of different races

Selection Review Nicole

A. In this personal narrative, Nicole describes how she feels about racism. Write three things that you learned about how Nicole deals with racism because you knew about her personal feelings.

1. Nicole doesn't think about being biracial.

2. Nicole won't fight with people who discriminate against her.

3. Nicole won't put herself into a category.

B. Answer the questions.

1. How did knowing how to clarify vocabulary help you understand Nicole's experiences better? Give one example from the text.

Possible response: Knowing that I should look for a definition, synonym, or an example in the text helped me understand how to find the meanings for words that were unclear. I did not understand the word temper, but when I read the words and phrases around it, such as angry, emotions, and difficult for me, I figured out that the word means "strong emotion" like anger.

2. How does Nicole want people to remember her? Support your answer with examples from the text.

Nicole wants people to know her as Nicole, not as a person in a racial category. She does not feel that she can define herself, so she does not check a box on the census survey. Nicole wants to be known as just Nicole.

Reflect and Assess

WRITING: Write About Literature

A. Plan your writing. List important insights Uncle Tommy makes in "Skins." Then list events from the story "Skins" and your own personal insights that relate to it. *Answers will vary.*

Uncle Tommy's Insight	Event	My Personal Experience
"You can never tell what's in someone's heart."	Jimmy T pretends to be Native American.	

B. Which of Uncle Tommy's insights can you relate to? Write a personal statement. Support your statement using the information in the chart.

Students should support their answers with examples from the selection.

_____

_____

_____

_____

_____

_____

_____

_____

_____

_____

_____

LITERARY ANALYSIS: Static and Dynamic Characters

Main characters interact with the minor characters to move the plot of a story along. Characters who change throughout a story are **dynamic characters**. Characters who remain the same are **static characters**.

A. Think about the main and minor characters in "Skins." Identify each as a dynamic or static character. Then explain why you think each character is dynamic or static.

Character	Dynamic or Static?	Why Do You Think So?
Mitchell	dynamic	*Possible response:* Mitchell learns that skin color doesn't reveal someone's identity.
Jimmy T	dynamic	*Possible response:* Jimmy T admits he lies to hide his true identity and feels badly about it. He seeks help from Mitchell at the end.
Randolph	static	*Possible response:* Randolph is confident about his race and his Native American heritage throughout the story.

B. List two minor characters from the story "Skins." Choose one and explain how the minor character affects the changes Mitchell goes through in the story. *Answers will vary. Possible responses are shown.*

Minor Character 1: Randolph

Minor Character 2: Uncle Tommy

As the story goes on, Mitchell becomes good friends with Randolph. Randolph is part Native American,

which shocks Mitchell. Through Randolph, Mitchell learns that you can't always tell a person's identity by

the way they look.

C. Think about someone in your life who has caused you to look at or think about things in a different way. Explain your experience below.

Answers will vary.

VOCABULARY STUDY: Greek and Latin Roots

Many English words include roots from the languages of Greek and Latin. If you know what Greek and Latin roots mean, you can figure out the meanings of the English words. *Answers will vary. Possible responses are shown.*

A. For each word below, use the meaning of the root to figure out the word's meaning. Then, use a dictionary to check the word's meaning.

Word	Root	Root Meaning	What I Think the Word Means	Definition
autograph	graph	write	my own writing	in the writer's handwriting
benefit	bene	good	a good outcome of something	advantage or useful aid
dialogue	log	word, speech	conversation between people	a conversation between two or more people
manual	manu	hand	doing something by hand	of, related to, or involving the hands
visible	vis	see	able to see	capable of being seen

B. The chart below shows common Greek and Latin roots and their meanings. Complete the chart by listing words you've heard that contain each root.

Root	Meaning	Words I've Used
bio	life	biology
geo	earth	geography
hydro	water	hydration
meter	measure	centimeter
scrib	write	scribble

C. Use the meanings listed in the chart above to write a definition of each of these words. Check your meanings in a dictionary

biodegradable something that is made of ingredients that can be decomposed by bacteria into recyclable elements

geologist a person who studies the earth

hydrate to water

thermometer something that measures temperature

transcribe to copy something in one's own handwriting (or typing)

Read for Understanding

1. Genre What kind of text is this passage? How do you know?

It is a poem. The text is

organized in short lines

instead of in paragraphs.

2. Topic What is the text mostly about?

This text mostly tells

about a wife's frustration

with her husband's use

of the word *yes*.

Reread and Summarize

3. Key Ideas In each section, circle three words or phrases that express the big ideas in that section. Note next to each word or phrase why you chose it.

· Section 1: lines 1–14
· Section 2: lines 15–23
· Section 3: lines 24–39
· Section 4: lines 40–49

4. Summary Use your topic sentence and notes to write a summary of the selection.

Possible response: An

American wife doesn't

know how to resolve

a conflict with her

Filipino husband, who

doesn't give her the

straightforward answers

she wants.

Yes

BY DENISE DUHAMEL

According to *Culture Shock:*
A Guide to Customs and Etiquette
of Filipinos, when my husband says yes,
he could also mean one of the following:
5   a.) *I don't know.*
  b.) *If you say so.*
  c.) *If it will please you.*
  d.) *I hope I have said yes unenthusiastically enough*
     for you to realize I mean no.
10 You can imagine the confusion
surrounding our movie dates, the laundry,
who will take out the garbage
and when. I remind him
I'm an American, that all his yeses sound alike to me.

◁ **Critical Viewing: Effect** How do the images of the people in this painting illustrate the relationship of the people in the poem?

◁ *Possible response to Critical Viewing:* The images--a simple drawing with clean, black lines and a complex drawing with a variety of lines and colors--illustrate the two people in the poem and what they want. The wife wants her husband to use yes more clearly, but for the husband the word *yes* is more nuanced.

In Other Words
Etiquette Rules of Social Behavior
unenthusiastically unexcitedly, unhappily

15

I tell him here in America we have shrinks
who can help him to be less of a people-pleaser.
We have two-year-olds who love to scream "No!"
when they don't get their way. <u>I tell him,</u>
<u>in America we have a popular book,</u>

20

<u>*When I Say No I Feel Guilty.*</u>
<u>"Should I get you a copy?" I ask.</u>
<u>He says yes, but I think he means</u>
"If it will please you," i.e., "I won't read it."
"I'm trying," I tell him, "but you have to try too."

25

"Yes," he says, then makes *tampo*,
a sulking that the book *Culture Shock* describes as
"subliminal hostility . . . withdrawal of customary cheerfulness
in the presence of the one who has displeased" him.
The book says it's up to me to make things all right,

30

"to restore goodwill, not by talking the problem out,
but by showing concern about the wounded person's
well-being." Forget it, I think, even though I know
if I'm not nice, *tampo* can quickly escalate into *nagdadabog*—
foot stomping, grumbling, the slamming

35

of doors. Instead of talking to my husband, I storm off
to talk to my porcelain Kwan Yin,
the Chinese goddess of mercy
that I bought on Canal Street years before
my husband and I started dating.

40

"The real Kwan Yin is in Manila,"
he tells me. "She's called Nuestra Señora de Guia.
Her Asian features prove Christianity
was in the Philippines before the Spanish arrived."
My husband's telling me this

45

tells me he's sorry. Kwan Yin seems to wink,
congratulating me—my short prayer worked.
"Will you love me forever?" I ask,
then study his lips, wondering if I'll be able to decipher
what he means by his yes.

Reread and Analyze

5. Analyze Character
Reread lines 1–23.
Underline the text that
shows how the characters
interact. What does the
interaction show about
how the characters
communicate? Then
underline another example
of character interaction.

Answers will vary.

Possible response:

The speaker doesn't

understand what her

husband wants.

6. Analyze Conflict Reread
lines 1–14. Highlight
the text that shows the
conflict. Is the conflict
internal or external?

Answers will vary.

Possible response: The

conflict is external. The

speaker wants her

husband to use "yes"

more clearly.

7. Analyze Conflict
Highlight text that shows
more about the conflict.
What happens between the
speaker and her husband?
Is the conflict internal or
external? Explain.

Answers will vary.

CLOSE READING YES

Discuss

8. **Synthesize** With the class, list some of the details that the author uses to show the speaker's interactions and their conflict.

    Answers will vary. Possible responses: lines 10–24;

    lines 29–35

    Then, with the class, discuss why the author chooses those details.
    Make notes.

    Answers will vary but should include explicit examples of instances when the speaker deals with the conflict.

9. **Write** Use your notes from question 8 to explain how authors show characters in conflict. Think about the details that the author uses to show how characters interact. Use the following to organize your thoughts.

    - **Describe the interaction. How do the characters communicate?**
    - **Describe how the interaction is a conflict. Why is the speaker not getting what she wants?**
    - **Describe how the conflict ends. Is it internal or external? How does the speaker change?**
    - **Summarize how the details the author presents tell you about the characters.**

    Answers will vary but should include answers to all the questions above.

Connect with the **EQ** When Do You Really Know Someone?

Consider the role of culture in relationships.

10. Respond to the Essential Question Reread lines 40–49. When does the author think that she can really know her husband? What details lead you to say that? Be sure to use text evidence to support your answer.

Answers will vary. Responses should include evidence from the text.

_____

_____

_____

_____

_____

11. Theme Review the two quotations on the Unit Opener. Ask: Would the author agree with either of these quotations? Why? What is the writer's message about understanding, or knowing, other people?

Answers will vary. Responses should include evidence from the text.

_____

_____

_____

_____

_____

Key Vocabulary Review

A. Read each sentence. Circle the word that best fits into each sentence.

1. Practice can help athletes develop their natural (**expectation** / **potential**).

2. If you make someone do something, you (**compel** / **stigmatize**) them to do it.

3. Devoting yourself to a project for three nights in a row shows that you are (**pathetic** / **ambitious**).

4. Fire alarms are intentionally loud and (**discordant** / **lucid**) in order to get your attention.

5. A child who is a mathematical genius is a (**prodigy** / **pretense**).

6. You can check the (**perspective** / **authenticity**) of a painting by asking an art expert.

7. When you describe the appearance and qualities of something, you (**characterize** / **assert**) it.

8. If you can't prevent something from happening, it is (**pathetic** / **inevitable**).

B. Use your own words to write what each Key Vocabulary word means. Then write a synonym and an antonym for each word. *Answers will vary. Possible responses are shown.*

Key Word	My Definition	Synonym	Antonym
1. assert	to state positively	state	deny
2. eliminate	to put an end to	remove	add
3. lucid	easy to understand	sane	insane
4. obscure	to make dark	conceal	reveal
5. pathetic	capable of sadness or suffering	sad	funny
6. predominate	to be the most powerful	dominate	submit
7. reproach	an expression of disapproval	blame	praise
8. stigmatize	to label or brand	shame	honor

accusation	characterize	• eliminate	lucid	• potential	racism
ambitious	compel	expectation	obscure	• predominate	reproach
assert	discordant	• inevitable	pathetic	pretense	stigmatize
authenticity	• discriminate	• intensity	• perspective	prodigy	• tension

• **Academic Vocabulary**

C. Answer the questions using complete sentences. *Answers will vary. Possible responses are shown.*

1. What is your **perspective** about stereotypes?

   I think having stereotypes about certain people is narrow-minded and wrong.

2. What do you do to get rid of **tension**?

   I take a hot bath.

3. What **expectation** do you have for the future?

   I will go to college.

4. What would you do if someone made a false **accusation** against you?

   I would tell people the truth about what happened.

5. Describe one way to combat **racism**.

   You could join a protest or confront people who are racist.

6. When do you show **intensity**?

   I show intensity when I practice the piano.

7. In what way do people **discriminate** against teenagers?

   People discriminate against teenagers by watching teens too closely in stores.

8. Have you ever put on a **pretense**? Explain.

   I put on a pretense to impress a girl I liked.

Prepare to Read

▶ **La Vida Robot**
▶ **Reading, Writing, and . . . Recreation**

Key Vocabulary

A. How well do you know these words? Circle a rating for each word. Check your understanding of each word by choosing the synonym. Then, complete the sentences. If you are unsure of a word's meaning, refer to the Vocabulary Glossary, page 926, in your student text.

Rating Scale

1	I have never seen this word before.
2	I am not sure of the word's meaning.
3	I know this word and can teach the word's meaning to someone else.

Key Word	Check Your Understanding	Deepen Your Understanding
❶ contemplate (**kon**-tem-plāt) *verb* **Rating:** 1 2 3	When you **contemplate** something, you _____ it. ignore (consider)	The place I like to go to contemplate my future is _____ *Possible response:* my room _____ _____ _____.
❷ designate (**de**-zig-nāt) *verb* **Rating:** 1 2 3	When you **designate** something, you _____ it. (name) hide	A name on an office door can designate _____ *Possible response:* who works in that office _____ _____ _____.
❸ disciplined (**di**-su-plund) *adjective* **Rating:** 1 2 3	When you are **disciplined**, you are _____. (careful) reckless	Disciplined athletes make sure that they _____ *Possible response:* eat the right foods, exercise, and practice their sport _____ _____.
❹ implement (**im**-plu-ment) *verb* **Rating:** 1 2 3	To **implement** something is to _____ it. (perform) ignore	One time I tried to implement a plan to *Possible* *response:* recycle soda cans at school _____ _____.

Key Word	Check Your Understanding	Deepen Your Understanding
5 **innovative** (**i**-ne-vā-tiv) *adjective* **Rating:** 1 2 3	An **innovative** designer is usually a _____ person. (creative) unoriginal	An example of an innovative product is _____ *Possible response:* an electric car _____ _____ _____.
6 **perpetually** (pur-**pe**-chü-we-lē) *adverb* **Rating:** 1 2 3	When you **perpetually** do something, you are _____ doing it. never (always)	My friends are perpetually *Possible response:* going to the mall or surfing the Internet _____ _____ _____.
7 **procrastinate** (prō-**kras**-te-nāt) *verb* **Rating:** 1 2 3	To **procrastinate** is to _____. (delay) rush	I usually procrastinate when *Possible response:* I need to do homework or wash dishes _____ _____ _____.
8 **spontaneously** (spon-**tā**-nē-us-lē) *adverb* **Rating:** 1 2 3	If you speak **spontaneously**, you say something _____. (impulsively) carefully	Once my friends and I spontaneously decided to _____ *Possible response:* go to a concert _____ _____ _____.

B. Use one of the Key Vocabulary words to write about an expectation that another person has, or that many people have, for you. How does this expectation make you feel?

Answers will vary.

_____

_____

LITERARY ANALYSIS: Analyze Nonfiction Text Features

Nonfiction **text features**, such as section heads, diagrams, labels, photos, and captions, help show important information.

A. Look at the diagram below. What information does each part of the diagram show? Write the information in the chart.

ANATOMY OF A ROBOT

By using polyvinyl chloride pipe, or PVC pipe, the team built a robot that was not only cheaper but better. The hollow pipes made the robot lighter and easier to move, trapped air to help it float, and provided waterproof housing for the electrical wiring.

1. articulated pincer
2. battery
3. camera
4. control box
5. hydrophones
6. laser
7. pump
8. PVC elbow
9. PVC pipes
10. tape measure

◄ **Use Visuals to Access Text** Compare the diagram to the text. Which sentences describe the information in the diagram?

Text Feature	Information
Title	tells the subject of diagram, "Anatomy of a Robot"
Labels	point out the parts of the robot
Caption	explains why PVC was helpful to the team

B. What information can a text feature, like the diagram above, give the reader that text cannot?

Possible response: It would be very difficult to picture this robot if I could only read about it in the

text. The diagram points out the parts clearly.

FOCUS STRATEGY: Identify Main Ideas and Details

> ## HOW TO IDENTIFY MAIN IDEAS AND DETAILS
>
> **1. Turn Section Heads into Questions** Asking the question will help you find the details.
>
> **2. Collect Important Details** Find details, and list them in a chart.
>
> **3. Answer the Question** Use the details to answer the question. This is the main idea.
>
> **4. Determine What's Important** Decide what to remember from each section.

A. Read the passage. Use the strategies above to identify the main idea and details. Answer the questions below.

> ### Look Into the Text
>
> ### The Team
>
> The four teenagers who built [the robot] are all undocumented Mexican immigrants who came to this country through tunnels or hidden in the backseats of cars. They live in sheds and rooms without electricity. But over three days last summer, these kids from the desert proved they are among the smartest young underwater engineers in the country.

1. Rewrite the section head as a question.

Who was on the team?

2. List two important details about the team.

a. There are four Mexican immigrants.

b. They proved to be smart underwater engineers.

3. Answer the question you wrote for question 1. This is the main idea.

The team is made up of four immigrants who are very smart.

B. Return to the passage above. How does identifying the important details help you identify the main idea?

Possible response: Once I identified the important details, I used them to answer the question I had asked.

A. In "La Vida Robot," you learned how four teenagers overcame obstacles and challenged everyone's expectations. Reread the article, and complete the diagram below to show how the text features helped you understand the main idea and gave you important information.

Main-Idea Diagram

Main Idea:
The Carl Hayden team overcame many obstacles to win the competition.

Text Feature:
The picture and caption of the robot showed that it was built out of common, inexpensive materials.

Text Feature:
Possible response: The pictures and captions of the students told me about their experiences. None of them had experience in these types of competitions, and they were all immigrants in high school.

Text Feature:
Possible response: The chart about resources showed how little money the boys had to build a robot with and how they had only four team members, compared to twelve on MIT.

Text Feature:
Possible response: The map showed how far the boys had to travel to get to the competition.

Text Feature:
Possible response: The picture of the teams' robots and the competition helped me see how the robots were different and what the robots had to do.

B. Use the information from the diagram you completed on page 52 to answer the questions about the Carl Hayden team.

1. Why did the Carl Hayden team win the competition?

Possible response: They had the right kind of members for the team. Even though they didn't have as

many team members and had no experience, their solid scores in other categories gave them the lead

that allowed them to win.

2. How did the Carl Hayden team challenge the expectations of others with their innovative robot at the underwater robot competition? Use **innovative** in your answer.

The team used their knowledge in other areas and used common, inexpensive materials to build

an innovative robot that was lighter and smaller than the other robots.

C. Use your understanding of the article to answer the questions.

1. Oscar and Lorenzo stayed up all night making repairs to the robot while the others slept. What might have happened had they not done this?

Possible response: If they had not repaired the robot, it would not have performed as well as it

did. If the other two teammates had not slept, they may not have done as well in their tasks.

2. What did the team discover about their potential?

Possible response: The team discovered that though they lacked the resources and experience

of the other teams, they had the potential to win the competition and possibly to go on to

become engineers.

Interactive

Interact with the Text

1. Develop Ideas
Circle the statements that answer any of your "5Ws + H" questions, and label each either *who, what, why, where, when,* or *how* in the margin. What questions have not been answered yet?

Answers will vary.

_____

_____

_____

_____

_____

2. Develop Ideas
Why did Otto join the speech team? How did the extracurricular activity help her?

Extracurricular activities

helped Otto get into

Dartmouth College.

_____

_____

Reading, Writing, and . . . Recreation?

NANCY C. RODRIGUEZ

Why extracurricular activities give you "extra credit" toward success

---

Find something you like and get involved. But remember, school and grades come first. That's what students have to say about participating in extracurricular activities.

High school isn't just about going to classes, then heading home. It is also an opportunity for students to explore interests, take in new experiences, and get connected to their school. Or in the case of Courtney Otto, conquer a fear of public speaking.

Otto, who graduated from high school in May, joined the school's speech team in seventh grade, **confronting** her dislike of speaking before large groups.

Through her experience, Otto placed first in the state of Kentucky in public speaking and won the National Catholic Forensic League title in 2004, which helped her get accepted to Dartmouth College.

"For me, it's a challenge, which is something I enjoy," she said of being on the speech team. "A large part of it is just having the confidence. I can be **scared to death**, but I can get up and speak about things. I can share an opinion."

Most schools offer athletics, band, and drama. But there also are a **plethora of** other clubs that focus on everything from

Most schools offer extracurricular activities that relate to a wide variety of hobbies and interests.

In Other Words
confronting dealing with
scared to death extremely afraid
plethora of very large number of

foreign language and community service to skateboarding and chess. And many schools will let students start their own clubs if there is enough interest and a faculty member agrees to be the adviser.

Ashley Brown, a senior at Atherton High School, got involved with the Future Educators of America/Minority Teacher Recruitment club last year. Ashley, who wants to be a special-education teacher, said the club led her to another program that allows her to tutor students during school.

"I love doing it," she said. "It gives me a **sense of being** and makes me feel like I'm needed somewhere."

Being part of the club also gives her access to scholarships and information about teaching.

"It also helps you get respect with your other teachers because they see you like a mini one of them."

But being involved requires finding a balance between activities and schoolwork.

"It's definitely hard," said Taylor Distler, 15, a sophomore at St. Xavier

Joining a school team or club may contribute to your future success.

High School who is on the school's lacrosse team. "You've got to be kind of **disciplined** and manage your time."

Students say they find time for schoolwork during school, after school, and before practice or club meetings. Keisha Knight, 18, who graduated from Central High in May, said that students should begin working on assignments as soon as they get them, even if their deadline is sometime in the future.

"Don't **procrastinate**," she said. ❖

Key Vocabulary
disciplined *adj.*, self-controlled
procrastinate *v.*, to wait, delay

In Other Words
sense of being purpose

3. Relate Main Ideas and Details
Foreign language, community service, skateboarding, and chess are details that support what main idea? Write the main idea in your own words.

Possible response:

Schools offer activities

that would interest a

variety of students.

4. Interpret
How can students find a balance between activities and schoolwork?

Students have to be

disciplined. They have to

find time to do homework

before, during, and after

school.

Selection Review Reading, Writing, and . . . Recreation?

A. Reread the article, and list three details about Ashley Brown
that relate to the main idea. Remember to look for the five
Ws + H questions.

1. Brown gets to do something she loves, like educating.

2. Brown has an opportunity to tutor students during school.

3. Brown has access to scholarships and information about teaching.

Now use the details to determine the important idea about Brown.

Main Idea: Some students, like Brown, use clubs to help them explore what they want to do in

the future.

B. Answer the questions.

1. How is this news feature different from a regular news story?
Include the characteristics of a news feature in your answer.

A news feature is a special report about a specific topic in the news or in daily life. News

features tell *who*, *what*, *when, where, why,* and *how.*

2. What additional skills do you think Otto and Brown developed
by joining their different clubs? Write a paragraph.

Possible response: Otto learned how to speak in front of others, which probably helped her

have confidence in her ideas and thoughts. Brown tutored students, so she probably practiced

being patient, listening to students' questions, and explaining ideas clearly.

Reflect and Assess

WRITING: Write About Literature

A. Do you believe that people are best at what they enjoy doing? Think about whether or not you agree with this idea. Then find examples from each selection to support your opinion. *Answers will vary.*

La Vida Robot	Reading, Writing, and . . . Recreation?

B. Do you believe that people are best at what they enjoy doing? Write an opinion statement. Support it with an example from each selection.

Students should support their answers with examples from both selections.

_____

_____

_____

_____

_____

_____

_____

_____

_____

_____

_____

_____

Integrate the Language Arts

LITERARY ANALYSIS: Analogy and Allusion

An **analogy** is a comparison that is used to describe or explain something.
An **allusion** is a reference to a famous person, event, or literary character.

A. Read each sentence. Mark an *X* in the correct column to show if the
sentence contains an analogy or an allusion.

Sentence	Analogy	Allusion
The wires were slightly thicker than a human hair.	X	
Stinky entered the water careening wildly like a rowboat with two wrestling men.	X	
Cristian had the genius of a modern young Einstein.		X

B. Read each sentence. Is it an analogy or an allusion? Explain what is
being compared, or what is being referred to, and why.

1. MIT's ROV looked like a graceful diving duck as it motored smoothly
   down into the water.

   Analogy; compares MIT's ROV to a graceful diving duck to show how smooth, natural, and efficient the

   ROV moved

2. Like the *Apollo 13* crew, Oscar and Lorenzo stayed up all night
   resoldering the control system.

   Allusion; refers to a famous space mission and the hard work that the crew did to survive

3. The team from Carl Hayden Community High School was like the 1988
   Jamaican bobsled team at their first Olympics.

   Allusion; refers to a bobsled team that was also viewed as complete outsiders to their competition

C. Write one analogy or one allusion about someone or something in your
own life.

   Answers will vary.

VOCABULARY STUDY: Context Clues (Definitions)

Authors sometimes include a word's definition in the text to clarify the word's meaning. This kind of context clue is often set off by commas.

A. Read the sentences below. Find the context clues in the sentence. Use the clues to figure out the meanings of the underlined words. Write the meanings in the chart.

Sentence	Word Meaning
The spectators, without planning, jumped up and cheered spontaneously for the team from Carl Hayden High School.	suddenly, without planning
It was an easy plan to enter the ROV competition, but to put the plan into action, or implement it, was not so easy.	put the plan into action
Cristian perpetually, or always, thought of science questions that were connected to the world around him.	always

B. Write the Key Vocabulary words in the paragraph below. Use the context clues in the sentences to help you.

disciplined   **innovative**   **designate**

The ROV team from Carl Hayden High School was successful at the competition. They created an ___innovative___, or new and original, ROV for the competition. They painted the PVC pipe structures with different colors to ___designate___, or show, the different systems inside the pipe. Each team member's ___disciplined___, or controlled, effort helped create this extraordinary ROV.

C. Write your own sentences about "La Vida Robot," using the words below. Include a context clue within the sentence. Remember to set off the context clue with commas. *Answers will vary. Possible responses are shown.*

procrastinate   The team did not procrastinate, or delay, fixing the problems they discovered with Stinky at the Santa Barbara pool.

contemplate   The team members did not have to contemplate, or think carefully, about the answers they gave the judges.

Prepare to Read

▶ My Left Foot
▶ Success Is a Mind-Set

Key Vocabulary

A. How well do you know these words? Circle a rating for each word. Check your understanding of the word by circling *yes* or *no*. Then, complete the sentences. If you are unsure of a word's meaning, refer to the Vocabulary Glossary, page 926, in your student text.

Rating Scale

1	I have never seen this word before.
2	I am not sure of the word's meaning.
3	I know this word and can teach the word's meaning to someone else.

Key Word	Check Your Understanding	Deepen Your Understanding
❶ consequence (**kon**-su-kwens) *noun* **Rating:** 1 2 3	A **consequence** of eating junk food is stronger bones. Yes (No)	One positive consequence of walking to school is _____ *Possible response:* enjoying the outdoors
❷ contend (kun-**tend**) *verb* **Rating:** 1 2 3	Many teachers **contend** that students do better on tests after having a good night's sleep. (Yes) No	A belief I strongly contend to be true is _____ *Possible response:* that it is important to be honest with people
❸ conviction (kun-**vik**-shun) *noun* **Rating:** 1 2 3	A person with a strong **conviction** will stand up for what is right, even if it is not popular. (Yes) No	A conviction I have about my family and friends is _____ *Possible response:* that I should support their decisions
❹ dictate (**dik**-tāt) *verb* **Rating:** 1 2 3	Drivers can **dictate** what speed is appropriate for driving on the highway. Yes (No)	The outcome I can dictate is _____ *Possible response:* how well I will do in school

Key Word	Check Your Understanding	Deepen Your Understanding
5 **endeavor** (in-**de**-vur) *noun* **Rating:** 1 2 3	An **endeavor** is the result of a bad experience. Yes (No)	My greatest endeavor so far is *Possible response:* that I am captain of the debate team _____ _____ _____
6 **momentous** (mō-**men**-tus) *adjective* **Rating:** 1 2 3	Going to the mall is a **momentous** occasion for most people. Yes (No)	A momentous occasion I would like to experience in the future is *Possible response:* getting married _____ _____ _____
7 **profound** (prō-**fownd**) *adjective* **Rating:** 1 2 3	**Profound** ideas are those that people think are meaningful. (Yes) No	A situation that would cause me to think about profound ideas is *Possible response:* a funeral or hearing a political leader speak _____ _____
8 **transition** (tran-**zi**-shun) *noun* **Rating:** 1 2 3	It is difficult for some students to make the **transition** from high school to college. (Yes) No	A difficult transition I have made in my life is _____ *Possible response:* moving to a new country _____ _____ _____

B. Use one of the Key Vocabulary words to tell how one of your future goals might exceed the expectations of others.

Answers will vary. _____

_____

Before Reading My Left Foot

LITERARY ANALYSIS: Analyze Development of Ideas

In an **autobiography**, a real person tells his or her life story. Readers understand what is important to the writer by thinking about the details that the writer chooses to share and the way in which he or she presents those details.

A. Read the passage below. Then, complete the chart with text evidence that develops some of the writer's ideas.

Look Into the Text

> I was born in the Rotunda Hospital, on June 5th, 1932. There were nine children before me and twelve after me, so I myself belong to the middle group. Out of this total of twenty-two, seventeen lived, four died in infancy, leaving thirteen still to hold the family fort.
>
> Mine was a difficult birth, I am told. Both mother and son almost died.

Idea That the Writer Presents	Statement That Develops the Idea
Christy Brown grew up in an earlier generation than that of many of his readers.	I was born in the Rotunda Hospital, on June 5th, 1932.
Brown was not the only child in the family to have health problems.	Out of this total of twenty-two, seventeen lived, four died in infancy, leaving thirteen still to hold the family fort.
Brown almost didn't survive to adulthood.	Both mother and son almost died.

B. In your own words, explain the importance of this information by completing the sentence.

These details develop the idea that ___Christy Brown, who grew up in an earlier time, faced physical___
___challenges from his earliest days___

FOCUS STRATEGY: Summarize

> ## HOW TO SUMMARIZE
>
>
> 1. **Think about** the title, the genre, and the author to help you figure out the topic.
>
> 2. **Read a section** of the text to see what it explains.
>
> 3. **Note important details** by underlining words or phrases.
>
> 4. **Sum up** the main ideas as you read more paragraphs. Write a one-paragraph summary of the important ideas of the text.

A. Read the passage. As you read, underline the important details. Then, answer the questions below.

Look Into the Text

My Left Foot

by Christy Brown

They now spoke of an <u>institution</u>.

"<u>Never!</u>" said my mother almost fiercely, when this was suggested to her. "I know <u>my boy is not an idiot</u>. It is his body that is shattered, <u>not his mind</u>. I'm sure of that." . . .

I was now five, and still I showed no real sign of intelligence. I showed no apparent interest in things except with my toes—more especially those of my left foot. . . . I used to lie on my back all the time in the kitchen. . . . a little bundle of crooked muscles and twisted nerves, surrounded by a family that loved me. . . . I was lonely, imprisoned in a world of my own, unable to communicate with others, cut off, separated from them as though a glass wall stood between my existence and theirs, . . . I longed to run about and play with the rest, but I was unable to break loose from my bondage.

---

1. What are the two main ideas in this paragraph?

Main idea 1: Brown's mother did not want to put him in an institution because she knew that his mind was normal. Main idea 2: Brown could not express himself and felt he was cut off from life and his family.

2. Summarize the important ideas.

Even though Brown could not communicate, his mother refused to put him in an institution because she knew that his mind was healthy.

Selection Review My Left Foot

EQ **How Do People Challenge Expectations?**
Learn how people do "the impossible."

A. In "My Left Foot," you learned how Brown challenged people's expectations. Complete the T Chart below with the expectations people had for Brown and his life.

T Chart

His Parents' Expectations	Others' Expectations
He would live with his family, not in an institution, and not in a special home.	He should be institutionalized and under special care.
He would not be treated by any member in his family as "the difficult one."	He should not be taken seriously because by being taken seriously, he would only break everyone's heart.
He should be treated the same as everyone else.	He was an "imbecile," or was mentally challenged. There was no way to teach him anything.
His mind was not handicapped, even though his body was.	He should be treated differently by his family.
He was a loved member of the family.	

B. Use the information in the chart to answer the questions.

   1. Why did Brown's parents continue to believe in him?

   They had the conviction that Brown could do more, and they were not about to give up hope. Brown's

   mother, in particular, knew that his mind was not disabled.

   _____

   _____

   2. What did Brown's parents contend about Christy? How did what they contend challenge other people's expectations? Use **contend** in your answer.

   Brown's parents continued to contend that his body was disabled, not his mind. Doctors, friends, and

   relatives did not agree with them and advised them to treat Brown differently. They treated Brown's mother

   as if she was "impertinent" for believing in him.

   _____

C. Use your understanding of Brown's autobiography to answer the questions.

   1. How did Brown exceed people's expectations? How did he exceed his own expectations?

   Possible response: Brown learned to write, which no one thought he could do. He never believed he could

   control his body, but he learned to use his left foot to write, which gave him freedom he never thought he

   would have.

   _____

   2. What do you think this autobiography, published in 1955, did to help people with cerebral palsy? Write a paragraph.

   Possible response: The autobiography probably educated people who knew very little about the disease.

   It was probably the first time people understood his thoughts because Brown found a way to communicate

   with people who had low expectations for him.

   _____

   _____

   _____

   _____

   _____

   _____

   _____

Interactive

Connect Across Texts

In "My Left Foot," Christy Brown succeeded against the odds. In this interview, brain surgeon Benjamin Carson comments on people's potential.

Success Is a Mind-Set

interview from *Hewitt Magazine Online*

As a kid, Benjamin Carson was considered the "dummy" of his class, and he had a violent temper. "I was most likely to end up in jail, reform school, or the grave," he remembers. So how did he become a world-famous neurosurgeon?

Dr. Benjamin Carson is the director of pediatric neurosurgery at the Johns Hopkins Medical Institutions in Baltimore, Maryland. He is shown here discussing his work at an international press conference.

Ben was just 8 years old when his mother found out that the man she wed at 13 had another wife and five more children living across town. Sonja Carson filed for divorce and worked as **a domestic** to support Ben and his older brother. She observed her wealthy employers and shared insights with her sons. "This is how successful people behave," she'd say. "This is how they think. You boys can do it, too, and you can do it better!"

His mother's refusal to accept excuses for failure enabled Ben to make the **transition** from—in his own words—"the dumbest kid in fifth grade to one of the smartest kids in seventh grade." When he found his studies overwhelming, she'd say, "You weren't born to be a failure. You can do it."

Soon, the boy with poor grades and **low self-esteem** began thinking of himself as smart and acting accordingly. Academic awards and achievements followed. He received a scholarship to Yale and later went on to study medicine at the University of Michigan Medical School.

Dr. Carson encourages young people to believe in themselves.

Key Vocabulary
transition *n.*, slow change

In Other Words
a domestic a maid
low self-esteem little belief in his abilities

1. Summarize
Highlight the words or phrases in the last paragraph on page 67 that tell the most important information. Then summarize the information in your own words.

Possible response: As soon as he started thinking that he was smart, he began to act smart.

2. Interpret
Underline the key points that the author wants you to understand about neurosurgery. Then tell why you think the author gives this information about neurosurgery before the interview.

Possible response: The author wants to inform the reader about what Dr. Carson does and to show how difficult this type of medicine is to study.

3. Relate Details
Underline two examples of successful people on page 69. Explain how the examples help present Carson's ideas.

Possible response: The examples of his own brother and of Walter Anderson show that people can overcome negative influences.

Today, Dr. Carson performs about 400 surgeries each year, more than double the **caseload** of the average neurosurgeon. He's the author of three books and the cofounder, with his wife, Candy, of the Carson Scholars Fund, a nonprofit organization that recognizes and rewards academic achievement with college-assistance funds.

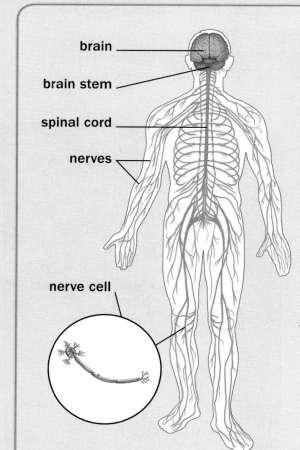

brain

brain stem

spinal cord

nerves

nerve cell

What Is Neurosurgery?
Neurosurgery is the area of medicine that focuses on the entire nervous system, including the brain and spine. Neurosurgeons treat a wide range of conditions, such as severe back injuries, brain tumors, and spinal cord injuries. In order to become a neurosurgeon, a medical student has to undergo an additional six to eight years of training after four years of medical school.

In Other Words
caseload amount of work

Q: Yours is an amazing success story. Why did you succeed when others in similar situations fail?

A: I'm always quick to point out that it's not just me; <u>my brother is also very successful.</u> We had, in our mother, someone who believed in us and was willing **to make sacrifices on our behalf**. She encouraged us to believe in ourselves. Success is **a mind-set**. If you have negative influences coming at you and you allow them to **dictate** your course in life, you'll never succeed. When you realize that the person with the greatest influence over what happens in your life is you, it makes a huge difference. <u>Look at Walter Anderson, the CEO and publisher of *Parade* magazine. Growing up, his father didn't think reading was a worthwhile</u> **endeavor**<u>; he would beat him if he caught him reading. Instead of using that as an excuse for failure, Walter grew up to be the publisher of the largest-circulation magazine in the world.</u>

Q: You've said, "Successful people don't have fewer problems, just different ways of looking at them." How so?

A: It all goes back to mind-set. How do you look at the problems you face—are they fences or are they hurdles? If you view them as fences, you allow them to contain you and they become excuses for inaction. But if you view problems as hurdles, then you have choices. You can go over them or under them or around them. It doesn't matter how you get by that hurdle; it just matters that you do. And each time you get by another hurdle, it strengthens you for the next one. In a corporate setting, it's essential that leaders not allow their employees to make excuses; eventually they'll stop constructing fences and start jumping hurdles. They learn to deal with and overcome their problems, and that leads to success.

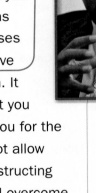

Interact with the Text

4. Relate Details
Circle the comparison that answers the interviewer's second question. Then explain the comparison in your own words.

Possible response: A

problem is like a fence if

you let it keep you from

taking action. It is like a

hurdle if can choose to

overcome it.

Key Vocabulary
dictate *v.*, to control, determine
endeavor *n.*, serious effort or try

In Other Words
to make sacrifices on our behalf to give up things for us
a mind-set a way of thinking, a belief

5. Summarize

Highlight the sentence that best summarizes the important idea in this paragraph. Then explain how you can use this concept in your own life.

Possible response: If I want to succeed, I really need to put the work into it. I also need to want the results for myself and no one else.

Q: **In your most recent book, *The Big Picture*, you talk about understanding why to succeed. Can you explain?**

A: People must want success for themselves, not because others demand it of them. Children are the best example. We say, "You need to study. You need to get A's." Soon they think they're doing it for Mom, Dad, or their teacher. They need to know they're doing it for themselves. They must understand that they have seventy to eighty years of life to live, the first twenty of which must be used to prepare. If they prepare, they'll have fifty years **to reap the benefits**. If they don't, they'll have fifty years to suffer the **consequences**. ❖

Key Vocabulary
• **consequence** *n.*, result, effect

In Other Words
to reap the benefits to enjoy the rewards

Selection Review Success Is a Mind-Set

A. Write a summary of one of these topics.

> **Topic 1:** **Dr. Carson's advice for success**
> **Topic 2:** **The role of Dr. Carson's mother in his life**

Possible responses: 1: He says that if you believe it, you can achieve it. 2: His mother had a great impact on his life by believing that he was just as good as anyone else.

B. Answer the questions.

1. How did the question-and-answer organization of this interview help you understand the information more clearly?

Possible response: I knew what the topic of each paragraph would be by reading the questions. I also was able to sum up important ideas before I moved to a new topic.

2. This article is based on the idea that success is mainly a result of your own thought process. Do you agree? Why or why not?

Possible response: I do agree that we can become anything we want. People need to believe in themselves and keep trying. If they do that, they will eventually succeed.

Reflect and Assess

WRITING: Write About Literature

A. Plan your writing. Read the opinion statement below. Think about whether you agree or disagree. Write examples from both texts that support your beliefs. *Answers will vary.*

> **Opinion:** Most people decide when they are young whether they can succeed.

My Left Foot	Success Is a Mind-Set

B. Do you agree that most people decide when they are young whether or not they can succeed? Write an opinion statement. Use examples from both texts to support your opinion.

Students should support their answers with examples from both selections.

_____

_____

_____

_____

_____

_____

_____

_____

_____

Integrate the Language Arts

LITERARY ANALYSIS: Author's Purpose, Text Structure, and Point of View

An **author's purpose** is the author's reason for writing. Stories told in **first-person point of view** allow the reader to experience the thoughts of the writer firsthand. Authors can organize the text in **chronological order**, or the order of events in which they happened.

A. Read the excerpt from "My Left Foot." Then answer the questions about first-person point of view.

> Suddenly I wanted desperately to do what my sister was doing. Then— without thinking or knowing exactly what I was doing, I reached out and took the stick of chalk out of my sister's hand—*with my left foot.*

1. How did the writer feel at the moment that is described?

He wanted desperately to do what his sister was doing.

2. How do you, as a reader, benefit from reading text that is written from the first-person point of view?

Possible response: I know exactly what the writer was feeling. I can trust that the writer will tell the events truthfully and accurately.

B. Write three main events from Brown's autobiography in chronological order.

Event 1	Event 2	Event 3
Christy was born with cerebral palsy.	Christy learned how to write with his left foot.	Christy became a writer.

Why do you think the author told the story in chronological order? How does this text structure help develop the author's ideas?

Possible response: The author used chronological order to show how each event impacted the ones that followed.

C. Write a paragraph describing an important event in your own life. Use first-person point of view and chronological order.

Answers will vary.

VOCABULARY STUDY: Context Clues (Multiple-Meaning Words)

Use **context clues** in a sentence to figure out the meaning of a word that has more than one meaning. *Answers will vary. Possible responses are shown.*

A. Read each sentence below. Use the context of the sentence to write the meaning of each underlined word.

1. Please <u>sign</u> your name on the bottom of the contract.

   write or autograph

2. My favorite <u>play</u> is *Death of a Salesman.*

   theatrical performance

3. My grandmother is a very <u>kind</u> person.

   caring

4. She lives in a two-<u>story</u> house.

   level or floor

5. Beautiful flowers grow in the <u>park</u> near my house.

   a place where people go to enjoy nature

B. Write two meanings for each word in the chart.

Multiple-Meaning Words	Meaning 1	Meaning 2
band	a musical group	something that is in the shape of a circle
check	to look over something	something written out in place of cash
light	not heavy	the opposite of dark
trip	a vacation	to fall

C. Write a sentence using one meaning for each word in the chart. Use context clues that would help other readers figure out this meaning.

1. The band played my favorite song.
2. I wrote a check for my new jeans and handed it to the cashier.
3. A feather is very light in comparison to a bowling ball.
4. I hope to take a trip to New York this summer.

Prepare to Read

▶ **The Freedom Writers Diary**
▶ **Strength, Courage, and Wisdom**

Key Vocabulary

A. How well do you know these words? Circle a rating for each word. Check your understanding by marking an *X* next to the correct definition. Then respond to the questions using complete sentences. If you are unsure of a word's meaning, refer to the Vocabulary Glossary, page 926, in your student text.

Rating Scale

1	I have never seen this word before.
2	I am not sure of the word's meaning.
3	I know this word and can teach the word's meaning to someone else.

Key Word	Check Your Understanding	Deepen Your Understanding
1 alienation (ā-lē-e-**nā**-shun) *noun* **Rating:** 1 2 3	[X] the state of being alienated [ ] the state of being alive	What is an example of alienation? *Possible response:* An example of alienation is being isolated from a group.
2 commiserate (ku-**mi**-zu-rāt) *verb* **Rating:** 1 2 3	[ ] to disregard [X] to sympathize	How could you show that you commiserate with someone? *Possible response:* I could console him or her.
3 empathize (**em**-pu-thīz) *verb* **Rating:** 1 2 3	[X] to understand [ ] to be inconsiderate	How can you empathize with others? *Possible response:* I can show them that I understand how they feel.
4 ethnicity (eth-**ni**-se-tē) *noun* **Rating:** 1 2 3	[ ] choice [X] race	What types of things are part of your ethnicity? *Possible response:* My religion and family background are part of my ethnicity.

Key Word	Check Your Understanding	Deepen Your Understanding
5 **integrate** (**in**-tu-grāt) *verb* **Rating:** 1 2 3	☐ to separate or divide ☒ to combine or mix together	If you integrate people, what might the effect be? _____ *Possible response:* Integration can lead to equality. ____ _____ _____ _____
6 **perception** (pur-**sep**-shun) *noun* **Rating:** 1 2 3	☒ an observation ☐ a preference	What can affect your perception of something? _____ *Possible response:* My perception can be affected by what I am told and who tells me about it. _____ _____ _____
7 **segregation** (se-gri-**gā**-shun) *noun* **Rating:** 1 2 3	☒ the separation of races ☐ the unity of all people	What does segregation mean to you? _____ *Possible response:* Segregation is a way of thinking that often leads to intolerance and injustice. _____ _____ _____
8 **tolerance** (**to**-lu-runs) *noun* **Rating:** 1 2 3	☒ respect ☐ indifference	How would you characterize people who show tolerance? *Possible response:* People who show tolerance are thoughtful and open-minded. _____ _____ _____.

B. Use one of the Key Vocabulary words to write about a time you proved yourself, despite the odds.

Answers will vary. _____

_____

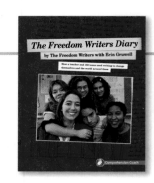

LITERARY ANALYSIS: Relate Ideas

A **diary** is a nonfiction account in which a writer records daily life events, thoughts, and feelings. The choice of details and the way in which those details are presented reveal what is important to the writer.

A. Read the passage below. Look for the events and the writer's thoughts and feelings about what is important. Then complete the chart.

Look Into the Text

Dear Diary,

We've been talking about the war in Bosnia and how similar some of the events are to the Holocaust. We have been reading about a young girl named Zlata, who many call the modern-day Anne Frank. Zlata and I seem to have a lot in common because while Zlata was living through a war in Sarajevo, I was living through a different kind of war—the L.A. riots. Ironically, Zlata and I were both eleven years old when our city was under siege. I can understand how afraid and scared she was to see her city go up in flames, because my city was on fire, too.

Event	What's Important to the Writer
the war in Bosnia	The war in Bosnia is similar to the Holocaust and the L.A. riots.
Zlata and the war in Sarajevo	It is ironic that Zlata was the same age as she was at the time and that both girls were experiencing violence.
L.A. riots	The writer was scared because her city was in flames.

B. Complete the sentence about the writer.

The writer feels a connection with Zlata because Zlata and the writer have lived through violent times.
They were both afraid when their cities were full of violence.

FOCUS STRATEGY: Determine What's Important

HOW TO DETERMINE WHAT'S IMPORTANT

Focus Strategy

Track your thoughts by taking notes on the following:

1. **Find the Main Idea** Write what the selection is mainly about.

2. **Take Note of Important Details** Write key information.

3. **Summarize** Write the most important ideas in your own words.

A. Read the passage. As you read, use the strategies above to determine what's important. Then answer the questions.

Look Into the Text

When I got a hold of the picture, I went ballistic. "This is the type of (propaganda) that (the Nazis) used during (the Holocaust)," I yelled. When a student timidly asked me, "What's the Holocaust?" I was shocked.

I asked, "How many of you have heard of the Holocaust?" (Not a single person) raised his hand. Then I asked, "How many of you have been shot at?" Nearly every hand went up.

I immediately decided to throw out my meticulously planned lessons and make (tolerance) the core of my (curriculum.)

From that moment on, I would try to (bring history to life) by using new books, inviting guest speakers, and going on field trips. . . .

---

1. What is this passage mainly about?

   This passage tells how a teacher decided to teach a lesson on tolerance after her students told her they had

   never heard of the Holocaust.

2. What is the most important idea?

   Answers will vary.

   _____

B. Return to the passage above. Circle the details that helped you answer the questions.

How Do People Challenge Expectations?
Find out why people challenge expectations.

A. In "The Freedom Writers Diary," you learned how people's expectations are challenged. Reread Student Diary #41, and compare what the student expected to learn with what the student actually learned. Complete the T Chart.

T Chart

What the Student Expected	What the Student Experienced
expected to learn about racial tolerance	student had life-altering experience
did not expect to make a connection with Holocaust survivor	identified with Holocaust survivor's life experiences
	compared Gestapo to gangs

B. Use the information in the chart to answer the questions.

1. How were the writer's expectations challenged?

The writer didn't expect to have such a connection with the Holocaust survivor. The writer identified with the survivor in a real way.

2. The diary writer was able to empathize with author Anne Frank and Holocaust survivor Gerda Seifer. How did this change her perception of the Holocaust? Use **perception** in your answer.

The writer's perception changed because she was able to understand the feelings of Holocaust victims Frank and Seifer.

3. Why are the diaries the Freedom Writers kept and the stories they share important for people to read?

The diaries explore the writers' thoughts and feelings about racial intolerance in the past and present. It is important for these stories to be heard and for people to tell them so that intolerance can be stopped before it starts.

Connect Across Texts
The students in "The Freedom Writers Diary" learned to **empathize** *with people who stood up for human rights. In this song, the singer realizes that she needs to stand up for her convictions.*

Strength, Courage, and Wisdom
by India Arie

Verse 1
Inside my head there lives a dream that I want to see in the sun.
Behind my eyes there lives a me that I've been hiding for much too long.
'Cause I've been too afraid to let it show
'Cause I'm scared of the judgment that may follow,
   Always putting off my living for tomorrow.

Pre-Chorus
   It's time to step out on faith. I've gotta show my faith.
      It's been elusive for so long, but freedom is mine today.
         I've gotta step out on faith. It's time to show my faith.
            Procrastination had me down, but look what I have found.
             I found

Chorus
   Strength, courage, and wisdom
   It's been inside of me all along.
   Strength, courage, and wisdom
   Inside of me.

Verse 2
   Behind my pride there lives a me that knows humility.
   Inside my voice there is a soul, and in my soul, there is a voice.
   But I've been too afraid to make a choice.
   'Cause I'm scared of the things that I might be missing,
Running too fast to stop and listen.

India Arie performs at a festival in Colorado.

In Other Words
It's been elusive It's been hard to find

Interact with the Text

1. Determine What's Important
Underline a line in the first verse that you consider important. Write a sentence that explains why you chose that line.

Possible response: When I think about what Arie goes on to say, I realize that in this line, she begins to state her decision to change.

2. Word Choice
Circle the repeated words and phrases in the Pre-Chorus and Chorus. Why does Arie use repetition in her song?

She uses repetition to emphasize the most important words, so the listener knows what the song is about.

3. Interpret

Circle the Bridge section. What do the lines in the Bridge section mean? Summarize the section in your own words.

These lines mean that if

you believe in yourself,

almost anything is

possible.

[Repeat Pre-Chorus]

[Repeat Chorus]

Bridge

I close my eyes and I think of all the things that I want to see.
'Cause I know now that I've opened up my heart
I know that anything I want can be.
So let it be. So let it be.
    So let it be. So let it be.

Strength, courage, and wisdom.
    It's been inside of me all along.
    Strength, courage, and wisdom.
    It's been inside of me all along.
    Strength, courage, and wisdom
Inside of me.

Selection Review Strength, Courage, and Wisdom

A. Reread the song, and circle the section that you consider the most important. Write its importance below.

The section that I think is most important is *Possible responses:* the Chorus

because it has powerful word choices—word choices that show not only what Arie realizes about

herself but also what listeners can apply in their own lives.

B. Answer the questions.

1. Choose a line Arie repeats. What is she trying to say? Why does she repeat these lines?

Answers will vary, but students should be able to determine that Arie repeats words and phrases

that are important to her.

2. Which line in the song do you think that most listeners would find most important? Why?

Answers will vary.

Reflect and Assess

WRITING: Write About Literature

A. Plan your writing. Both texts include advice about overcoming obstacles. List the most important and useful recommendations from each text in the chart below. *Answers will vary.*

The Freedom Writers Diary	Strength, Courage, and Wisdom

B. Imagine it is Ms. Gruwell's first day as an English teacher. How do you think she feels? Write a short advice letter to her, using the ideas from the chart.

Students should support their letters with examples from both selections.

_____

_____

_____

_____

_____

_____

_____

_____

_____

_____

_____

LITERARY ANALYSIS: Analyze Point of View

In **first-person point of view**, a person or character uses the pronouns *I*, *my*, and *me* to describe what he or she did, thought, or felt.

In **third-person point of view**, a person or character uses the pronouns *she*, *he*, and *they* to describe what someone else did or thought.

A. Read each sentence. Circle the first-person pronouns.

1. When (I) got a hold of the picture, (I) went ballistic.

2. It's uncanny how many similarities (my) students have with Anne and Zlata.

3. (I) did find (myself) within the pages of the book, like she said (I) would.

4. After all, history tells (me) that (I) am not alone.

B. Rewrite the sentences in Activity A in third-person point of view.
Answers will vary. Possible responses are shown.

1. When she got a hold of the picture, she went ballistic.

2. It's uncanny how many similarities her students have with Anne and Zlata.

3. She did find herself within the pages of the book, like she said she would.

4. After all, history tells her that she is not alone.

Which version of the sentences sounds more believable? Why?
Possible response:
The sentences that include first-person point of view sound more believable. I can hear the person's feelings and voice. The sentences that include third-person point of view are not as believable because the speaker could be wrong.

C. Think of a recent experience you have had. Write about it in first-person point of view. Then write about the same experience in third-person. *Answers will vary.*

First-person: _____

_____

Third-person: _____

_____

VOCABULARY STUDY: Context Clues: Examples

Context clues, or clues in nearby words and sentences, can help you figure out the meaning of an unfamiliar word. An **example** is one type of context clue. Words that signal an example include *like*, *such as*, *including*, and *for example*.

A. Circle the signal words in the sentences.

1. The Freedom Writers studied historic events, (such as) the Holocaust, the war in Sarajevo, and civil rights.

2. The protagonists of these books, (like) Anne Frank and Zlata Filipovic, opened the students' eyes to a new way of seeing the world.

3. Houses can have different types of annexes—(for example,) attics, secret rooms, and tornado shelters.

B. Use the words and definitions to write sentences with examples and signal words in the chart below.   *Answers will vary. Possible responses are shown.*

Word	Definition	My Sentence
elusive	hard to find	There are many things that are elusive in my messy bedroom, including my socks and my books.
perception	observation or feeling	*Possible response:* The book contained people's perceptions of ancient art, such as their admiration and curiosity.
utopia	a perfect place	*Possible response:* We studied different writers' ideas about utopia, like an island paradise, heaven, and a perfect city.

C. Read the sentences below. Use the context clues in each sentence to figure out which word completes the sentence.

chronicles   convictions   ethnicities

1. Sometimes it is necessary to stand up for important _____convictions_____, such as integrity, freedom, and strength.

2. Americans are all different _____ethnicities_____, like Asian American, Latino, and Native American.

3. Reading _____chronicles_____, including diaries, letters, and songs, is a useful way to learn history.

Read for Understanding

1. Genre What kind of text is this passage? How do you know?

This is a nonfiction

personal narrative. Its

events seem to be true,

and they are told by a

first-person narrator.

2. Topic What is the passage mostly about?

The text mostly tells

about Salak's journey

down the Niger River

and how she feels about

her adventure.

Reread and Summarize

3. Word Choice In each section, circle three words or phrases that express the big ideas in that section. Note next to each word or phrase why you chose it.

· Section 1: paragraphs 1–2
· Section 2: paragraphs 3–7
· Section 3: paragraphs 8–11
· Section 4: paragraphs 12–20

4. Summary Use your topic sentence and notes to write a summary of the selection.

Possible response: A

woman recounts her

solitary journey down the

Niger River.

from
The Cruelest Journey
by Kira Salak

1 In the beginning, my journeys feel at best **ludicrous**, at worst insane. This one is no exception. The idea is to paddle nearly 600 miles on the Niger River in a kayak, alone, from the Malian town of Old Ségou to Timbuktu. And now, at the very hour when I have decided to leave, a thunderstorm bursts open the skies, sending down **apocalyptic** rain, washing away the very ground beneath my feet. It is the rainy season in Mali, for which there can be no comparison in the world. Lightning pierces trees, slices across houses. Thunder racks the skies and pounds the earth like **mortar fire**, and every living thing huddles in **tenuous** shelter, expecting the world to end. Which it doesn't. At least not this time. So that we all give a collective sigh to the salvation of the passing storm as it rumbles its way east, and I **survey** the river I'm to leave on this morning. Rain or no rain, today is the day for the journey to begin. And no one, not even the oldest in the village, can say for certain whether I'll get to the end.

2 "Let's do it," I say, leaving the shelter of an **adobe** hut. My guide from town, Modibo, points to the north, to further storms. He says he will pray

Remi Benali, 2003.

Kira Salak paddles
down the Niger River.

In Other Words
ludicrous foolish
apocalyptic powerful and intense
mortar fire bombs
tenuous fragile, weak
survey look over, study
adobe clay

Geographical Background
Timbuktu is in the African country of Mali. From 1400 to 1600, it was a key trading post and center of learning. The Niger River flows south of Timbuktu.

Timbuktu, MALI
Niger River
AFRICA

for me. It's the best he can do. To his knowledge, no man has ever completed such a trip, though a few have tried. And certainly no woman has done such a thing. This morning he took me aside and told me he thinks I'm crazy, which I understood as concern and thanked him. He told me that the people of Old Ségou think I'm crazy too, and that only uncanny good luck will keep me safe.

3   Still, when a person tells me I can't do something, I'll want to do it all the more. It may be a failing of mine. I carry my inflatable kayak through the narrow passageways of Old Ségou, past the small adobe huts melting in the rains,

> **This morning he took me aside and told me he thinks I'm crazy...**

past the huddling goats and smoke of cooking fires, people peering out at me from the dark entranceways. It is a **labyrinth** of ancient homes, built and rebuilt after each storm, plastered with the very earth people walk upon. Old Ségou must look much the same as it did in Scottish explorer Mungo Park's time when, exactly 206 years ago to the day, he left on the first of his two river journeys down the Niger to Timbuktu, the first such trip by a Westerner. It is no coincidence that I've planned to leave on the same day and from the same spot. Park is my benefactor of sorts, my guarantee. If he could travel down the Niger, then so can I. And it is all the guarantee I have for this trip—that an obsessed nineteenth-century adventurer did what I would like to do. Of course Park also died on this river, but I've so far managed to overlook that.

4   Hobbled donkeys cower under a new onslaught of rain, ears back, necks craned. Little naked children dare each other to touch me, and I make it easy for them, stopping and holding out my arm. They stroke my white skin as if it were velvet, using only the pads of their fingers, then stare at their hands for wet paint.

5   Thunder again. More rain falls. I stop on the shore, near a centuries-old kapok tree under which I imagine Park once took shade. I open my bag, spread out my little red kayak, and start to pump it up. A couple of women nearby, with colorful cloth wraps called *pagnes* tied tightly about their breasts, gaze at me cryptically, as if to ask: *Who are you and what do you think you're doing?* The Niger churns and slaps the shore, in a **surly** mood. I don't pretend to know what I'm doing. Just one thing at a time now, kayak inflated, kayak loaded with my gear. Paddles fitted together and ready. Modibo is standing on the shore, watching me.

In Other Words
labyrinth maze, network
surly annoyed, unfriendly

Reread and Analyze

5. Nonfiction Text Features
In the Geographical Background feature on page 84, circle the name of Salak's destination. What does this information add to the main idea?

Possible response:

Timbuktu is a place that

is important to African

history.

6. Determine Importance
Reread paragraph 3. Underline the text that explains why Mungo Park is important as a "benefactor" to Salak.

7. Development of Ideas
Go back to paragraph 5. Highlight the details that show how Salak prepares to leave in her kayak.

8. Development of Ideas
How do the details about getting ready to launch show what is important to Salak?

Possible response:

The details name steps

that Salak performs

despite the rain and the

onlookers. The short,

plain sentences suggest

that she is forcing herself

to do these things and

not to turn back.

9. Determine Importance
In paragraph 8, underline the reason that Salak finds Mungo Park's writing fascinating. Why do you think Salak thought it was important to include these ideas?

Possible response: Salak identifies with Mungo Park, who risked many dangers in his Niger River journey but never allowed fear to show in his writing about the journey.

10. Analyze Development of Ideas Reread paragraph 10. Highlight the words in the paragraph that presents a new event. Circle the words that show the author's reaction. What important idea do we learn about the author?

Possible response:
We learn that she is mentally and physically strong and that she is a determined individual.

---

6   "I'll pray for you," he reminds me.

7   I balance my gear, adjust the straps, get in. And, finally, **irrevocably**, I paddle away.

8   When Mungo Park left on his second trip, he never admitted that he was scared. It is what fascinates me about his writing—his insistence on maintaining an illusion that all was well, even as he began a journey that he knew from previous experience could only beget tragedy. Hostile peoples, unknown rapids, malarial fevers. Hippos and crocodiles. The giant Lake Debo to cross, like being set adrift on an inland sea, no sight of land, no way of knowing where the river starts again. Forty of his forty-four men dead from sickness, Park himself afflicted with dysentery when he left on this ill-fated trip. And it can **boggle** the mind, what drives some people to risk their lives for the mute promises of success. It boggles my mind, at least, as I am caught up in the same affliction. Already, I fear the irrationality of my journey, the relentless stubbornness that drives me on.

9   The storm erupts in a new overture. Torrential rains. Waves higher than my kayak, trying to **capsize** me. But my boat is self-bailing and I stay afloat. The wind drives the current in reverse, tearing and ripping at the shores, sending spray into my face. I paddle madly, crashing and driving forward. I travel inch by inch, or so it seems, arm muscles smarting and rebelling against this journey.

10   A popping feeling now and a screech of pain. My right arm lurches from a ripped muscle. But this is no time and place for such an injury, and I won't tolerate it, stuck as I am in a storm. I try to get used to the **metronome-like** pulses of pain as I fight the river. There is only one direction to go: forward.

11   I wonder what we look for when we embark on these kinds of trips. There is the pat answer that you tell the people you don't know: that you're interested in seeing a place, learning about its people. But then the trip begins and the hardship comes, and hardship is more honest: it tells us that we don't have enough patience yet, nor humility, nor gratitude. And we thought that we had. Hardship brings us closer to truth, and thus is more difficult to bear, but from it alone comes **compassion**. And I've told the

> ## Already, I fear the irrationality of my journey…

In Other Words
irrevocably permanently
boggle confuse, puzzle
capsize overturn
metronome-like regular
compassion concern for others

world that it can do what it wants with me if only, by the end, I have learned something more. A **bargain**, then. The journey, my teacher.

12 And where is the river of just this morning, with its whitecaps that would have liked to drown me, with its current flowing backward against the wind? Gone to this: a river of smoothest glass, a placidity unbroken by wave or eddy, with islands of lush greenery awaiting me like distant **Xanadus**.

13 I barely travel at one mile an hour, the river preferring—as I do—to loiter in the sun. I lean down in my seat and hang my feet over the sides of the kayak. I eat turkey jerky and wrap up my injured arm, part of which has swollen to the size of a grapefruit. I'm not worried about the injury anymore. I'm not worried about anything. I know this feeling won't last, but for now I wrap myself in it, feeling the rare peace. To reach a place of not worrying is a greater freedom than anything I could hope to find on one of these trips. It is my true Undiscovered Country.

14 The Somono fishermen, casting out their nets, puzzle over me as I float by.

15 "*Ça va, madame?*" they yell.

16 Each fisherman carries a young son perched in the back of his pointed canoe to do the paddling. The boys stare at me, transfixed; they have never seen such a thing. A white woman. Alone. In a red, inflatable boat. Using a two-sided paddle.

17 I'm an even greater novelty because Malian women don't paddle here, not ever. It is a man's job. So there is no good explanation for me, and the people want to understand. They want to see if I'm strong enough for it, or if I even know how to use a paddle. They want to determine how sturdy my boat is. They gather on the shore in front of their villages to watch me pass, the kids screaming and jumping in excitement, the women with hands to foreheads to shield the sun as they stare, men yelling out questions in Bambarra which by now I know to mean: "Where did you come from? Are you alone? Where's your husband?" And of course they will always ask: "Where are you going?"

18 "Timbuktu!" I yell out to the last question.

19 "*Tombouctou!?!*" they always repeat, just to be sure.

20 "*Awo,*" I say in the Bambarra I've learned. "Yes." ❖

Remi Benali, 2003.

In Other Words
bargain agreement, deal
Xanadus grand, luxurious places
Ça va, madame? Is everything OK, ma'am? (in French)

11. Relate Ideas
Highlight one fact and one personal observation in paragraph 13. How do they work together to express an important idea?

Possible highlighting is shown. *Possible response:* The fact of the slow, calm rate gives Salak a feeling of peace. These details show Salak's physical and emotional progress.

12. Relate Ideas Underline the questions that appear in paragraphs 14–20. How do these questions reflect important ideas in the narrative?

Possible response:
The men's questions suggest that it is unusual for a woman to make a dangerous journey alone. Salak's unusual determination is an important idea throughout the narrative. In addition, the reference to Timbuktu points to of the importance of this journey to Salek.

Discuss

13. **Synthesize** With the class, list some of the details that help you understand important ideas in this nonfiction narrative.

Answers will vary. Possible responses: the example of Mungo Park, the contrast between the author and the local residents, the contrast between the vivid description of the bad weather and her own matter-of-fact preparations.

Then, with the class, discuss how authors choose details to show readers what is important. Make notes.

Answers will vary but should note authors' personal reflections as well as the factual details that they relate.

14. **Write** Use your notes from item 13 to write about the ways that the author expresses important ideas. Use the questions below to organize your thoughts.

- · What are the important ideas in this narrative?
- · How do the events the author chose to include in this narrative suggest the important ideas?
- · How do the author's reactions to the events suggest the important ideas?
- · Analyze the development of ideas in the narrative: How do the events and the author's reactions fit together to suggest the important ideas?

Answers will vary but should include answers to all the questions above.

Connect with the **EQ** How Do People Challenge Expectations?

Consider what challenges teach us about ourselves.

15. Respond to the Essential Question Compare the beginning and the end of this selection. How does Salak show that she is challenging expectations about what is "appropriate" behavior—especially behavior for a woman? Be sure to use text evidence to support your answer.

Answers will vary. Responses should include evidence from the text.

_____

_____

_____

_____

_____

16. Theme Review the two quotations on the Unit Opener. Would the author agree with either of these quotations? Why? What is the writer's message about challenging expectations?

Answers will vary. Responses should include evidence from the text.

_____

_____

_____

_____

_____

Key Vocabulary Review

A. Read each sentence. Circle the word that best fits into each sentence.

1. People who (**procrastinate**/ **designate**) wait until the last minute to do something.

2. If you are late to school, you may have to face a (**conviction** / **consequence**) such as a detention.

3. Graduation is a (**momentous**/ **disciplined**) event.

4. Some people might identify themselves by their (**ethnicity**/ **perception**).

5. Hospitals are (**spontaneously** / **perpetually**) open.

6. Laws passed in the 1960s forced schools to (**commiserate** / **integrate**).

7. A powerful speaker might have a(n) (**profound**/ **innovative**) effect on an audience.

8. Laws (**dictate**/ **contend**) what people can and cannot do.

B. Use your own words to write what each Key Vocabulary word means. Then write a synonym for each word. *Answers will vary. Possible responses are shown.*

Key Word	My Definition	Synonym
1. alienation	a feeling of separation	isolation
2. contend	to struggle for	argue
3. conviction	a strong belief	opinion
4. designate	to point out or specify	identify
5. implement	to accomplish	apply
6. innovative	new and clever	original
7. segregation	the isolation of a group of people	separation
8. spontaneously	suddenly and instinctively	impulsively

Unit 2 Key Vocabulary

alienation	contend	disciplined	• implement	• perception	segregation
commiserate	conviction	empathize	• innovative	perpetually	spontaneously
• consequence	designate	endeavor	• integrate	procrastinate	tolerance
contemplate	dictate	• ethnicity	momentous	profound	transition

• **Academic Vocabulary**

C. Answer the questions using complete sentences. *Answers will vary. Possible responses are shown.*

1. What is your **perception** of hardworking people?

They are dedicated to achieving a goal.

2. Why might you want to **commiserate** with someone?

I would commiserate with a friend to help her feel better.

3. How might a **disciplined** person behave?

He or she might be very organized and responsible.

4. Why can a **transition** be difficult for some people?

It is sometimes difficult to adjust to new situations.

5. Why is it important to have **tolerance** for others?

If you treat people with respect, they will treat you the same way.

6. What do you think about people who attempt a difficult **endeavor**?

I have a lot of respect for people who try really hard to achieve a goal.

7. When might you **empathize** with someone?

I would empathize with a friend who was sick.

8. Why should you **contemplate** something before you make a big decision?

It is important to think about all of the possible consequences.

Prepare to Read

▶ Amigo Brothers
▶ Lean on Me

Key Vocabulary

A. How well do you know these words? Circle a rating for each word. Check your understanding of each word by circling *yes* or *no*. Then write a definition in your own words. If you are unsure of a word's meaning, refer to the Vocabulary Glossary, page 926, in your student text.

Rating Scale

1 I have never seen this word before.

2 I am not sure of the word's meaning.

3 I know this word and can teach the word's meaning to someone else.

Key Word	Check Your Understanding	Deepen Your Understanding
❶ acknowledgment (ik-**nah**-lij-munt) *noun* **Rating:** 1 2 3	Audience members show **acknowledgment** of a person's performance by applauding. (**Yes**) No	My definition: *Answers will vary.*
❷ devastating (**de**-vu-stāt-ing) *adjective* **Rating:** 1 2 3	Something **devastating** is helpful and beneficial to you. Yes (**No**)	My definition: *Answers will vary.*
❸ dispel (di-**spel**) *verb* **Rating:** 1 2 3	The best way to **dispel** rumors is to tell them to others. Yes (**No**)	My definition: *Answers will vary.*
❹ evade (i-**vād**) *verb* **Rating:** 1 2 3	If you **evade** doing chores, you offer to do them. Yes (**No**)	My definition: *Answers will vary.*

Key Word	Check Your Understanding	Deepen Your Understanding
5 **improvise** (**im**-prah-vīz) *verb* **Rating:** 1 2 3	Most good actors do not know how to **improvise** a character or situation. **Yes** (No)	My definition: *Answers will vary.* _____ _____ _____ _____
6 **opponent** (u-**pō**-nunt) *noun* **Rating:** 1 2 3	An **opponent** is a player on the same team. **Yes** (No)	My definition: *Answers will vary.* _____ _____ _____ _____
7 **pensively** (**pen**-siv-lē) *adverb* **Rating:** 1 2 3	A person who reacts **pensively** to a piece of news would cheer and clap. **Yes** (No)	My definition: *Answers will vary.* _____ _____ _____ _____
8 **surge** (**surj**) *verb* **Rating:** 1 2 3	If a crowd begins to **surge**, it remains still. **Yes** (No)	My definition: *Answers will vary.* _____ _____ _____ _____

B. Use one of the Key Vocabulary words to write about a time your loyalty was tested.

Answers will vary.
_____

_____

Before Reading Amigo Brothers

LITERARY ANALYSIS: Analyze Style: Language

Style is the way an author uses language to express ideas. **Word choice,** sentence length, and **point of view**—the perspective from which a story is told—all influence style.

An author's style can be formal, informal, or a combination of both. "Amigo Brothers" is written in a casual, conversational style and third-person omniscient point of view.

A. Read the passage from "Amigo Brothers." Use word choices and other text clues from the passage to complete the chart.

> **Look Into the Text**
>
> Each youngster had a dream of someday becoming lightweight champion of the world. . . .
>
> One morning less than a week before their bout, they met as usual for their daily workout. They fooled around with a few jabs at the air, slapped skin, and then took off, running lightly along the dirty East River's edge. . . .
>
> After a mile or so, Felix puffed and said, "Let's stop a while, bro. I think we both got something to say to each other."

Elements of Informal Style	How Do You Know?
Word choice is casual, conversational	*The author chooses words and phrases for his narrator such as "fooled around" and "slapped skin."*
Sentence length	The author has his narrator use long, rambling sentences.
Third-person omniscient point of view	The narrator is all-knowing and uses third-person pronouns.

B. Answer the question about the style of the passage.

Why might the author have had his narrator use an informal style to describe the relationship between Felix and Antonio? _Possible response:_ The author may have wanted to have his narrator show that the boys are good friends, so the language the author uses is casual and conversational.

FOCUS STRATEGY: Make Inferences

> ## HOW TO MAKE INFERENCES
>
> **Focus Strategy**
>
> 1. **I Read** Write down details that help you understand characters and their relationships.
>
> 2. **I Know** Use your own knowledge to make sense of the text.
>
> 3. **And So** Track your thoughts in a chart.

A. Read the passage. Use the strategies above to make inferences about Felix and Antonio. Track your thoughts in the chart.

Look Into the Text

> Felix leaned heavily on the river's railing and stared across to the shores of Brooklyn. Finally, he broke the silence.
> "Man, I don't know how to come out with it."
> Antonio helped. "It's about our fight, right?"
> "Yeah, right." Felix's eyes squinted at the rising orange sun. "I've been thinking about it too, panín. In fact, since we found out it was going to be me and you, I've been awake at night, pulling punches on you, trying not to hurt you.'"

I Read	I Know	And So
"Felix leaned heavily on the river's railing"	When something is bothering me, I feel heavy.	Felix is worried about something and doesn't know what to do.
Antonio helped. "It's about our fight, right?"	When friends are close, each knows what the other is thinking.	Antonio knows what Felix is worried about because he has been worried about it, too.

B. How does your personal knowledge about people and their relationships help you make inferences about Felix and Antonio?

Possible response: Thinking about my friends and how we act and feel helps me understand what Felix and

Antonio are feeling.

Selection Review Amigo Brothers

EQ **What Tests a Person's Loyalty?**
Find out how competition can test people's loyalty.

A. In "Amigo Brothers," you find out how Felix and Antonio's friendship is tested. Complete the map below with the events in the beginning, middle, and end of the story.

Beginning-Middle-End Map

> **Beginning:** Felix and Antonio decide not to see one another before the big fight. Both boys want to win the fight badly, but their friendship is getting in the way of the competition.

> **Middle:** The boys begin the fight that will take them to the Golden Gloves tournament. Although they are good sportsmen, Antonio comes very close to knocking Felix out. Both boys keep fighting hard.

> **End:** The fight ends. The two boys embrace each other. Before the winner is announced, both boys leave the ring together.

B. Use the information in the map on page 96 to answer the questions.

1. In what ways does the fight affect Felix and Antonio's friendship? Does the competition test their loyalty? Why or why not? Write your response in a short paragraph below.

   Possible response: The fight affects their friendship because they stop hanging out together. However, they still think about each other and show respect for each other on the day of the fight. The competition tests their loyalty somewhat, because both characters want to win. In the end, their friendship is strong enough to survive the competition.

2. What actions between Felix and Antonio show an acknowledgment of their loyalty to each other on the day of the fight? Give at least two examples. Use **acknowledgment** in your answer.

   Possible response: Felix and Antonio show an acknowledgment of their friendship by waving at each other before the fight begins, nodding before the fight starts, being sportsman-like by not punching each other once the bell rings, and hugging each other after the fight ends.

3. Are you surprised by the ending of the story? Why do you think the author ends the story this way? Write a short paragraph.

   Possible response: The ending surprised me, because I thought the author would reveal who won the fight. I think the author wanted to show that it did not matter who won. The ending made it clear that the boys felt that their friendship was more important than winning or losing.

4. What might have happened after the two boys left the ring? Write the next scene. Use what you know about the author's style in your writing.

   Answers will vary.

SONG LYRICS

Connect Across Texts

In "Amigo Brothers," Felix and Antonio's friendship is put to the test. In this song, read about the meaning of friendship during challenging times.

Lean on Me
by Bill Withers

Sometimes in our lives we all have pain,
We all have sorrow,
But if we are wise
We know that there's always tomorrow.

Chorus

Lean on me when you're not strong,
And I'll be your friend;
I'll help you carry on,
For it won't be long
'Til I'm gonna need
Somebody to lean on.

Please swallow your pride
If I have things you need to borrow,
For no one can fill those of your needs
That you won't let show.

Central Park Skate II, 2005, Joseph Holston. Oil on canvas, collection of the artist.

▲ **Critical Viewing: Design** What connections can you make between the composition of these figures and the lyrics of this song?

In Other Words
Lean on rely on
swallow forget about, don't think about

You just call on me brother when you need a hand. *a*
We all need somebody to lean on. *b*
I just might have a problem that you'd understand. *a*
We all need somebody to lean on. *b*

[Chorus]

You just call on me brother when you need a hand.
We all need somebody to lean on.
I just might have a problem that you'd understand.
We all need somebody to lean on.

If there is a load you have to bear
That you can't carry,
I'm right up the road.
I'll share your load
If you just call me.

1. Make Inferences
Underline a line on page 98 that reminds you of your own life. Explain what it means to you. Why does the songwriter include this line?

Possible response:

Sometimes I try to

do things alone. The

songwriter is saying

you shouldn't be

embarrassed to accept

help.

2. Structure: Rhyme Scheme
Using the letters *a* and *b*, mark the rhyme scheme of the first 4 lines on this page. Explain how you figured out the rhyme scheme.

Possible response:

I looked at the last word

in each line and found

a word in another line it

rhymed with.

3. Interpret
Reread the last 5 lines of the song. Highlight the most important line. Write the main idea of this verse.

Possible response:

When you need help,

you should not be afraid

to ask for it.

4. Make Inferences

Underline the songwriter's description of what his song is about. Why do you think he chose to sing about this type of love instead of romantic love?

Possible response: He

might believe this love

is just as important, or

more important, than the

other kind of love.

The Power of Words

What started as a simple phrase grew into a number-one song. One day as singer/songwriter Bill Withers was playing around on a new piano, he came up with the words "lean on me." That called to mind his experiences growing up in a West Virginia coal mining town. When times were hard for someone in the community, everyone would lend a helping hand.

"You know, most songs are about romantic love, perhaps the most inconsistent kind there is. Well, <u>there's another kind of love where people say, 'Hey, if there's anything I can do for you, let me know.'</u> At the same time, they're smart enough to say, 'And if there's any way you can help me out, I'd sure appreciate it.'"

Selection Review Lean on Me

A. Read each example below and its rhyme scheme. How does knowing the rhyme scheme help you understand the song?

Example 1: "I'm right up the road. / I'll share your load"

Example 2: "Lean on me when you're not strong, / And I'll be your friend."

Example 1 is an end rhyme. Example 2 is an internal rhyme. Knowing which words rhyme helps me understand the structure and meaning of the song.

B. Answer the questions.

1. How does thinking about your own experiences help you infer the song's meaning and the songwriter's purpose?

Possible response: When my friends have problems, I try to help them. I realize that all people have times when they need support, and the author wants to remind people that they should ask for help when they need it.

2. What does the songwriter say about loyalty in this song?

Possible response: The songwriter says that loyalty is an important part of friendship. You should be there when your friends need you, and your friends should support you when you need them.

Reflect and Assess

WRITING: Write About Literature

A. Find specific examples of dialogue between the characters in "Amigo Brothers" and lines from "Lean on Me" that show thoughts or feelings. List them in the chart. *Answers will vary.*

Amigo Brothers	Lean on Me
"In fact, since we found out it was going to be me and you, I've been awake at night, pulling punches on you, trying not to hurt you."	

B. Write a diary entry from the perspective of a character from the story or the singer of the song. Include the thoughts or feelings you listed above.

Dear Diary, _Students should support their answers with examples from the chosen selections._

_____

_____

_____

_____

_____

_____

_____

_____

_____

Integrate the Language Arts

LITERARY ANALYSIS: Word Choice in Description

Description is a detailed account of a scene, event, or character. Writers use words that appeal to a reader's senses to help the reader see, hear, smell, taste, or feel events and details in a story.

> Example: As the two climbed into the ring, the crowd <u>exploded with a roar</u>.

A. Read the sentences from "Amigo Brothers" in the chart below. Underline the descriptive words. Then write which of your senses the words appealed to.

Sentence	Sense
"Only the <u>frenzied</u> <u>screaming</u> of those along ringside let him know that he had dropped Antonio."	sound
"The <u>cold water sponges</u> brought clarity to both *amigo* brothers."	touch
"Felix wore <u>sky blue</u> trunks, <u>red</u> socks, and <u>white</u> boxing shoes."	sight

B. How do the word choices in the sentences above help you picture the characters and events?

Possible response: The word choices made everything seem more vivid. I could see a very clear image in my mind of what each character looked like and how he moved. I could hear the cheering of the crowd and imagine how cold the sponges felt. The descriptive words made the event more real, and I felt involved in the action with the characters.

C. Write a description of a person, place, or event in your own life. Think about what you want readers to picture in their minds. Use words that appeal to the five senses.

Answers will vary.

VOCABULARY STUDY: Word Families

A **word family** is a group of words with the same base word but different prefixes or suffixes. For example, the words *oppose*, *opponent*, and *opposition* are all in the same word family because they come from the base word *oppose*.

A. The base word *preserve* means "to keep safe." Use your understanding of the base word and what you know about prefixes or suffixes to define each of the words in the chart. Then use a dictionary to confirm the meanings.

Word	What I Think It Means	Definition
preservation	*Possible response:* keeping something safe	the act of keeping something safe from harm
preservationist	*Possible response:* someone who makes old things new	a person who wants to preserve objects, such as buildings or landmarks
preservative	*Possible response:* something that keeps food fresh	something that has the power to protect against spoilage or decay

B. Explore the word family for the base word *honest.* Complete each sentence with the correct word.

1. Someone who does not tell the truth is _____dishonest_____.

2. When you are frank with someone about your opinion, you are speaking _____honestly_____.

3. The man's _____honesty_____ surprised everyone because he was known for telling lies.

4. A store that cheats its customers is behaving _____dishonestly_____.

5. Everyone appreciated the woman's _____honesty_____ about her mistake.

C. Use each base word to brainstorm other words in the same word family.
Answers will vary. Possible responses are shown.

add _____ adding, addition, additive _____

agree _____ disagree, agreeable, agreeing, disagreeable _____

respect _____ disrespect, respectful, disrespectful, respectfully _____

round _____ rounding, around, rounded, surround _____

run _____ running, runner, rerun _____

Prepare to Read

▶ **My Brother's Keeper**
▶ **What Price Loyalty?**

Key Vocabulary

A. How well do you know these words? Circle a rating for each word. Check your understanding of each word by circling *yes* or *no*. Then complete the sentences. If you are unsure of a word's meaning, refer to the Vocabulary Glossary, page 926, in your student text.

Rating Scale	
1	I have never seen this word before.
2	I am not sure of the word's meaning.
3	I know this word and can teach the word's meaning to someone else.

Key Word	Check Your Understanding	Deepen Your Understanding
1 abstract (**ab**-strakt) *noun* **Rating:** 1 2 3	A specific direction is an example of something in the **abstract**. Yes (No)	An example of something in the abstract is *Possible* *response:* the idea of honor
2 adhere (ad-**hear**) *verb* **Rating:** 1 2 3	Good drivers **adhere** to the speed limit. (Yes) No	I adhere to rules when *Possible response:* I play a game
3 advocate (**ad**-vu-kāt) *verb* **Rating:** 1 2 3	Most doctors **advocate** a healthy diet and plenty of exercise. (Yes) No	I would never advocate *Possible response:* lying to a friend
4 deliberately (di-**li**-bah-rut-lē) *adverb* **Rating:** 1 2 3	Criminals always **deliberately** carry out crimes. Yes (No)	My friend deliberately *Possible response:* avoided band practice

Key Word	Check Your Understanding	Deepen Your Understanding
5 desolately (**de**-su-lut-lē) *adverb* Rating: 1 2 3	After a tragedy, a person might act **desolately**. (Yes) No	I feel like crying desolately when _*Possible response:* I_ see animals in need _____ _____ _____ _____ .
6 dilemma (dah-**le**-mah) *noun* Rating: 1 2 3	A **dilemma** is always easy to resolve. Yes (No)	I faced a dilemma when I had to choose between _____ *Possible response:* going to the movies with my friends or going to dinner with my family _____ _____ _____ .
7 ethical (**e**-thi-kul) *adjective* Rating: 1 2 3	An **ethical** decision would be to return a lost wallet to its owner. (Yes) No	I made an ethical decision when _*Possible response:* I_ told my parents the truth _____ _____ _____ _____ .
8 reinforce (rē-un-**fors**) *verb* Rating: 1 2 3	Lying to a friend is one way to **reinforce** a friendship. Yes (No)	One way I reinforce a friendship is to _____ *Possible response:* be honest with my friend at all times _____ _____ _____ .

B. Use one of the Key Vocabulary words to write about a decision you recently made that was difficult for you.

Answers will vary.
_____

_____

Before Reading My Brother's Keeper

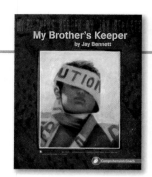

LITERARY ANALYSIS: Analyze Style: Sentence Structure

An author's **sentence structure** helps create his or her style. An author can use repetition or fragments to create the story's overall feeling.

A. Read the passage below. Think about how sentence structure affects the feeling of the text. Complete the chart to show the effect of the author's style.

Look Into the Text

> Jamie was alone.
> And now the phone was ringing.
> He reached over to the night table and picked up the dark, gleaming receiver.
> The summer curtain rustled noiselessly.
> Then he heard the voice.
> "Jamie?"
> A slight chill went through him and he was silent.
> "Jamie?"
> It was his brother.
> His only brother.

Structure	What Each Does	Effect or Feeling
Long sentences	*take longer to read and require more thought*	*help reader reflect or visualize*
Short sentences	are fast and to the point	*Possible response:* create urgency, importance, fear
Fragments	seem abrupt, or choppy	*Possible response:* create tension
Repeated words	help you remember the ideas	*Possible response:* emphasize dramatic moments

B. How does the author use sentence structure to show how Jamie feels about his brother?

Possible response: The author uses short sentences to create tension and suspense. These short sentences keep the reader focused on the action and on Jamie's cold reaction to his brother.

FOCUS STRATEGY: Make Inferences

> ## HOW TO MAKE INFERENCES
> **Focus Strategy**
>
> 1. **Connect Details** What do you already know about the details in the story? How do these details relate to the story's characters?
> 2. **Track Your Thoughts** Write your notes in a chart.

A. Read the passage. Use the strategies above to make inferences about Jamie and his brother's relationship. Answer the questions below.

> **Look Into the Text**
>
> Then he heard it.
> "I'm in trouble, Jamie."
> And you need me to bail you out, <u>Jamie thought bitterly.</u>
> <u>"Trouble."</u>
> This time the voice was almost a whisper.
> But Jamie heard it clearly.
> <u>His lips thinned into a straight line.</u>
> <u>I'm your kid brother. Five long years younger than you are and all the time, all through the years I had to act like I was the older brother.</u>
> <u>All the time.</u>
> <u>Jamie's hand tightened</u> around the receiver.
> "What have you done, Ted?"

1. How does Jamie feel toward his brother? Why?

   He is angry and annoyed because his older brother is always in trouble. He expects Jamie to help him get

   out of it.

2. What do you already know that helped you make an inference about how Jamie feels about his brother?

   Possible response: I know that I would be annoyed if my older brother was always in trouble and needed

   my help.

B. Return to the passage above and underline sentences and phrases that helped you answer the first question. On a separate sheet of paper, track your thoughts about Jamie's relationship with his brother as you read the story.

Selection Review My Brother's Keeper

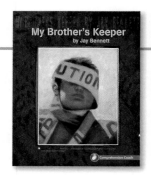

EQ **What Tests a Person's Loyalty?**
Consider whether loyalty is always the best policy.

A. In "My Brother's Keeper," you found out how Jamie's loyalty to his brother conflicted with his beliefs. Complete the T Chart below about Jamie's dilemma.

T Chart

Reasons to Help Ted	Reasons Not to Help Ted
Jamie should be loyal to his brother.	
Ted needs help.	Ted should honor the court system.
Ted really didn't mean to hit the man with his car. The man Ted hit is okay; it was the man's fault anyway.	Ted will keep getting in trouble, so Ted should learn to be responsible for his actions.

B. Use the information in the chart above to answer the questions.

1. What dilemma does Jamie have?

   Jamie has to decide if he should help his brother or stay true to his beliefs and tell the truth about Ted.

2. Does Jamie make an ethical decision? Why or why not? Use **ethical** in your answer.

   Possible responses: Yes, because it is ethical to tell the truth in court; No, because it is not ethical to be disloyal to family.

3. What would you have done if you had the same dilemma as Jamie?
Use **dilemma** in your answer.

Possible response: If I had the same dilemma as Jamie, I would respect myself and not support my brother.

He would need to learn how to be responsible without my help.

4. Reread "My Brother's Keeper." Identify two sentence styles the
author uses, and list them in the chart below. Write how the author's
sentence structure affects the story's overall feeling.

Author's Sentence Style	Story's Feeling
short and choppy with sentence fragments	creates tension adds drama
long and complex	provides a contrast to tension gives the reader important information

5. How might the feeling of the story change if the author used fewer
fragments and less repetition to create the story's style?

Possible response: The feeling might change because it would not effectively show Jamie's tense feelings

toward his brother.

What Price Loyalty?
by Gerald Pomper

1. Determine Viewpoint
Highlight the author's examples of loyalty and disloyalty in American history. What viewpoint does the author support with these examples?

The author uses these
examples to show that
loyalty is an abstract
idea that is more
complicated in real life.

2. Make Inferences
On pages 110–111, underline the people and things that the author claims people are loyal to. What is the author trying to tell readers about loyalty?

Loyalties sometimes
conflict, and we are
sometimes forced to
choose which loyalty is
more important.

Connect Across Texts

In "My Brother's Keeper," you read about a **dilemma** *between family loyalty and telling the truth. In this news commentary, read about the role of loyalty in society.*

Loyalty is in the news. But what does it mean?

Loyalty has been a concern throughout American history. The Declaration of Independence, remember, was an act of disloyalty toward the British Crown, and opponents of the rebellion called

Martin Luther King, Jr., delivered his famous "I Have a Dream" speech in Washington, D.C. on August 28, 1963.

themselves "Loyalists." In the Civil War, Northerners **swore fealty to** the federal union, Southerners to their individual states.

In the **abstract**, loyalty is an unquestioned virtue; nobody **advocates** disloyalty. But it gets more complicated in the real world. Because of their oaths to Adolf Hitler, the German General Staff ignored the Holocaust.

Dissenters such as Martin Luther King, Jr., have been accused of disloyalty because they disobeyed the law, even as they claimed a **higher allegiance to the nation's overriding principles**. Can it be, in the words of the late journalist Alan Barth, that "Loyalty in a free society depends upon the toleration of disloyalty"?

We in fact have many loyalties, each **commendable** in itself. We believe in loyalty to family, friends, employers

Key Vocabulary
dilemma *n.*, situation that requires you to choose between two unfavorable options
• **abstract** *n.*, idea, nonreal situation
• **advocate** *v.*, to speak in favor of

In Other Words
swore fealty to promised to be loyal to
higher allegiance to the nation's overriding principles more important loyalty to the nation's basic beliefs
commendable worthy of praise

and employees, the institutions where we work, perhaps our political party, our country, our God, and our conscience. Often these loyalties **reinforce** each other.

But **ethical** problems arise when these loyalties conflict—as often happens. Should we protect a criminal relative? Should an employee stay with a failing corporation, or an employer keep his workers on the payroll even as profits fall?

These dilemmas are not resolved by the easy answer that we should always stick to our principles; each of the conflicting loyalties is, after all, a **statement of principle**.

Loyalty to friends, for example, is a good principle, but it can create problems. In 1950 during the Cold War, Secretary of State Dean Acheson said he refused to "turn my back" on Alger Hiss, even when his friend was revealed to be a Soviet spy.

Is such loyalty always commendable?

We should be suspicious of **glib claims of loyalty** to principle. Instead, we need to consider the consequences of individual actions, public and private. One basic question to ask: How many people may be harmed by **adhering** to one form of loyalty or another?

We may get closer to resolving these conflicts if we recall a famous statement of loyalty—naval commander Stephen Decatur's toast, "Our country, right or wrong."

Students recite the Pledge of Allegiance, which is a patriotic oath of loyalty to the United States.

Key Vocabulary
- **reinforce** *v.*, to strengthen
- **ethical** *adj.*, moral
  adhere *v.*, to stick with

In Other Words
statement of principle way of expressing what we truly believe
glib claims of loyalty casual statements about loyalty

3. Determine Viewpoint

What conclusion does the author make about loyalty?

The author concludes

that loyalty at all costs,

or to one principle, is

dangerous. Loyalty

should be a thoughtful

choice.

Fifty-five years later, Carl Schurz, a United States general and United States senator, provided a better rule: "Our country, right or wrong. When right, to be kept right; when wrong, to be put right." That is appropriate conduct for thinking men and women in a free land. ❖

Selection Review What Price Loyalty?

A. Read the viewpoints the author expresses about loyalty. Then, list one fact he uses to support each. How do the facts support the author's viewpoints?

> **Viewpoint 1:** We should be suspicious of glib claims of loyalty to principle.
> **Viewpoint 2:** Loyalty to friends . . . is a good principle, but it can create problems.

Viewpoint 1; Fact: During World War II, the German General Staff ignored the Holocaust out of loyalty to Hitler. The Holocaust was a horrible tragedy; being suspicious of Hitler's principle would have been the right thing to do. Viewpoint 2; Fact: Dean Acheson refused to go against Alger Hiss. Hiss turned out to be a Soviet spy who was being disloyal to the U.S. government. The facts support the author's opinions well because the author uses famous events that caused damage to people and governments.

B. Answer the questions.

1. What do you think the author's purpose was for writing this news commentary?

Possible response: He wanted people to understand that loyalty is not a defense for doing unethical things. People need to think about how their choices affect others.

2. How can adhering to one form of loyalty harm people?

Possible response: People who do not question others can cause harm to others. The author used Hitler as an example to show how loyalty can harm people.

Reflect and Assess

► **My Brother's Keeper**
► **What Price Loyalty?**

WRITING: Write About Literature

A. Plan your writing. In the chart below, list what Jamie from "My Brother's Keeper" and Gerald from "What Price Loyalty?" each thinks loyalty means. *Answers will vary.*

My Brother's Keeper	What Price Loyalty?
Jamie thinks loyalty is . . .	Gerald thinks loyalty is . . .

B. Imagine that you have an online advice column. What advice would you give Jamie? Write a question from Jamie, and then an e-mail that gives Jamie advice. Support your advice with details from the text.

Students should support their answers with examples from both selections.

_____

_____

_____

_____

_____

_____

_____

_____

_____

_____

_____

Unit 3: The Ties That Bind 113

Integrate the Language Arts

LITERARY ANALYSIS: Analyze Style and Theme

The way a writer uses word choice and sentence length, and the tone created by that language, is the writer's **style**. A writer's style can help you identify and understand the **theme** of a story as well.

A. Write examples from "My Brother's Keeper" that show the author's style. Then determine what each shows you about the writer's style.

Answers will vary. Possible responses are shown.

Elements of Style	Examples from Text	What the Style Shows You
Word choice	alone, bitterly, chill, trouble, bail you out, the voice, whisper	The writer's word choice shows that Jamie is unhappy.
Sentence length	Thinking. Ever thinking.	The sentences are short and in phrases. This shows, along with other elements, that Jamie is upset.
Dialogue	"Oh." "I'm in trouble, Jamie."	The dialogue is short but loaded with unsaid things.

B. Read the quotes from "My Brother's Keeper" below. List possible themes for the story.
Answers will vary. Possible responses are shown.

1. "But he was a human being. Not a dog. You don't even leave a dog lying in the street and run off."

Theme: _People need to help each other._

2. "I panicked and left him lying there."

Theme: _Some people choose not to do the right thing._

3. "I'd give my right arm to help you decide. But I just can't. It's your call, Jamie. Yours alone."

Theme: _People need to make their own decisions._

C. Imagine that the theme in "My Brother's Keeper" was about Ted doing the right thing. Write a new ending to the story.

Answers will vary.

_____

_____

_____

_____

VOCABULARY STUDY: Word Families

Many English words are related because they have Greek or Latin roots. If you recognize a root, you can figure out the meaning of more words in the same **word family**. *Answers will vary. Possible responses are shown.*

A. Read the roots and their meanings below. List more words with the same roots. Use a dictionary if you need to.

Root	Meaning	Words with Root
graph	write	autograph, photography
grat	pleasing	congratulate, grateful
leg	law	legal, legislature
poli	city	police, politics

B. Look at the underlined roots below. Write what you think the root means. Then list three new words in the same word family.

micro<u>scope</u>: _small; microphone, microchip, microwave_

sym<u>pathy</u>: _feeling; empathy, pathetic, telepathy_

<u>popul</u>ar: _people; populate, population, popularity_

<u>vis</u>ible: _see; vision, visual, visit_

C. Write sentences using the words in Activity B.

1. _I use a microscope in science class to study different kinds of bacteria._

2. _My friend showed sympathy for me when my dog died._

3. _A lot of my friends worry about being popular._

4. _Fog keeps the signs from being visible on the road._

Prepare to Read

▶ **The Hand of Fatima**
▶ **Old Ways, New World**

Key Vocabulary

A. How well do you know these words? Circle a rating for each word. Check your understanding of each word by choosing the correct definition. Then provide examples. If you are unsure of a word's meaning, refer to the Vocabulary Glossary, page 926, in your student text.

Rating Scale	
1	I have never seen this word before.
2	I am not sure of the word's meaning.
3	I know this word and can teach the word's meaning to someone else.

Key Word	Check Your Understanding	Deepen Your Understanding
❶ abolish (ah-**bah**-lish) *verb* **Rating:** **1 2 3**	☐ to make clean ☒ to get rid of	Example: _Possible response: getting rid of a dress_ code rule
❷ admonish (ad-**mah**-nish) *verb* **Rating:** **1 2 3**	☒ to scold ☐ to erase	Example: _Possible response: scolding someone for_ telling a lie
❸ coherent (kō-**hir**-unt) *adjective* **Rating:** **1 2 3**	☒ easy to understand ☐ confusing or unclear	Example: _Possible response: using plenty of_ examples and words that connect ideas
❹ conscientious (kahn-shē-**en**-shus) *adjective* **Rating:** **1 2 3**	☐ carefree ☒ responsible	Example: _Possible response: feeding and walking my_ dog, doing my homework

Key Word	Check Your Understanding	Deepen Your Understanding
5 **controversial** (kahn-trah-**vur**-shul) *adjective* **Rating:** 1 2 3	☐ accepted ☒ disputed	Example: *Possible response:* book banning, animal testing
6 **naive** (nah-**ēv**) *adjective* **Rating:** 1 2 3	☒ easily fooled ☐ easily forgotten	Example: *Possible response:* a student's first day at school
7 **pursue** (pur-**sü**) *verb* **Rating:** 1 2 3	☐ to attach ☒ to go after	Example: *Possible response:* a police car chase
8 **subdued** (sub-**düd**) *adjective* **Rating:** 1 2 3	☒ quiet and controlled ☐ submerged or immersed	Example: *Possible response:* a formal gathering, a religious ceremony

B. Use one of the Key Vocabulary words to explain how your loyalties have changed as you have gotten older.

Answers will vary.

Before Reading The Hand of Fatima

LITERARY ANALYSIS: Analyze Viewpoint

Viewpoint refers to the attitudes of a story's characters, narrator, and author. An author reveals viewpoints through words, descriptions, and sentence structure.

A. Read the passage. Find words and phrases from the passage that show how the author feels about Aneesi and how Aneesi feels. List examples of the author's word choice and descriptions in the chart below.

> **Look Into the Text**
>
> Aneesi paused outside the dining room. She had spent the long, hot summer morning helping Sitt Zeina prepare a lavish lunch, had waited on the guests without a single slip, and had just finished clearing the dessert dishes. She was tired and hungry and her plastic sandals chafed from so much running back and forth. All she wanted right now was to sit down in the kitchen and enjoy the leftovers.
>
> But something had caught her attention. Holding the serving plates still half full of pastries, she lingered in the hallway to listen.
>
> Sitt Zeina was telling her husband, in no uncertain terms, "We must have that garden wall repaired, Yusuf. You know, where the old fig tree is pushing it over. You've put it off long enough, and costs are going up every day. Besides, there's a lot more we should do with the garden."

Character	Word Choice	Descriptions
Aneesi	*long, hot; tired, hungry; chafed*	*waited on the guests without a single slip; wanted to sit*

B. Answer the question about the author's viewpoint.

What does the author's attitude toward Aneesi tell you about life in Sitt Zeina's household?

Possible response: The author seems sympathetic toward Aneesi and her situation. The author makes me feel what everyday life in this family is like. The author seems to know every detail of their lives.

FOCUS STRATEGY: Make Inferences

> ## How to MAKE INFERENCES
>
> Focus Strategy
>
> 1. **Take notes** about the characters' inferences about each other.
>
> 2. **List the event or statement** that supports an inference.
>
> 3. **Confirm** whether a character's inference is correct or incorrect.

A. Read the passage. Use the strategies above to make inferences as you read. Answer the questions below.

> ### Look Into the Text
>
> For a moment Aneesi recalled Sitt Zeina speaking to her—more than once, in fact—about not listening to the family's private conversations. It was an improper, low kind of behavior to "eavesdrop," as Sitt Zeina had put it. Aneesi had bristled inwardly at being admonished, but at least it was better than being thought of as too dull to care what people were saying, like a pet dog. . . . So now she'd eavesdropped again—but maybe this time Sitt Zeina would be glad of it. . . . "Sitt Zeina, I couldn't help hearing something—I didn't mean to, but I was just leaving the dining room—" . . . . With raised eyebrows Sitt Zeina shot a disapproving look at Aneesi.

1. What inference does Aneesi make about Sitt Zeina? Why does she make this inference?

   Possible response: Aneesi infers that Sitt Zeina will not mind that Aneesi had eavesdropped this time.

   Aneesi thinks she has a good idea and Sitt Zeina will be happy to hear it.

2. Which of the strategies did you use to answer question 1? Was the character's inference correct or incorrect? Why?

   Possible responses: I used strategies 1 and 3. I think Aneesi's inference about Sitt Zeina was incorrect.

   Aneesi was too excited about her idea. I also think Aneesi thought Sitt Zeina might not always be so

   disapproving.

B. Return to the passage above and circle the words or sentences that helped you answer question 1.

Selection Review The Hand of Fatima

EQ **What Tests a Person's Loyalty?**
Explore the ways loyalties may change over time.

A. In "The Hand of Fatima," you found out how events test Aneesi's loyalty. Write the events and the effects that the events have on Aneesi and her father in the Cause-and-Effect Chart.

Cause-and-Effect Chart

Events	How the Events Affect Aneesi
1. Aneesi's brother, Hussein, needs to go to college.	1. Aneesi must become a maid in Lebanon to support the family.
2. The Jubeilis need a new stone wall on their estate.	2. Aneesi recommends her father to build it.
3. Aneesi's father asks her to marry a man back home.	3. Aneesi becomes upset because she does not want to marry.
4. Aneesi's father gives Aneesi the Hand of Fatima.	4. Aneesi wonders at her father's reasons for the gift.
5. Maya thinks her money has been stolen.	5. The Jubeilis accuse Aneesi's father of stealing the money.
6. The Jubeilis ask Aneesi's father to leave.	6. Aneesi's father returns to Syria in shame.
7. Aneesi finds the money.	7. Aneesi returns to Syria to be with her father.

B. Use the information in the chart to answer the questions.

1. In what ways is Aneesi's loyalty to her family tested? Give three examples.

Possible response: Aneesi wants to be loyal to her family, but she hates her life as a maid. Aneesi does not want to marry as her father asks, but she wants to be loyal to her family. Aneesi cannot believe her father has stolen the money, but she wonders about how he gets it for the Hand of Fatima.

2. Why do you think the Jubeilis are so quick to admonish Aneesi's father for stealing? What lesson do they learn? Use the word **admonish** in your answer.

Possible response: The Jubeilis are quick to admonish Aneesi's father because they are rich and are used to treating their servants and workers with little respect. They learn that Aneesi's father is an honest man and that Maya's carelessness is to blame.

3. How will Aneesi behave toward her father in the future? Why will she behave this way?

Possible response: Aneesi will be respectful and apologetic because she brought her father to the Jubeili family. She might give up her dreams of an independent life and agree to marry the man her father wants her to marry.

Old Ways, NEW WORLD

by Joseph Berger

Connect Across Texts

In "The Hand of Fatima," Aneesi is torn between loyalty to her family and her own dreams. As you read the following news report, consider how loyalty to family and culture might impact people's life decisions.

A Delicate Balance

For Afghan and Indian immigrants in the United States, dating and marriage present special challenges. Ashrat Khwajazadah and Naheed Mawjzada are in many ways modern American women, **spurning** the headscarves and modest outfits customarily worn by Afghan women.

Both in their early twenties, they have taken a route still **controversial** for Afghan women living in America: going to college to pursue professions. And both defy the ideal of **submissive** Afghan womanhood. Mawjzada speaks up forcefully when men talk politics at the dinner table.

But at the same time, neither woman has ever dated. Like most women in the Afghan community in New York, they are waiting for their parents to pick their spouses.

Elsewhere in New York, Bodh Das, a physician from India, wanted his daughters to marry within his Hindu **caste**. His eldest daughter, Abha,

A young couple takes part in a traditional Hindu marriage ceremony in New York's Central Park.

Key Vocabulary
● **controversial** *adj.*, causing disagreement

In Other Words
spurning rejecting
submissive quiet and obedient
caste society, social division

Interact with the Text

1. Make Inferences
Underline phrases that show the women's controversial actions. What inferences can you make about these women and their loyalties to family and to themselves?

Possible response: The loyalties of these women to their families and cultural traditions may not be as strong as their loyalties to themselves.

2. Make Inferences

Underline a phrase that shows how Rekha did not follow Afghan tradition. Why do you think she did not follow this tradition?

Possible response:

Rekha may have had

less pressure from her

parents since her other

sisters followed tradition.

She may have adopted

the American culture

more than her sisters.

3. Determine Viewpoint

Circle the phrases that describe how immigrant parents react to their children's changing loyalties. How can you tell that the author is unbiased?

Possible response: The

author chooses objective

language to show how

each group behaves

and the difficulty of the

situation. He reports

facts without making

opinionated comments.

returned to India in 1975 to wed a man she had never met from her father's Kayashta caste. Das's second daughter, Bibha, also married a Kayashta.

But Rekha, who is the most Americanized of Das's three daughters, <u>married a man outside her father's caste whom she met in school</u>. It was what Indians call "a love marriage": that is, a marriage that is not arranged by the parents.

Indians and Afghans living in America, particularly women, must often **strike a delicate balance** as they grow up in a relatively

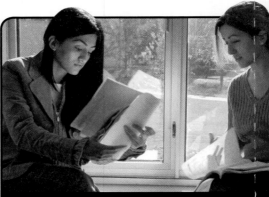

Ashrat Khwajazadah (right) and her sister Alliy both attend Queens College in New York.

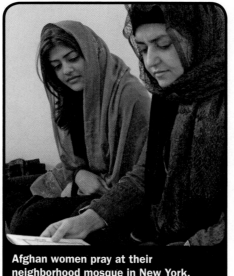

Afghan women pray at their neighborhood mosque in New York.

freewheeling society, but with immigrant parents who are holding on to the customs of their homeland. The tension between immigrant parents and children today is no different from that experienced by the Irish, Italian, Jewish, and other immigrant groups of the nineteenth and twentieth centuries. Those newcomers also looked on with anger or resignation as their children gradually **adopted the prevailing culture**.

Among Afghans, no tradition is more ironclad than parents arranging their children's marriages. It is generally felt that if a daughter chooses her own husband, it damages her father's **stature in the community**.

In Other Words

strike a delicate balance act with care
freewheeling society free world with few restrictions
adopted the prevailing culture became more like the dominant culture or mainstream society
stature in the community status or reputation among other Afghans

"The girl is a trophy piece," says Mawjzada. "If the girl has a good reputation, the family has a good reputation."

Marriage customs for men are **more lenient**. Bashir Rahim, 29, says that if he meets a girl who interests him at a family gathering he will find out her address, then send his parents to her home to start a conversation about marriage.

An Ancient
Hierarchy

India's caste system goes back thousands of years to the origins of Hinduism. At the top were the Brahmin scholars and priests;

Hariharan Janakiraman, 31, trusts his parents to find him a Brahmin wife.

at the bottom were the Dalit, or "untouchables." After India gained its independence from Britain in 1947, the legal forms of the caste system were **abolished**. But attitudes shaped by **an ancient and pervasive social system** don't change easily.

Some young people are still attached to the old ways. Hariharan Janakiraman, a 31-year-old software engineer, has agreed to let his parents find a Brahmin wife for him. They will consult his horoscope and that of his prospective bride. The young woman will then be asked to prepare some food and sing and dance to show that all her limbs work. If he were to marry a woman outside of his caste, says Janakiraman, "My uncle and aunt won't have a good impression of my parents, so I won't do that."

But sometimes an arranged marriage can be painful. Masuda Sultan, 26, grew up in New York and is now a graduate student at Harvard. When she was 15, her father arranged for her to marry a doctor twice her age.

Key Vocabulary
  abolish *v.*, to do away with or get rid of

In Other Words
  more lenient not as strict
  an ancient and pervasive social system old and widespread traditions in society

4. Make Inferences
Underline a sentence that explains how Janakiraman shows his loyalty to his family. Why is he choosing to follow this tradition?

Possible response: He knows that his actions reflect his parents' reputation. He does not want others to have a bad impression of them.

5. Determine Viewpoint
Circle a phrase that explains why attitudes about the caste system remain today. What is the writer's attitude toward the subject of the caste system?

Possible response:
The writer is fair and neutral. He knows that it is difficult for people to let go of traditions they have followed for a long time.

6. Interpret

Why does the author end the article with the quote from Sultan?

Possible response:

Sultan has experience

with an arranged

marriage. Her

experience helps the

reader understand

why Afghan and Indian

women struggle with

their loyalties.

Afghan or American?

"I actually thought it could work," recalls Sultan. "When your actions are limited and you're from a certain world and you respect your family, you go along with their wishes."

Sultan wanted to finish college before they began having children, and tensions with her husband became **irreconcilable**. After three years, they divorced, which is a rare and humiliating event in the Afghan community.

"The core issue was really a different philosophy of what it means to be Afghan and what it means to be American," says Sultan. "Ultimately I was being treated as a child and my role was set and I was being told what I could and couldn't do." ❖

In Other Words
irreconcilable impossible to repair

Selection Review Old Ways, New World

A. How does the author present information in an unbiased way? List two examples.

1. _*Possible response:* He uses many examples and quotes to show how Afghan and Indian immigrants view arranged marriages._

2. _*Possible response:* He uses facts about the caste system and how people still view it._

B. Answer the questions.

1. Why do some young Afghans and Indians follow marriage traditions?

   *Possible response:* An arranged marriage maintains a family's reputation, and it is one of the most important traditions.

2. What factors may stop someone from following a family tradition?

   *Possible response:* People may choose not to follow a tradition because they feel it goes against a belief that they now have. The tradition may limit their sense of freedom, or they may not see the sense in it anymore.

Reflect and Assess

WRITING: Write About Literature

A. Plan your writing. Complete the Venn diagram with details from both selections that show how life in the Middle East and the United States is the same and different. *Answers will vary.*

Venn Diagram

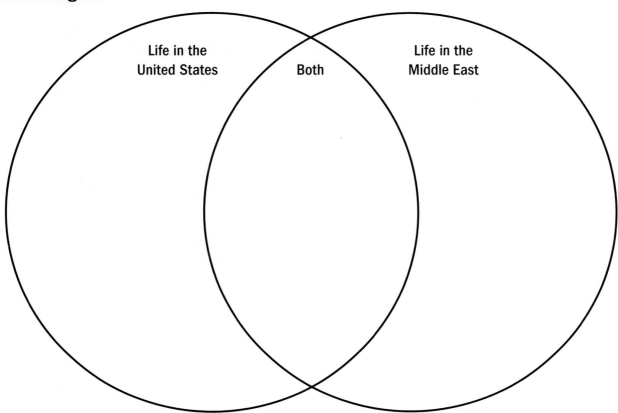

Life in the
United States

Both

Life in the
Middle East

B. What are two ways that life in the Middle East appears to be similar to or different from life in the United States? Write a comparison paragraph. Use examples from both texts.

Students should support their answers with examples from both selections.

_____

_____

_____

_____

_____

_____

_____

_____

Integrate the Language Arts

LITERARY ANALYSIS: Symbolism

A **symbol** in literature is a person, place, event, or object that symbolizes, or represents, something else. For example, a tiger might represent strength or power.

A. Brainstorm a list of symbols you see around you. Tell what each symbol represents to you. *Answers will vary. Possible responses are shown.*

Symbol	What It Symbolizes
Statue of Liberty	freedom, opportunity
cross or Star of David	faith
ring	marriage, love
dove	peace

B. The gold charm symbolizes different things for Aneesi at different points in the story. Listed below are story events that cause Aneesi to view the charm differently. What does the charm symbolize after each event? Complete the chart below.

Story Event	What the Charm Symbolizes
Aneesi receives the charm from her father.	a father's love for his daughter
Aneesi thinks about her arranged marriage to Fareed.	her family's control over her life
Maya reports that she has lost her money.	Aneesi's doubt about her father's honesty
Aneesi returns to her family in Syria.	strength, independence, and loyalty

C. Write a short paragraph that describes how the meaning of a symbol changed for you after an event. What caused it to change?

Answers will vary.

_____

_____

_____

_____

_____

VOCABULARY STUDY: Word Families

Many English words have roots that come from Greek and Latin. Words that have the same root belong to the same **word family**. For example, the words *inspect*, *respect*, and *spectacular* all belong to the same word family because the words come from the root *spect*. *Answers will vary. Possible responses are shown.*

A. Complete the chart. List as many words as you know that have the roots listed below.

Root	Words with the Same Root
aqua	aquatic, aquarium, aquamarine, aqua
cycl	bicycle, cycle, cyclist, cyclone
uni	unit, union, unison, unisex, united, universal

B. The chart below shows common Greek and Latin roots, their meanings, and a sample word. Write the meaning of each sample word. Use a dictionary to confirm the meaning.

Greek or Latin Root	Meaning	Word with Root	Meaning of the Word
extra	outside of	extraordinary	*out of the ordinary*
inter	between	intermission	a break between performances
lect	to choose or to read	elect	choose by voting
terr	earth	terrestrial	belonging to the land

C. Write sentences using the sample words in the chart above.

1. extraordinary   My cousin's math skills are extraordinary for her age.

2. intermission   We went to the restroom during intermission.

3. elect   We will elect a new president next year.

4. terrestrial   The lizard is a terrestrial animal.

Read for Understanding

1. Genre What kind of text is this passage? How do you know?

The text is fiction

because the characters

and setting are imagined

rather than real.

2. Topic Write a topic sentence to tell what the text is mostly about.

The text mostly tells

about Equality 7-2521

and how he struggles to

fit into his society.

Reread and Summarize

3. Word Choice In each section, circle three words or phrases that express big ideas in that section. Note next to each word or phrase why you chose it.

· Section 1: paragraphs 1–12
· Section 2: paragraphs 13–21

4. Summary Use your topic sentence and notes from item 3 to write a summary of the selection.

Possible response:

Equality 7-2521 wants to

be a Scholar. However,

he accepts the career of

Street Sweeper as a way

to atone for the "sin" of

being different.

from Anthem

BY AYN RAND

1 Our name is Equality 7-2521, as it is written on the iron bracelet which all men wear on their left wrists with their names upon it. We are twenty-one years old. We are six feet tall, and this is a burden, for there are not many men who are six feet tall. Ever have the Teachers and the Leaders pointed to us and frowned and said:

2 "There is evil in your bones, Equality 7-2521, for your body has grown beyond the bodies of your brothers." But we cannot change our bones nor our body.

3 We were born with a **curse**. It has always driven us to thoughts which are forbidden. It has always given us wishes which men may not wish. We know that we are evil, but there is no will in us and no power to resist it. This is our wonder and our secret fear, that we know and do not resist.

4 We strive to be like all our brother men, for all men must be alike. Over the portals of the Palace of the World Council, there are words cut in the marble, which we repeat to ourselves whenever we **are tempted**:

5 *"WE ARE ONE IN ALL AND ALL IN ONE.*
THERE ARE NO MEN BUT ONLY THE GREAT WE,
ONE, INDIVISIBLE AND FOREVER."

Lecture, News, Advertising, for the Social Science Hall, "A Century of Progress" Exposition, Chicago, Illinois, 1933, Alfonso Iannelli. Scale model, The Wolfsoinian–Florida International University, Miami Beach, Florida, The Mitchell Wolfson, Jr. Collection.

▲ **Critical Viewing: Character** How would you describe the people in this art? How are they like the people described in the story?

▲ *Possible responses to Critical Viewing:* The people are colorless workers, almost identical to each other. Like the people in the story, the people in this art are "equal"; they illustrate the statement "WE ARE ONE IN ALL AND ALL IN ONE."

In Other Words
curse terrible problem
are tempted desire to do wrong

6   We repeat this to ourselves, but it helps us not.

7   These words were cut long ago. There is green mold in the grooves of the letters and yellow streaks on the marble, which come from more years than men could count. And these words are the truth, for they are written on the Palace of the World Council, and the World Council is the body of all truth. Thus has it been ever since the Great Rebirth, and farther back than that no memory can reach.

8   But we must never speak of the times before the Great Rebirth, else we are sentenced to three years in the Palace of Corrective Detention. It is only the Old Ones who whisper about it in the evenings, in the Home of the Useless. They whisper many strange things, of the towers which rose to the sky, in those Unmentionable Times, and of the wagons which moved without horses, and of the lights which burned without flame. But those times were evil. And those times passed away, when men saw the Great Truth which is this: that all men are one and that there is no will save the will of all men together.

9   All men are good and wise. It is only we, Equality 7-2521, we alone who were born with a curse. For we are not like our brothers. And as we look back upon our life, we see that it has **ever been thus** and that it has brought us step by step to our last, supreme **transgression**, our crime of crimes hidden here under the ground.

> ...we are not like our brothers.

10   We remember the Home of the Infants where we lived **till** we were five years old, together with all the children of the City who had been born in the same year. The sleeping halls there were white and clean and bare of all things save one hundred beds. We were just like all our brothers then, save for the one transgression: we fought with our brothers. There are few offenses blacker than to fight with our brothers, at any age and for any cause whatsoever. The Council of the Home told us so, and of all the children of that year, we were locked in the cellar most often.

11   When we were five years old, we were sent to the Home of the Students, where there are ten wards, for our ten years of learning. Men must learn till they reach their fifteenth year. Then they go to work. In the Home of the Students we arose when the big bell rang in the tower and we went to our

In Other Words
ever been thus always been this way
transgression misbehavior
till until

5. Author's Purpose   What is the author's purpose for writing this selection?

Possible response: The author both entertains and persuades.

How do you know?

Possible response: The story, like most stories, is entertaining. It also is persuasive because the author makes you think about keeping society from becoming like this.

6. Author's Style   Reread paragraph 1. Underline three groups of words that show that Rand's narrator uses simple statements and plain words when talking about himself.

7. Style   Reread section 1. Highlight four more examples where the narrator uses plain words to make simple statements about himself.

8. Evaluate the Language Why does the author choose a style that has her narrator speaking in such plain language?

Possible response: The author's stylistic choices reinforce the idea that the narrator is part of a rigid, colorless society.

9. Style Circle the first sentence in paragraph 14 in which the narrator shows that he identifies with the group but still has personal feelings. What word choices in this paragraph help show the contrast?

Possible response: The

narrator refers to himself

as "we," "our," and "us."

At the same time, he

expresses unhappiness

over the "evil" he

commits by being

smarter than others.

10. Style On the rest of this page, find and underline three other examples of this contrast between thinking with the group and having personal feelings. Discuss and write about how these examples help develop Rand's ideas and make this narrator a memorable character.

Responses should

recognize that the

plain style reflects the

plainness of the society

and that the conflict

between the narrator's

identification with the

group and his personal

feelings make the

narrator memorable.

beds when it rang again. Before we removed our **garments**, we stood in the great sleeping hall, and we raised our right arms, and we said all together with the three Teachers at the head:

12 "We are nothing. Mankind is all. By the grace of our brothers are we allowed our lives. We exist through, by and for our brothers who are the State. Amen."

13 Then we slept. The sleeping halls were white and clean and bare of all things save one hundred beds.

14 We, Equality 7-2521, were not happy in those years in the Home of the Students. It was not that the learning was too hard for us. It was that the learning was too easy. This is a great sin, to be **born with a head which is too quick**. It is not good to be different from our brothers, but it is evil to be superior to them. The Teachers told us so, and they frowned when they looked upon us. . . .

15 So we wished to be sent to the Home of the Scholars. We wished it so much that our hands trembled under the blankets in the night, and we bit our arm to stop that other pain which we could not endure. It was evil and we dared not face our brothers in the morning. For men may wish nothing for themselves. And we were punished when the Council of Vocations came to give us our life Mandates which tell those who reach their fifteenth year what their work is to be for the rest of their days.

16 The Council of Vocations came on the first day of spring, and they sat in the great hall. And we who were fifteen and all the Teachers came into the great hall. And the Council of Vocations sat on a high **dais**, and they had but two words to speak to each of the Students. They called the Students' names, and when the Students stepped before them, one after another, the Council said: "Carpenter" or "Doctor" or "Cook" or "Leader." Then each Student raised their right arm and said: "The will of our brothers be done."

17 Now if the Council has said "Carpenter" or "Cook," the Students so assigned go to work and they do not study any further. But if the Council has said "Leader," then those Students go into the Home of the Leaders, which is the greatest house in the City, for it has three stories. And there they study for many years, so that they may become candidates and be elected to the City Council and the State Council and the World Council—by a free and general vote of all men. But we wished not to be a Leader, even though it is a great honor. We wished to be a Scholar.

In Other Words
garments clothes
born with a head which is too quick too smart
dais stage

Pillars of the Game, 2000, Hugh Shurley. Photo collage © Hugh Shurley/Corbis.

▲ **Critical Viewing: Effect** How would this painting be different if the artist had chosen to include all of the people shown?

18   So we awaited our turn in the great hall and then we heard the Council of Vocations call our name: "Equality 7-2521." We walked to the dais, and our legs did not tremble, and we looked up at the Council. There were five members of the Council, three of the male gender and two of the female. Their hair was white and their faces were cracked as the clay of a dry river bed. They were old. They seemed older than the marble of the Temple of the World Council. They sat before us and they did not move. And we saw no breath to stir the folds of their white **togas**. But we knew that they were alive, for a finger of the hand of the oldest rose, pointed to us, and fell down again. This was the only thing which moved, for the lips of the oldest did not move as they said: "Street Sweeper."

19   We felt the cords of our neck grow tight as our head rose higher to look upon the faces of the Council, and we were happy. We knew we had been **guilty**, but now we had a way to **atone** for it. We would accept our Life Mandate, and we would work for our brothers, gladly and willingly, and we would erase our sin against them, which they did not know, but we knew. So we were happy, and proud of ourselves and of our victory over ourselves. We raised our right arm and we spoke, and our voice was the clearest, the steadiest voice in the hall that day, and we said:

We would accept our Life Mandate…

20   "The will of our brothers be done."

21   And we looked straight into the eyes of the Council, but their eyes were as cold blue glass buttons. ❖

▲ *Possible responses to Critical Viewing:* Seeing their faces would make the people seem more human.

In Other Words
togas robes
guilty to blame
atone make up

Reread and Analyze

11. Style   Reread paragraph 18. Place a box around an example of the narrator's language. Explain why you think the author chose a different kind of language for the narrator at this moment in the story.

Possible response:

The narrator is thinking

much more about the

importance of the Council

than about himself. He

also realizes that this

will be a life-changing

moment for him. Perhaps

his language changes

because of the excitement

of the moment.

12. Style   Highlight other strong descriptions in paragraphs 18–20. Discuss and write about how the change in language also shows a change in the narrator's thinking.

Possible response:

Ironically and sadly, the

change in the narrator's

language comes as he

gives up his dream of

becoming a Scholar and

surrenders his will to the

will of the State.

Discuss

13. **Synthesize** With the class, list some of the infomation that Equality 7-2521 shares with readers. Discuss the style—the language and sentence structure—that the author chooses for presenting the information.

Answers will vary. Possible responses are shown.

Information	Style of Presentation
All men are good and wise. It is only we, Equality 7-2521, we alone who were born with a curse.	short, simple words (almost all one-syllable words) that show little imagination; one very simple sentence followed by a sentence that is not quite as simple and yet is not complicated

Then, with the class, discuss how the author uses language and sentence structure to characterize Equality 7-2521 and his society. Make notes.

Answers will vary but should include examples of plain words and uncomplicated sentence

structures that reflect the dull, barren life of the narrator and of the society seen in *Anthem*.

14. **Write** Use your notes from question 13 to explain how an author can present his or her view of a society and its people. Use the questions below to organize your thoughts.

- · What does the author have the narrator show us about the society in *Anthem*?
- · Analyze the author's language: What does she show about the society by choosing this kind of language?
- · Analyze the author's sentence structure: What does she show about the society by using certain sentence structures most of the time?
- · How can an author use language and word choice to express ideas?

Answers will vary but should show how students have carried forward their thinking from item 13.

Connect with the EQ — What Tests a Person's Loyalty?

Consider whether loyalty can be enforced.

15. Viewpoint Reread paragraphs 18–21. Does the author believe that Equality 7-2521 has passed the test of his loyalty? How do you know?

Answers will vary. Responses should include evidence from the text.

_____

_____

_____

_____

_____

16. Theme What is the author's message about loyalty?

Answers will vary. Responses should include evidence from the text.

_____

_____

_____

_____

_____

_____

Key Vocabulary Review

A. Use these words to complete the paragraph.

adhere	advocate	dilemma	evade
admonish	conscientious	ethical	reinforce

People are sometimes faced with an ___ethical___ problem. What if a friend committed a
(1)

crime? Would you ___evade___ responsibility and not tell anyone about the
(2)

___dilemma___? Would you ___advocate___ your friend's behavior, or would you
(3) (4)

___adhere___ to your principles? Perhaps you could ___admonish___ your friend and
(5) (6)

___reinforce___ the reasons he or she should be more ___conscientious___.
(7) (8)

B. Use your own words to write what each Key Vocabulary word means.
Then write an example for each word. *Answers will vary. Possible responses are shown.*

Key Word	My Definition	Example
1. abstract	not easily understandable	a concept such as loyalty, honor
2. acknowledgment	a recognition	thank-you letter
3. coherent	clear and understandable	a cake recipe
4. dispel	to drive away	a crowd after a game
5. improvise	to invent in an offhand way	giving a speech without notes
6. naive	innocent or ignorant	a young child
7. subdued	quiet and calm	someone in control of his or her emotions
8. surge	to rise or swell	a growing ocean wave

Unit 3 Key Vocabulary

abolish	admonish	• controversial	dilemma	improvise	• pursue
• abstract	• advocate	deliberately	dispel	naive	• reinforce
• acknowledgment	• coherent	desolately	• ethical	opponent	subdued
adhere	conscientious	devastating	evade	pensively	surge

• **Academic Vocabulary**

C. Complete the sentences. *Answers will vary. Possible responses are shown.*

1. A person might behave **desolately** when <u>he or she fails a test</u>

   _____ .

2. A **controversial** issue I support is <u>changing the voting age</u>

   _____ .

3. I behave **pensively** when <u>I know my actions can affect other people</u>

   _____ .

4. A speaker should talk **deliberately** to an audience because <u>the audience needs to be able to</u>

   <u>understand the speaker's argument</u> .

5. One goal I want to **pursue** is <u>going to medical school</u>

   _____ .

6. One thing I would like to **abolish** is <u>my town's curfew for teenagers</u>

   _____ .

7. A natural disaster can be **devastating** because <u>people often lose their homes and personal</u>

   <u>belongings</u> .

8. When I face an **opponent**, I <u>try my best to win</u>

   _____ .

Prepare to Read

▶ **Face Facts: The Science of Facial Expressions**
▶ **Silent Language**

Key Vocabulary

A. How well do you know these words? Circle a rating for each word. Check your understanding of each word by circling *yes* or *no*. Then write a definition. If you are unsure of a word's meaning, refer to the Vocabulary Glossary, page 926, in your student text.

Rating Scale	
1	I have never seen this word before.
2	I am not sure of the word's meaning.
3	I know this word and can teach the word's meaning to someone else.

Key Word	Check Your Understanding	Deepen Your Understanding
❶ **competent** (**kom**-pu-tent) *adjective* **Rating:** 1 2 3	A **competent** bus driver has the skills and capability to drive a bus well. (**Yes**) No	My definition: *Answers will vary.* _____ _____ _____ _____
❷ **emphasis** (**em**-fu-sis) *noun* **Rating:** 1 2 3	News magazines put great **emphasis** on reporting current events. (**Yes**) No	My definition: *Answers will vary.* _____ _____ _____ _____
❸ **emulate** (**em**-yū-lāt) *verb* **Rating:** 1 2 3	When you **emulate** someone, you do the opposite of everything they do. Yes (**No**)	My definition: *Answers will vary.* _____ _____ _____ _____
❹ **enhance** (in-**hants**) *verb* **Rating:** 1 2 3	Picking up litter is one way to **enhance** the appearance of a neighborhood. (**Yes**) No	My definition: *Answers will vary.* _____ _____ _____ _____

Key Word	Check Your Understanding	Deepen Your Understanding
5 **precision** (pri-**si**-zhun) *noun* **Rating:** 1 2 3	A clumsy and careless person completes tasks with **precision.** **Yes**　　(**No**)	My definition: *Answers will vary.*
6 **subtle** (**su**-tul) *adjective* **Rating:** 1 2 3	The smell of a **subtle** perfume is hard to ignore. **Yes**　　(**No**)	My definition: *Answers will vary.*
7 **vary** (**vair**-ē) *verb* **Rating:** 1 2 3	When you **vary** the way you dress, you wear something different every day. (**Yes**)　　**No**	My definition: *Answers will vary.*
8 **visualize** (**vi**-zhu-wu-līz) *verb* **Rating:** 1 2 3	If you want to **visualize** something, you imagine how it looks. (**Yes**)　　**No**	My definition: *Answers will vary.*

B. Use one of the Key Vocabulary words to describe a time you communicated with someone without speaking.

Answers will vary.

LITERARY ANALYSIS: Analyze Text Structure: Cause and Effect

Many nonfiction texts show **cause-and-effect relationships** between major events and ideas. Words and phrases such as *because, since, as a result,* and *if/then* signal these relationships. A writer can describe an effect and then its causes, or the cause and then one or more effects.

A. Read the passage below. Find the cause-and-effect relationships and write them in the Cause-and-Effect Chart.

> **Look Into the Text**
>
> Emotion usually leads to an expression, but studies have shown that the process can also work in reverse: If you force your face to look sad or angry, then the rest of your body will react as well, and you may involuntarily begin to feel those emotions. A look of anger will make your heart speed up and your blood vessels dilate until your skin turns red; a look of fear can make your hands cold and clammy and your hairs stand on end; a look of disgust can make you nauseated.

Cause-and-Effect Chart

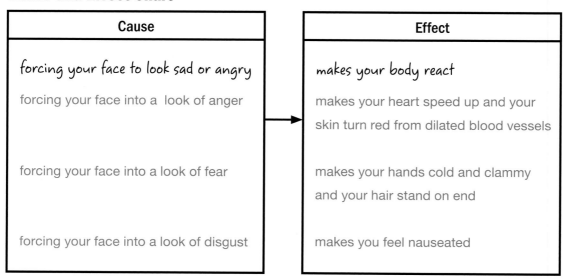

Cause	Effect
forcing your face to look sad or angry	makes your body react
forcing your face into a look of anger	makes your heart speed up and your skin turn red from dilated blood vessels
forcing your face into a look of fear	makes your hands cold and clammy and your hair stand on end
forcing your face into a look of disgust	makes you feel nauseated

B. Answer the question by using the information in the chart. Use a signal word or phrase.

How do facial expressions cause emotions? _Possible response: If you force a facial expression, then your body reacts to that and actually feels emotions._

FOCUS STRATEGY: Self-Question

> ## HOW TO SELF-QUESTION
>
> Focus Strategy
>
> 1. **Pause Your Reading and Ask Yourself One of the "Five Ws + H" Questions** *Who? What? When? Where? Why?* or *How?* helps check your understanding.
>
> 2. **State the Answers** In your own words, answer the questions clearly.
>
> 3. **Reread** If you cannot answer your question, go back and find the answer in the text.

A. Read the passage. Use the strategies above to self-question as you read. Answer the questions below.

> **Look Into the Text**
>
> Chances are, you're not very good at faking a smile. You can raise the corners of your lips into a neat grin—as one does for the camera—and you can probably tighten your eyelids a bit to enhance the effect. But unless you're amused, excited, grateful, relieved, or just plain happy, you probably can't pull your cheeks up and your eyebrows down to form a smile that looks genuine. No more than one in ten people can voluntarily control the outer orbicularis oculi, the muscles surrounding the eye sockets, with that much precision.

1. Ask a "Five Ws + H" question about the passage.

   Possible response: Why is it hard for most people to fake a smile?
   _____

   _____

2. Answer your question in your own words.

   Possible response: Only one in ten people can control the facial muscles around the eyes satisfactorily

   enough to look genuinely happy when he or she doesn't feel happy.

B. How did the strategy help you to check your understanding as you read?

   Possible response: Using the strategy stopped me from reading the text quickly. Asking questions forced me

   to pause and think about the information I was reading.

Selection Review Face Facts: The Science of Facial Expressions

EQ **What Does It Really Mean to Communicate?**
Discover the variety of ways people communicate.

A. In "Face Facts: The Science of Facial Expressions," you learned about Ekman's research into facial expressions. Complete the Details Web by listing the results of Ekman's research.

Details Web

learned that facial expressions are universal

more research on anger now

Results of Ekman's Research

developing a computer system to read expressions

police officers trained to read facial expressions

B. Use the information in the web to answer the questions.

1. Describe the benefits of Ekman's studies. Give examples from the text to support your answer.

   Possible response: Ultimately, Ekman's research will benefit society. More research is being done now on the expression of anger, and the research on facial expressions will help police officers and the CIA to catch criminals.

2. How does Ekman's research in Papua New Guinea enhance our knowledge of facial expression across cultures? Use **enhance** in your response.

   Possible response: Ekman's research was able to enhance our knowledge because it shows that the same basic facial expressions communicate the same things in all cultures. Facial expressions are universal.

3. What other professions might find the study of facial expressions useful? Explain.

   Possible response: Actors and actresses could make their acting more believable if they studied facial communication. Professional photographers could use the information to take better photographs of people.

Connect Across Texts

"Face Facts" focuses on facial expressions. In "Silent Language," discover what your body movements may communicate.

Silent Language

Can we tell what someone is thinking or feeling just by noticing how he or she moves?

BY DR. BRUCE PERRY AND CHARLOTTE LATVALA

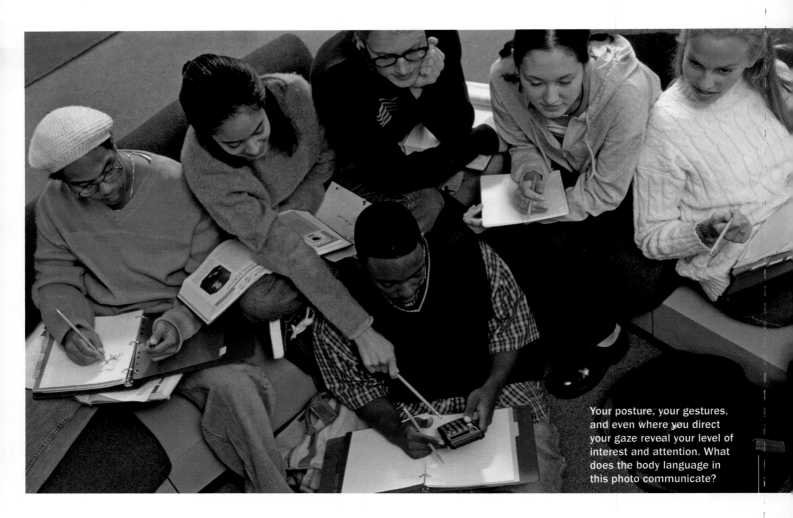

Your posture, your gestures, and even where you direct your gaze reveal your level of interest and attention. What does the body language in this photo communicate?

READING THE SIGNS

We all read minds every day, and we read minds continuously. We're always trying to understand what our parents, teachers, friends, and classmates are thinking or feeling. So think for a moment and you'll realize you can often tell what's on—or in—the mind of someone else. You usually know when a person "likes" you or not; you know when a friend is **preoccupied**, sad, or angry. You can even tell if your parents are disappointed or proud.

We humans are specifically designed to read and respond to each other's **nonverbal cues**, with a special ability to judge safety-related signals: Is this a friend or **a foe**? Will this person hurt me or help me?

In Other Words

preoccupied thinking about something else
nonverbal cues signals without words
a foe an enemy

Some people are better at "mind reading" than others. You can become better if you pay attention to body language, such as hand gestures and facial expressions. For example, when people are feeling uncomfortable, they may squirm, blush, bite their lip, pick at their fingernails, and have a hard time maintaining eye contact. When someone likes you, he or she may often look into your eyes, touch his or her hair, smile, or touch your arm when talking to you. You'll find the subtle cues a person gives off are somewhat unique—for one friend, you may find one nervous habit (fingernail biting) and with another friend a different cue (fidgety feet).

Try to pay attention to how you behave when you feel anxious, happy, interested, or bored. What signals do you give off? Watch, listen, and build up a catalog of experience and you'll become a better "mind reader."

IS YOUR BODY LANGUAGE HOLDING YOU BACK?

You probably think a lot about what you say to others, but did you know that you also send some very strong messages without **uttering** a word? Your gestures and posture say more than you know. Indeed, body language is the single most important means of getting a point across, say experts. Below, you'll find help for some of the most common body language **goofs**.

Avoiding Eye Contact

THE PROBLEM: Refusing to meet someone's eyes says that you're unconfident, nervous, or, even worse—untrustworthy.

HOW TO FIX IT: Ease yourself in—practice maintaining eye contact for slightly longer periods of time. You might feel uncomfortable at first, notes communication specialist Debra Fine, author of *The Fine Art of Small Talk*. "One good trick is to look the person right between the eyes; somehow, this little shift will make you feel more comfortable and connected," she says.

In Other Words
uttering saying
goofs mistakes

Interact with the Text

1. Interpret
Look at the photograph on page 141. What do you think the soccer player who has his hands on his head is feeling, based on his body language?

Possible response: I think the player is feeling upset and angry that he did not make the goal. He looks frustrated.

2. Self-Question
Underline a sentence on page 142 that caused you to pause as you read. What did the sentence make you think about? Write a question that connects to your thoughts about this sentence.

Possible response: I can't always tell that my friend is angry. How can you tell that people are angry if they hide it well?

3. Text Structure: Problem and Solution
Reread the last section on this page. What problem do the authors describe, and what solution do they offer?

The problem is avoiding eye contact. The solution is to relax and practice making eye contact.

4. Text Structure: Problem and Solution

In your own words, write the first problem described on this page. Circle two solutions the author suggests.

Possible response:

Crossing your arms or

legs makes you look

unfriendly. People will

think you want to be

somewhere else.

5. Self-Question

Ask yourself a question about the bigger issue regarding the problem of slouching. Write your question and then circle the solutions to slouching on page 145 that you think would work for you.

Possible response: If you

correct your posture, will

you feel happier?

Crossing Your Arms and Legs

THE PROBLEM: This gesture says, "I'm closed to whatever you're saying," "I wish I weren't here," or "I'm protecting myself from something."

HOW TO FIX IT: Find something comfortable to do with your arms other than crossing them, says communication coach Carmine Gallo, author of *10 Simple Secrets of the World's Greatest Business Communicators.* Try putting one hand in your pocket to train your body to get used to a more open feeling. "Placing both hands in your pockets will make you look nervous or uninterested," Gallo says. "Plus, having the other hand free to gesture makes you seem more confident." Holding something (a glass, a notebook) can also remind you not to cross your arms. And practice sitting with your arms relaxed, hands in lap, and legs side by side.

Looking Around the Room When You're in a Group of Three or More

THE PROBLEM: The conversation **steers away from** you and you think, This is a good time to check out what's happening around us. Well, guess what: "It comes across as **arrogant** or rude," says Fine. (Same goes for continually glancing at your cell phone.)

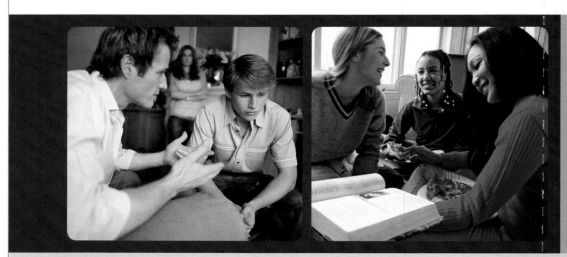

In Other Words
steers away from is no longer about
arrogant self-important

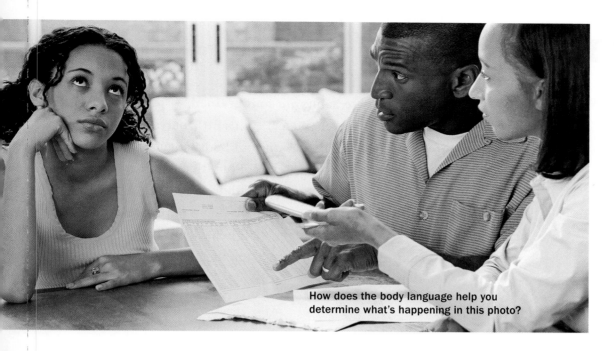

How does the body language help you determine what's happening in this photo?

HOW TO FIX IT: Even if the subject matter drifts away from you, look interested—lean in or nod your head in agreement with the person speaking. Too bored to **even bother**? Excuse yourself politely and walk away. And if you're caught glancing around, you might simply say (with an apologetic smile),"Sorry, but I've got to keep my eye on the door; I'm waiting for a friend to arrive."

Slouching

THE PROBLEM: Poor posture almost shouts, "I'm not handling this well," "I don't feel **competent**," or "I'm depressed."

HOW TO FIX IT: Just force yourself to stand (and sit) up straight! "And while you do it, hold your head up and smile," says Fine. "**Visualize** how you look to others. It may seem stiff at first, but these behaviors will eventually become natural." Before social situations, she adds, remind yourself to sit tall and keep your chin up. Or, role-play the experience you're about to go through (job interview, teacher conference) with an **emphasis** on body language. Regardless of which mental tricks you use, says Fine, once you improve your posture, "You'll feel more confident."

Key Vocabulary
competent *adj.*, capable, qualified
● **visualize** *v.*, to imagine what something looks like
● **emphasis** *n.*, type of special attention

In Other Words
even bother do that

Possible response:

Become aware of your

own body language in

order to stop unflattering

habits.

Twisting Your Jewelry, Playing with Your Hair

THE PROBLEM: You look nervous.

HOW TO FIX IT: Because these habits are **so ingrained**, we're often not aware of what we're doing. So, whenever you feel even a little nervous, **take a mental inventory of** what's going on with your body language. (Are your feet jiggling? Are you playing with your jewelry?) Every time you're tempted to start the **unflattering** habit, take a deep breath instead. Another trick, says Fine: "The next time you're in a group of people, focus on [those] who look self-confident and relaxed, and **emulate** their behavior. It'll make you aware of your nervous **mannerisms** and help you stop them." ❖

Key Vocabulary
emulate *v.*, to imitate

In Other Words
so ingrained so much a part of our daily lives
take a mental inventory of pay attention to
unflattering unattractive
mannerisms behaviors, habits

Selection Review   Silent Language

A. Think about a concept or idea you read about in "Silent Language," and briefly describe it below. What bigger issues does it raise? List your questions below.

Concept/Idea:	Crossing your arms or legs
Questions:	Why am I feeling so nervous that I have to cross my arms and legs?
	What else could I do to keep from crossing my legs?

B. Answer the questions.

1. How did the problem-and-solution text structure help you understand the magazine article?

Possible response: The problem-and-solution text structure was a good way to organize the magazine article. It was obvious where I needed to look to find each piece of information.

2. Which of the problems listed in the magazine article is one you have experienced? What was your solution?

Possible response: One time I was slouching at the dinner table, so my grandmother thought I didn't like the meal she had prepared. Next time at dinner, I was more aware of my body language, so I sat up straight and showed my grandmother that I enjoyed the meal.

Reflect and Assess

- Face Facts: The Science of Facial Expressions
- Silent Language

WRITING: Write About Literature

A. Plan your writing. Identify the topic of each selection and the author's purpose for writing. Then identify the text structure and give an example that shows the text structure. *Answers will vary. Possible responses are shown.*

	Face Facts: The Science of Facial Expressions	Silent Language
Topic	Paul Ekman studies facial expressions for scientific and cultural purposes.	Body language conveys feelings and attitudes more than you might realize.
Author's purpose	to inform	to inform
Text structure	The author explains the cause-and-effect relationships between facial expressions and emotions.	The author describes five problems and several possible solutions to each problem.
Example of text structure	When you feel surprised, your jaw drops and your eyes widen.	Slouching is one of the problems described. The solution is to force yourself to sit up straight by imagining how you look to others.

B. In your opinion, which selection is better organized? Evaluate the text structure of that selection in a paragraph. Include why it is effective or serves the author's purpose.

Students should support their answers with examples from that selection.

_____

_____

_____

_____

_____

_____

_____

_____

_____

_____

Unit 4: Express Yourself 147

Integrate the Language Arts

LITERARY ANALYSIS: Literary Paradox

A **paradox** is an idea or statement that seems illogical or impossible but has an element of truth.

> Example: Body language is the single most important means of getting a point across.

A. Read each statement below. Decide if the underlined phrase is a paradox or not. Mark an *X* in the appropriate column.

Statement	Paradox	Not a Paradox
<u>Internal responses</u>, such as an increased heartbeat, can last longer than the expressions themselves.		*X*
The police officer gave a <u>grim smile</u> to show his satisfaction that the criminal had finally been captured.	*X*	
It is uncommon for a person to be able to <u>voluntarily control</u> the muscles surrounding the eye sockets.		*X*

B. Choose two of the phrases above. Explain why each phrase is or is not a paradox.
Answers will vary. Possible responses are shown.

   1. Phrase: <u>internal responses</u>

      Explanation: <u>This is not a paradox because it is true that your internal organs are able to respond along</u>

      <u>with your facial expressions.</u>

   2. Phrase: <u>grim smile</u>

      Explanation: <u>This is a paradox because a smile usually indicates that someone is happy. It is illogical that</u>

      <u>a smile would be grim. However, there is truth to the statement. For example, the police officer may be happy</u>

      <u>that the criminal has been caught but unhappy that the criminal escaped in the first place.</u>

C. Write your own paradox based on a recent experience. Explain why the paradox is impossible and truthful in a short paragraph below.

   Answers will vary.

VOCABULARY STUDY: Multiple-Meaning Words

Many **multiple-meaning words** have specialized meanings in different subject areas, such as social studies, science, and math.

A. Each word in the chart below has more than one meaning. Use a dictionary to find the specialized meanings in math and in English for each word.

Word	Math Meaning	English Meaning
angle	the space between two lines or surfaces that meet	point of view
foot	a unit of length equal to 12 inches	one of the units of rhythm into which a line of poetry is divided
line	the path traced by a moving point, extending at both ends	a row of words across a page
root	a number that produces another number when multiplied by itself	a word or word part from which other words are made

B. Use a dictionary to find the meaning for the word *flat* in the sentence below. Then write the definitions for the same word in the subject areas of math and music.

> *I prefer novels with adventurous and interesting main characters because flat protagonists bore me.*

English meaning: lacking life, interest, or flavor

Math meaning: smooth and level

Music meaning: half a note below natural pitch

C. Write sentences for *flat* using the math and music meanings.
Answers will vary. Possible responses are shown.

1. My geometry teacher asked us to imagine a flat plane.

2. The song seemed especially mournful when the choir sang the flat notes most loudly.

Prepare to Read

▶ **They Speak for Success**
▶ **Breaking the Ice**

Key Vocabulary

A. How well do you know these words? Circle a rating for each word. Check your understanding of each word by circling the correct synonym or antonym. Then complete the sentences. If you are unsure of a word's meaning, refer to the Vocabulary Glossary, page 926, in your student text.

Rating Scale	
1	I have never seen this word before.
2	I am not sure of the word's meaning.
3	I know this word and can teach the word's meaning to someone else.

Key Word	Check Your Understanding	Deepen Your Understanding
❶ abbreviated (u-**brē**-vē-ā-ted) *adjective* **Rating:** 1 2 3	If something is **abbreviated**, it is _____. (**shortened**) lengthened	When I take notes, I use abbreviated words and phrases because *Possible response:* I can write faster .
❷ ambience (**am**-bē-ents) *noun* **Rating:** 1 2 3	When a place has **ambience**, it has a certain _____. logic (**mood**)	The ambience of my bedroom is *Possible response:* relaxed and comfortable
❸ articulate (ar-**ti**-kyü-let) *adjective* **Rating:** 1 2 3	The opposite of an **articulate** person is a _____ person. lucid (**stammering**)	I am articulate when I talk about *Possible response:* subjects that interest me .
❹ humiliation (hyū-mi-lē-ā-shun) *noun* **Rating:** 1 2 3	If you feel **humiliation**, you feel _____. (**shame**) honor	I experienced humiliation when *Possible response:* I tripped on the curb in front of a group of friends .

Key Word	Check Your Understanding	Deepen Your Understanding
5 **intimidating** (in-**ti**-mu-dā-ting) *adjective* **Rating:** 1 2 3	An **intimidating** person is a _____ person. comforting (frightening)	Something that is intimidating to me is _____ *Possible response:* singing in front of people _____ _____ _____.
6 **obligation** (ah-blu-**gā**-shun) *noun* **Rating:** 1 2 3	The opposite of an **obligation** is a _____. (choice) responsibility	I have an obligation to *Possible response:* take care of my little sister whenever my mom asks me to _____ _____ _____.
7 **stimulating** (**stim**-yū-lā-ting) *adjective* **Rating:** 1 2 3	The opposite of a **stimulating** conversation is a _____ conversation. fun (dull)	A stimulating experience I have had was _____ *Possible response:* watching a live recording in a music studio _____ _____.
8 **surpass** (sur-**pas**) *verb* **Rating:** 1 2 3	If you **surpass** people's expectations, you _____ them. (exceed) lose	When I surpass my own expectations, I feel _____ *Possible response:* proud and excited _____ _____ _____.

B. Use one of the Key Vocabulary words to write about a time when it was difficult for you to communicate with others. What did you do?

Answers will vary. _____

_____

LITERARY ANALYSIS: Analyze Text Structure: Main Idea and Details

Nonfiction writers often provide specific **examples** to support main ideas. Example details often follow signal words; they also can appear after a colon (:) or a dash (—), in a numbered or bulleted list, or in a text box.

A. Read the passage below. Complete the diagram by listing the example details that support the main idea given for the passage.

> **Look Into the Text**
>
> ### What Is Forensics?
>
> Today forensics is offered as a class or extracurricular activity at many high schools and colleges. Many students who participate enjoy the theatrical aspect or want to improve their public speaking skills. Members of a forensics team compete against others in one or more of the following areas:
> - debate
> - dramatic interpretation
> - expository (informational) speech
> - extemporaneous talk

Main Idea: Forensics is a study that involves public speaking.

Example:	debate
Example:	dramatic interpretation
Example:	expository (informational) speech
Example:	extemporaneous talk

B. What do the examples tell you about forensics?

Possible response: There are several different kinds of speeches in forensics.

FOCUS STRATEGY: Find Question-Answer Relationships

> ## HOW TO FIND QUESTION-ANSWER RELATIONSHIPS
> **Focus Strategy**
>
> - **"Writer and Me"** Think about what you already know and what the author tells you. Decide how these two parts answer the question.
>
> - **"On My Own"** Use your personal experiences to answer the question.

A. Read the passage. Use the strategies above to find question-answer relationships as you read. Answer the questions below.

> ### Look Into the Text
>
> "They all help each other," says their teacher. "They find refuge here. I've tried to create an environment where it's safe for them to stand up and speak in public." He knows it can be scary. "Speaking in public is as frightening to many people as coming down with cancer," says Lindsey, 53. "But I believe that getting good at it can be the key to success." And his students prove him right. While only 40 percent of Logan graduates go on to four-year colleges, virtually all of Lindsey's students do—but not before they show off their talents at tournaments across the country.

1. Write one question you asked yourself as you read the passage.

Possible response: How does being a part of the forensics team help students become more successful in school?

2. What is the answer to your question?

Possible response: Being on the forensics team teaches students to speak well in public. It also prepares them for college.

3. Which strategy did you use to answer your question? Explain.

Possible response: "Writer and Me"; I thought about the author's ideas and combined that knowledge with what I already know about public speaking and preparing for college.

B. Return to the passage above and underline the words or phrases that gave you the answer to the question.

Selection Review They Speak for Success

 EQ **What Does It Really Mean to Communicate?**
Explore everyday challenges to communication.

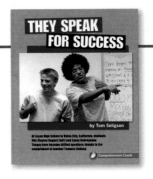

A. In "They Speak for Success," you read about students who improved their communication skills through forensics. Complete the chart below with examples of what each student learned.

Student	What the Student Learned
Jamie Walker	good posture, rhythm of good speech, a strong work ethic
Jennifer Chang Kuo	how to be confident, happy, successful, and articulate; how to work hard
Steve Kuo	poise and confidence are important aspects of communication
Sharahn LaRue McClung	the need to communicate should surpass the need to compete

B. Use the information in the chart to answer the questions.

1. What are some examples of good communication skills? Why are these skills so important?

Good communication skills include good posture, confidence, and poise. These skills can help students prepare for the future and make them successful.

2. Why is it intimidating for some people to speak in public? Use **intimidating** in your answer.

Possible response: Speaking in public can be intimidating for people who are shy or who have never spoken in front of people. People might be afraid that they will stutter or that the audience will laugh at them.

3. Why do you think that forensics students are often the most successful graduates of their high school?

Possible response: The students set goals and they work hard. They practice regularly and do not give up easily. They are motivated to succeed.

Connect Across Texts

In "They Speak for Success," students overcome challenges to communication. In "Breaking the Ice," Dave Barry recalls his toughest communication challenge—how to ask a girl out on a date.

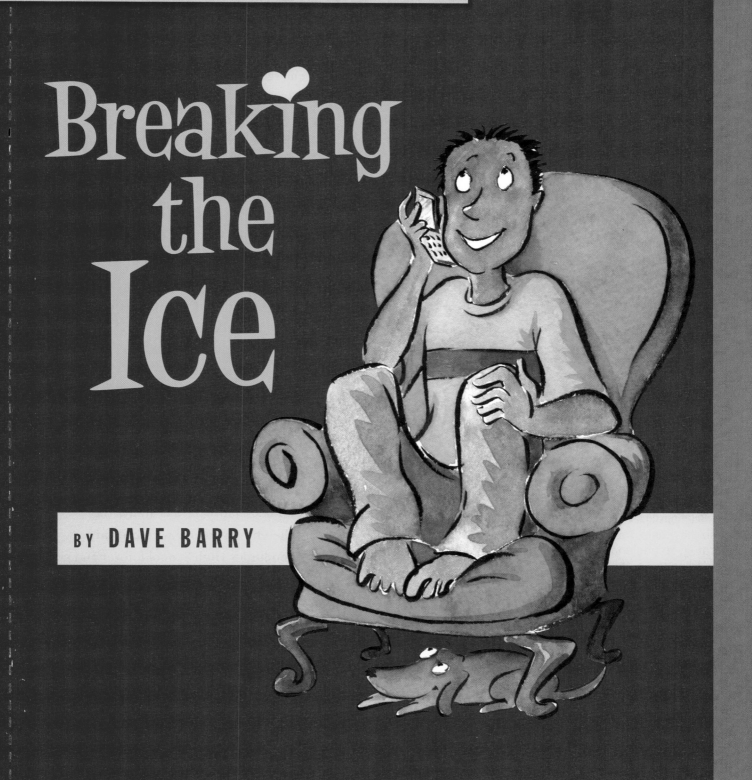

Breaking the Ice

BY **DAVE BARRY**

1. Interpret

Look at the art on page 155 and then describe how the image makes you feel.

Possible response: The

image makes me feel

that this might be a

funny column because it

begins with a cartoon.

2. Humor

The author begins the article by comparing how much time he spent thinking about dating when he was young and how much time he spent thinking about school or zits. Why do these comparisons add humor to the article?

Possible response:

They exaggerate how

much the author was

concerned about dating.

3. Find Question-Answer Relationships

Use the "Right There" strategy to find and underline the author's suggestion for the most sensible way to ask out a girl. What do you think about his suggestion?

Possible response: It

seems too intimidating.

The girl might say no.

As a mature adult, I feel an **obligation** to help the younger generation, just as the mother fish guards her unhatched eggs, keeping her lonely **vigil** day after day, never leaving her post, not even to go to the bathroom, until her tiny babies emerge and she is able, at last, to eat them. "She may be your mom, but she's still a fish" is a wisdom nugget that I would pass along to any fish eggs reading this column.

But today I want to talk about dating. This subject was raised in a letter to me from a young person named Eric Knott, who writes:

> *I have got a big problem. There's this girl in my English class who is really good-looking. However, I don't think she knows I exist. I want to ask her out, but I'm afraid she will say no, and I will be the freak of the week. What should I do?*

Eric, you have sent your question to the right mature adult, because as a young person I spent a lot of time thinking about this very problem. Starting in about eighth grade, my time was divided as follows:

- Academic Pursuits: 2 percent
- Zits: 16 percent
- Trying to Figure Out How to Ask Girls Out: 82 percent

I don't think she knows I exist

The most sensible way to ask a girl out is to walk directly up to her on foot and say, "So, you want to go out? Or what?" I never did this. I knew, as Eric Knott knows, that there was always the possibility that the girl would say no, thereby leaving me with **no viable option** but to leave Harold C. Crittenden Junior High School forever and go into the woods and become a bark-eating **hermit** whose only companions would be the gentle and understanding woodland creatures.

"Hey, ZITFACE!" the woodland creatures would shriek in cute little

---

Key Vocabulary
obligation *n.*, duty, responsibility

In Other Words
vigil period of watching
no viable option no other choice
hermit person who lives away from society

Chip 'n' Dale voices while raining acorns down upon my head. "You wanna DATE? HAHAHAHAHAHA."

So the first rule of dating is: Never risk direct contact with the girl in question. Your role model should be the nuclear submarine, gliding silently beneath the ocean surface, tracking an enemy target that does not even begin to suspect that the submarine would like to date it.   I spent the vast majority of 1960 **keeping a girl named Judy under surveillance**, maintaining a minimum distance of fifty lockers to avoid the danger that I might somehow get into a conversation with her, which could have led to disaster.

JUDY: Hi.

ME: Hi.

JUDY: Just in case you have ever thought about having a date with me, the answer is no.

WOODLAND CREATURES: HAHAHAHAHA.

The only problem with the nuclear-submarine technique is that it's difficult to get a date with a girl who has never, technically, been asked. This is why you need Phil Grant. Phil was a friend of mine who had the ability to talk to girls. It was a mysterious superhuman power he had, comparable to X-ray vision. So, after several thousand hours of intense discussion and planning with me, Phil approached a girl he knew named Nancy, who approached a girl named Sandy, who was a direct personal friend of Judy's and who passed the word back to Phil via Nancy that Judy would be willing to go on a date with me. This procedure protected me from direct **humiliation** . . .

Thus it was that, finally, Judy and I went on an actual date, to see a movie in White Plains, New York. If I were to sum up the romantic **ambience** of this date in four words, those words would be: "My mother was driving." This made for an extremely quiet drive, because my mother, realizing that her presence

Key Vocabulary
humiliation *n.*, shame, embarrassment
ambience *n.*, feeling or mood of a place or thing

In Other Words
keeping a girl named Judy under surveillance watching a girl named Judy closely

4. Find Question-Answer Relationships
Highlight the author's first rule of dating. Use the "Think and Search" strategy to explain why a boy should be like a nuclear submarine.

Possible response: The author compares a boy to a submarine because the first rule of dating requires silence and secrecy.

5. Humor
Highlight phrases on page 158 that show how the author uses humor to explain his date with Judy. What elements of humor does the author use to show he was nervous?

Possible response: The author uses impossible events, odd or absurd comparisons, exaggeration, and unexpected statements.

was hideously embarrassing, had to pretend she wasn't there. If it had been legal, I think she would have got out and sprinted alongside the car, steering through the window. Judy and I, sitting in the back seat about seventy-five feet apart, were also silent, unable to communicate without the assistance of Phil, Nancy, and Sandy.

After what seemed like several years, we got to the movie theater, where my mother went off to sit in the Parents and **Lepers** Section. The movie was called *North to Alaska*, but I can tell you nothing else about it because I spent the whole time wondering whether it would be necessary to **amputate** my right arm, which was not getting any blood flow as a result of being perched for two hours like a **petrified** snake on the back of Judy's seat exactly one molecule away from physical contact.

After what seemed like several years, we got to the movie theater.

So it was definitely a fun first date, featuring all the relaxed spontaneity of a real-estate closing, and in later years I did regain some feeling in my arm. My point, Eric Knott, is that the key to successful dating is *self-confidence*. I bet that good-looking girl in your English class would LOVE to go out with you. But YOU have to make the first move. So just do it! Pick up that phone! Call Phil Grant. ❖

Selection Review Breaking the Ice

A. Answer the questions using one of the reading strategies. Name the strategy you used for each.

1. Why did the author write this article?

"Right There"; The author felt an obligation to tell the younger generation about dating.

2. Why was the author's date not romantic?

"Think and Search"; Because the author was nervous, his mother drove them to the movies, and he did not communicate with his *date*. As a result, the date was not romantic.

B. How did the humor help you understand the author's message?

Possible response: Humor can help you put humiliating experiences into perspective.

Reflect and Assess

WRITING: Write About Literature

A. Plan your writing. Read the opposing opinions. Mark an *X* next to the opinion you agree with. List examples from the text that support your opinion.   *Answers will vary.*

☐ **Opinion 1:**   Speaking formally to a group is more challenging than talking seriously to someone on a first date.

☐ **Opinion 2:**   Talking seriously to someone on a first date is more challenging than speaking formally to a group.

They Speak for Success	Breaking the Ice

B. What is your opinion? Write an opinion statement. Support your opinion with examples from both texts.

Students should support their answers with examples from both selections.

_____

_____

_____

_____

_____

_____

_____

Integrate the Language Arts

LITERARY ANALYSIS: Flashback

A **flashback** is an interruption in a text that describes an experience that occurred in the past. Flashbacks can give more information about a person, place, or event, or they can relate a memory or dream. Flashbacks can also emphasize the importance of a story element.

> Eric, you have sent your question to the right mature adult, because as a young person I spent a lot of time thinking about this very problem. Starting in about eighth grade, my time was divided as follows …

A. Reread "Breaking the Ice." After you read, brainstorm reasons why you think the author used flashback in his humor column. *Answers will vary.*

Reasons for Flashback
1. to tell about a similar experience he had when he was a teenager
2.
3.
4.

B. List specific details from the flashback in "Breaking the Ice." Then explain how the flashback adds to the selection. *Answers will vary. Possible responses are shown.*

Details	How It Adds to the Selection
The flashback begins when Barry is in 8th grade.	The flashback helps me to understand how the writer can help Eric.
Barry tells how much time he spent thinking about girls.	I know he can relate to Eric because he experienced the same thing.
Barry tells about his dating experience in great detail.	The author tells Eric that it is important to relax, be himself, and ask the girl out.
Barry uses humor to write about his dating experiences.	He uses his own experience to show Eric that it is normal to feel nervous.

C. Write about a time when you or someone you know failed to communicate. Use flashback to describe your memory.

When I think back on it now, it seems _____ *Answers will vary.*

VOCABULARY STUDY: Jargon

Jargon is the specialized vocabulary used in a job or activity to describe materials, actions, and tools. Baseball is one activity that has its own jargon. For example, words such as *home run* and *out* are specific to baseball.

A. In the chart are three examples of baseball jargon. Write what you think each special word or phrase means. Then use a dictionary to confirm the meanings. *Answers will vary. Possible responses are shown.*

Word or Phrase	What I Think It Means	Definition
dugout	the area where the teams sit	the low shelters that face the baseball diamond and contain the players' benches
grand slam	a home run with runners on all three bases	a home run with the bases loaded
strike	failing to hit the ball	a pitched ball that is swung at; a perfectly thrown ball

B. The chart below lists jargon related to forensics, or public speaking. Write a definition for each word or phrase in the chart below. Use a dictionary to confirm the meanings.

Jargon	My Definition
debate	a discussion of opposite viewpoints
dramatic interpretation	the performance of a part of a play or novel
expository (informational) speech	an informative speech
extemporaneous talk	a speech in which only the outline of the speech is prepared
impromptu speech	an unprepared speech
original oratory	a speech on a subject of the speaker's own choosing

C. Use the jargon above to explain how a public speaker might choose to communicate with an audience and why. Include at least three of the terms from the chart in Activity B. The paragraph is started for you.

Public speakers can use a variety of speeches to get their message across. Speakers can choose ___*Answers will vary.*___

_____

_____

Prepare to Read
▶ **My English**
▶ **How I Learned English**

Key Vocabulary

A. How well do you know these words? Circle a rating for each word. Check your understanding of each word by marking an X next to the correct definition. Then provide an example. If you are unsure of a word's meaning, refer to the Vocabulary Glossary, page 926, in your student text.

Rating Scale

1	I have never seen this word before.
2	I am not sure of the word's meaning.
3	I know this word and can teach the word's meaning to someone else.

Key Word	Check Your Understanding	Deepen Your Understanding
❶ **accentuate** (ik-**sen**-shü-wāt) *verb* **Rating:** 1 2 3	☐ to make something smaller ☒ to make something noticeable	Example: *Possible response:* showing off your muscles by flexing
❷ **banish** (**ba**-nish) *verb* **Rating:** 1 2 3	☒ to send away ☐ to help someone	Example: *Possible response:* being sent home from school for disobeying the rules
❸ **countenance** (**kown**-tun-ents) *noun* **Rating:** 1 2 3	☒ a person's look or expression ☐ a person's clothing	Example: *Possible response:* an expression of anger or sadness
❹ **discerning** (di-**sur**-ning) *adjective* **Rating:** 1 2 3	☐ showing good manners ☒ showing good judgment	Example: *Possible response:* someone who thinks carefully before buying a car

Key Word	Check Your Understanding	Deepen Your Understanding
5 **disrespectful** (dis-ri-**spekt**-ful) *adjective* **Rating:** 1 2 3	☐ willing ☒ insulting	Example: *Possible response:* interrupting others when they are speaking
6 **enlist** (in-**list**) *verb* **Rating:** 1 2 3	☐ to make a list ☒ to ask for assistance	Example: *Possible response:* to ask friends to help make food for a big party
7 **enumerate** (i-**nü**-mu-rāt) *verb* **Rating:** 1 2 3	☐ to question ☒ to list	Example: *Possible response:* listing your ten favorite songs or musicians
8 **interminably** (in-**tur**-mi-nu-blē) *adverb* **Rating:** 1 2 3	☒ continuing on without end ☐ sickly	Example: *Possible response:* a boring movie or a long speech

B. Use one of the Key Vocabulary words to describe one of the many ways you communicate with people in your life.

Answers will vary.

Before Reading My English

LITERARY ANALYSIS: Analyze Text Structure: Chronological Order

A nonfiction writer uses **chronological order,** or time order, to present events in the order that they take place. Words such as *before, during, after, first, last, next, then,* and *when* indicate chronological order.

A. Read the passage below. Underline the time-order words in the passage. Then write the narrator's thoughts or feelings in the chart.

Look Into the Text

> When we arrived in New York, I was shocked. A country where everyone spoke English! . . . It took some time before I understood that Americans were not necessarily a smarter, superior race. . . . Soon it wasn't so strange that everyone was speaking English instead of Spanish.

Chronology	Narrator's Thoughts or Feelings
First	I felt shocked. Everyone spoke English.
Next	I understood that Americans were not a smarter race.
Then	I didn't feel strange hearing English anymore.

B. Complete the sentence about the writer's experience in New York.

The writer becomes used to people speaking English after she spends some time in her new country
and realizes Americans are not so different

FOCUS STRATEGY: Question the Author

HOW TO QUESTION THE AUTHOR

Focus Strategy

1. **Pause and Ask Questions** Direct your questions to the author.

2. **State the Answer** Say it clearly in your own words.

3. **Reread** If you cannot answer the questions, read the text again and think about why the author made certain decisions.

A. Read the passage. Use the strategies above to question the author as you read. Then answer the questions below.

Look Into the Text

> Why my parents didn't first educate us in our native language by enrolling us in a Dominican school, I don't know. Part of it was that Mami's family had a tradition of sending the boys to the States to boarding school and college, and she had been one of the first girls to be allowed to join her brothers. At Abbot Academy, whose school song was our lullaby as babies ("Although Columbus and Cabot never heard of Abbot, it's quite the place for you and me"), she had become quite Americanized. It was very important, she kept saying, that we learn our English. She always used the possessive pronoun: *your* English, an inheritance we had come into and must wisely use. Unfortunately, my English became all mixed up with our Spanish.

1. Why is the author telling the reader this information?

   Possible response: It explains why the author couldn't speak English very well and was learning to speak English in the first place.

2. What other question did you have after reading this passage? How did you answer it?

   Possible response: Could the author have said it better? I went back, reread the passage, and noticed all the details about her family. This helped me better understand why she learned English.

B. Return to the passage above and highlight the words or sentences that helped you answer question 2.

Selection Review My English

EQ **What Does It Really Mean to Communicate?**
Observe how people learn new forms of communication.

A. In "My English," you found out how the author learned to speak a new language. Complete the Sequence Chain by listing the events in order.

Sequence Chain

1. Alvarez began to learn English in an American school.

2. She mixed Spanish words with English words.

3. She made mistakes as she learned.

4. She practiced English with her grandfather and learned idioms from others.

5. She arrived in New York and was surrounded by English speakers.

6. A sixth-grade teacher taught her to love language.

7. Alvarez finally felt comfortable speaking English.

B. Use the information in the Sequence Chain to answer the questions.

1. What event caused Alvarez to finally feel comfortable with the English language? When did this event occur?

   She had a good sixth-grade teacher who helped her to become more comfortable with the language.

   This event happened after she arrived in the United States.

2. Whose help did Alvarez enlist to help her learn English? Use **enlist** in your answer.

   Possible response: Alvarez enlisted her grandfather to help her practice her English. She also learned

   idioms from others.

3. What questions did you have for the author as you read? Write one question and the strategy you used to find the answer. Write the answer.

   Possible response: How did it feel to make mistakes as you were learning English? I reread the text in

   order to answer my question. The author might respond to the question by saying that it felt frustrating

   and embarrassing to make mistakes while learning English.

4. Write a paragraph describing how you would feel if you were in Alvarez's situation. How is this similar to the way Alvarez felt?

   Answers will vary.

1. Free Verse

How do you know that this is a free verse poem?

Possible response:

There is no set pattern,

rhythm, or rhyme. The

poet separated the

descriptions using

commas and also line

breaks.

2. Question the Author

Circle the line on the first page that is indented, or begins differently from all the others. Why do you think the poet wrote the line this way?

Possible response: The

poet may have written

it this way to emphasize

how he was feeling—

alone.

3. Interpret

What position does the speaker play on the team? Highlight where you found this in the text. Why do you think he is given this position?

Possible response:

He plays outfield. He

probably isn't a good

player, so he is put in a

position where he won't

see much action.

Connect Across Texts

In "My English," Julia Alvarez accentuates the variety of ways in which she made the English language her own. In this poem, the writer tells how he became more comfortable with English by playing baseball with friends.

How I Learned English

By Gregory Djanikian

It was in an empty lot
Ringed by elms and fir and honeysuckle.
Bill Corson was pitching in his buckskin jacket,
Chuck Keller, fat even as a boy, was on first,
5   His t-shirt riding up over his gut,
Ron O'Neill, Jim, Dennis, were talking it up
In the field, a blue sky above them
Tipped with cirrus.
        And there I was,
10 Just off the plane and plopped in the middle
Of Williamsport, Pa. and a neighborhood game,
Unnatural and without any moves,
My notions of baseball and America
Growing fuzzier each time I whiffed.
15 So it was not impossible that I,
Banished to the outfield and daydreaming
Of water, or a hotel in the mountains,
Would suddenly find myself in the path

Key Vocabulary
banish *v.*, send away

In Other Words
without any moves not having baseball skills

Of a ball stung by Joe Barone.
20   I watched it closing in
Clean and untouched, transfixed
By its easy arc before it hit
My forehead with a thud.
$\qquad$(I fell back,)
25   Dazed, clutching my brow,
Groaning, "Oh my shin, oh my shin,"
And everybody peeled away from me
And dropped from laughter, and there we were,
All of us writhing on the ground for one reason
30   Or another.
$\qquad$(Someone said "shin" again,)
There was a wild stamping of hands on the ground,
A kicking of feet, and the fit
Of laughter overtook me too,
35   And that was important, as important
As Joe Barone asking me how I was
Through his tears, picking me up
And dusting me off with hands like swatters,
And though my head felt heavy,
40   I played on till dusk
Missing flies and pop-ups and grounders
And calling out in desperation things like
"Yours" and "take it," but doing all right,
Tugging at my cap in just the right way,
45   Crouching low, my feet set,
"Hum baby" sweetly on my lips.

In Other Words
transfixed frozen into one position
peeled away ran away suddenly
writhing twisting

Cultural Background
Williamsport, Pennsylvania, is the home of the Little League youth baseball program, which began in 1939. At the end of every summer, teams from around the world come to Williamsport to participate in the Little League World Series championship tournament.

Interact with the Text

4. Question the Author
Why does the speaker play on until dusk, in spite of his injury?

Possible response:

The speaker might feel accepted by the players, so he begins to enjoy playing the game with them.

5. Free Verse
The poet uses the unique line break two more times. Circle the two unique lines. Why does the poet use this pattern?

Possible response: The poet uses these lines to show important points in his story—points where he wants to catch the reader's attention and emphasize an idea.

Selection Review How I Learned English

A. The poet uses free verse to write about an important moment in his life. Complete the web that shows which elements of free verse the poet uses in "How I Learned English." Then answer the question.

Details Web

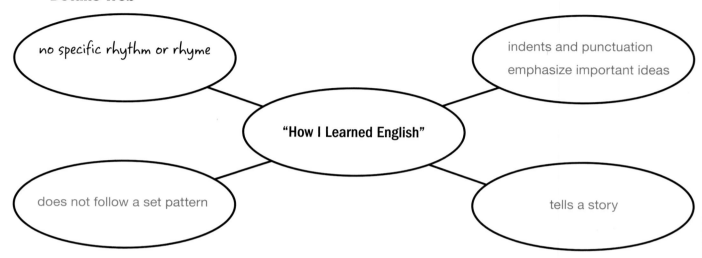

no specific rhythm or rhyme

indents and punctuation emphasize important ideas

"How I Learned English"

does not follow a set pattern

tells a story

1. Describe how the poet effectively uses the elements of free verse in his poem. How does it help you understand his story about the baseball game better?

   Possible response: The poet does not use rhyme, so the poem is easier to read. He indents lines

   and punctuates in certain ways so the reader will take special notice of certain ideas. The poet

   also writes the poem like a story, so it keeps my interest. The poem does not follow a set pattern;

   it flows from one idea to the next.

B. Answer the questions.

1. Why do you think the poet used the setting of a baseball game to show how he "learned English"?

   Possible response: The setting of a baseball game could be a metaphor describing the difficulties

   and accomplishments involved in learning a new language. Baseball is also a very popular game

   in America.

2. How do the speaker's actions at the end of the poem change? What does this say about his ability to communicate?

   Possible response: He is more confident. He is enjoying the game. He tries yelling out to the

   other players. This shows that he has more confidence in himself. If he made another mistake, his

   friends would support him, or they could enjoy laughing together.

Reflect and Assess

▶ **My English**
▶ **How I Learned English**

WRITING: Write About Literature

A. Plan your writing. Compare how the writer in "My English" and the speaker in "How I Learned English" had similar and different experiences with learning a new language. Complete the Venn diagram with details from both selections.

Venn Diagram

"My English"

Possible response:
The writer learned English in an American school in a foreign country.

Family members helped her.

Both

Possible response:
Both made mistakes as they were learning the language.

"How I Learned English"

Possible response:
The speaker learned English by playing with American kids who later became his friends.

B. Think about your own experiences learning a new language or as you learn to be a better communicator. Write a letter or an e-mail to a friend explaining how your experiences compare to those in "My English" and "How I Learned English."

Students should support their answers with examples from both selections.

_____

_____

_____

_____

_____

_____

_____

_____

Unit 4: Express Yourself **171**

Integrate the Language Arts

LITERARY ANALYSIS: Multiple Levels of Meaning

The English language includes words and sayings that have more than one meaning depending upon the context in which they are used. For example, the phrase *the cream of the crop* might literally mean "the cream on top of fresh milk." More often, it means "the best of a group."

A. Brainstorm some common phrases that people use that might be confusing for a person who is learning English. *Answers will vary.*

Common Phrases	
1. cool as a cucumber	**5.**
2.	**6.**
3.	**7.**
4.	**8.**

B. Read these phrases from "My English." Explain the literal meaning of each phrase. Then write what the phrase meant in the context of the selection. *Answers will vary. Possible responses are shown.*

Phrase	Literal Meaning	Meaning in Context
"Talking up an English storm."	talking about the weather in England	talking a lot
"Cat got your tongue?"	Did a cat scratch your tongue?	Can't you say anything?
"Go jump in a lake!"	Go jump in a lake!	Stop talking nonsense to me!

C. Describe an experience you had when you misunderstood a word or a saying that had multiple levels of meaning.

Answers will vary.

_____

_____

_____

_____

_____

_____

_____

_____

VOCABULARY STUDY: Content-Area Words

Content-area words have specialized meanings in a specific subject area. For example, the word *photosynthesis* is a content-area word used in science. Other content areas include math, social studies, and English.

A. Look up each word in a dictionary and write the definition. Then list the content area in which the word might be used.

Word	Definition	Content Area
algorithm	a precise order to follow to best solve a problem	math
almshouse	a charitable home for those in need	social studies
anemometer	a device used to measure wind	science
electrolysis	splitting a substance into the separate chemicals that make it up by passing an electric current through it	science
latitude	the imaginary lines running east and west on the globe that run parallel to the equator	geography

B. Write a sentence using each of these words. *Answers will vary. Possible responses are shown.*

algorithm Once I learned the algorithm, it was easy to complete my math assignment.

almshouse The homeless man lived at the almshouse temporarily.

anemometer When I visited the weather station, I saw an anemometer in action.

electrolysis The scientists produce electrolysis in the lab.

latitude I found the city on the map by looking for its latitude and longitude coordinates.

C. Describe a method that you might be able to use that would help you understand new content-area words when they are used in texts that you are reading.

Possible response: I can keep a dictionary by my side so that when I see one of these words, I can look it up. I can also record the words and the definitions in a notebook so that if I run across them again, I will already have written or recorded the definition in my own words.

Read for Understanding

1. Genre What kind of text is this passage? How do you know?

Possible response: It

is an essay in which

the author presents an

argument and defends it.

2. Topic Write a topic sentence to tell what the text is mostly about.

The text mostly tells

about texting and how

it doesn't weaken

language skills.

Reread and Summarize

3. Key Ideas In each section, circle three words or phrases that express big ideas in that section. Note next to each word or phrase why you chose it.

· Section 1: numbers 1–12
· Section 2: numbers 13–18

4. Summary Use your topic sentence and notes from item 3 to write a summary of the selection.

Possible response:

The author argues

that texting reflects

texters' language

skills and motivates

communication and

creativity.

from **Txtng: The Gr8 Db8**

BY DAVID CRYSTAL

1 A remarkable number of **doom-laden prophecies** arose during the opening years of the new millennium, all relating to the **linguistic evils** which would be unleashed by texting. The prophecies went something like this:

2 • Texting uses new and nonstandard **orthography**.

3 • This will **inevitably erode** children's ability to spell, punctuate, and capitalize correctly—an ability already thought to be poor.

4 • They will inevitably transfer these new habits into the rest of their schoolwork.

5 • This will inevitably give them poorer marks in examinations.

6 • A new generation of adults will inevitably grow up unable to write proper English.

7 • Eventually the language as a whole will inevitably decline.

8 Misinformation of this kind can be crushed only by solid research findings. And research is slowly beginning to show that texting actually benefits literacy skills. The studies are few, with small numbers of children,

In Other Words

doom-laden prophecies negative predictions
linguistic evils language-related problems
orthography spelling
inevitably erode surely harm

so we must be cautious; but a picture is emerging that texting does not harm writing ability and may even help it. Here are the findings of some recent studies:

...texting does not harm writing ability...

9 • Veenal Raval, a speech and language therapist working at the City University in London, compared group of 11- to 12-year-old texters with a similar group of non-texters. She found that neither group had noticeably worse spelling or grammar than the other, but that both groups made some errors. She also noted that **text abbreviations** did not appear in their written work.

10 • A team of Finnish researchers found that the informal style of texting was an important motivating factor, especially among teenage boys, and provided fresh opportunities for linguistic creativity.

11 • In a series of studies carried out in 2006-7, Beverly Plester, Clare Wood, and others from Coventry University found strong positive links between the use of text language and the skills underlying success in standard English in a group of pre-teenage children. The children were asked to compose text messages that they might write in a particular situation—such as texting a friend to say that they had missed their bus and they were going to be late. The more text abbreviations they used in their messages, the higher they scored on tests of reading and vocabulary. The children who were better at spelling and writing used the most texting abbreviations. Also interesting was the finding that the younger the children received their first phone, the higher their scores.

12 These results surprise some people. But why should one be surprised? Children could not be good at texting if they had not already developed considerable literacy awareness. Before you can write **abbreviated** forms effectively and play with them, you need to have a sense of how the sounds of your language relate to the letters. You need to know that there are such things as alternative spellings. You need to have a good visual memory and good **motor** skills. If you are aware that your texting behavior is different, you must have already **intuited** that there is such a thing as a standard. If you are

---

Key Vocabulary
abbreviated *adj.*, shortened

In Other Words
text abbreviations shortened versions of words
motor hand movement
intuited understood

Reread and Analyze

5. Viewpoint Reread numbers 1–8. Underline the author's viewpoint on texting.

6. Text Structure Reread numbers 1–7. Circle the main idea of this part of the text and highlight the supporting details.

7. Text Structure Reread pages 174–175. Find another example of the main ideas and details structure. Circle the main idea and highlight the supporting details.

8. Evaluate the Text Structure Why is main idea and details a helpful way for Cyrstal to present his information?

Possible response:

The author can clearly

present important ideas

about his viewpoint

and support them with

details.

9. Content-Area Words
Reread number 12. Find and place a square around at least two words used only for electronic communication. Then write each word and the phrase it stands for. Underline the letters in each word that form the new abbreviated word.

Possible response: brb,

be <u>r</u>ight <u>b</u>ac<u>k</u>., imho, <u>i</u>n

<u>m</u>y <u>h</u>umble <u>o</u>pinion

10. Content-Area Words
Reread section 2. Find and place a square around two words that indicate the writer is a scholar using academic language. Then write the words and their definitions below.

Possible response:

phenomena: event;

communicative: relating

to how people share

11. Text Structure Find and circle the main idea of number 14. Then highlight details Crystal uses to support this idea. Explain in your own words the main idea Crystal presents here and how he supports it.

Answers will vary but

should indicate that

texting is not responsible

for all nonstandard use.

---

using such abbreviations as 🔲*lol* ("laughing out loud") and 🔲*brb* ("be right back"), you must have developed a sensitivity to the communicative needs of your textees, because these forms show you are responding to them. If you are using 🔲*imho* ("in my humble opinion") or 🔲*afaik* ("as far as I know"), you must be aware of the possible effect your choice of language might have on them, because these forms show you are self-critical. Teenage texters are not stupid nor are they socially inept within their peer group. They know exactly what they are doing.

Teenage texters are not stupid...

13   Texting is one of the most **innovative linguistic 🔲phenomena** of modern times, and perhaps that is why it has generated such strong emotions—"a kind of laziness," "an affectation," "ridiculous." Yet all the evidence suggests that belief in an **impending** linguistic disaster is a consequence of a mythology largely created by the media. Children's use of text abbreviations has been **hugely exaggerated**, and the mobile phone companies have played a part in this by emphasizing their "cool" character, compiling dictionaries, and publishing usage guides—doubtless, thereby, motivating sales.

14   (Texting has been blamed for all kinds of evils that it could not possibly have been responsible for.) Virtually any piece of nonstandard English in schoolwork is now likely to be considered the result of texting, even if the evidence **is incontrovertible** that the nonstandardism has been around for generations. The other day I read about someone **condemning** *would of* (for *would have*) as a consequence of texting. That misspelling has been around for at least 200 years. You will find it in Keats. I have encountered similar misapprehensions in Japan, Finland, Sweden, and France, and it is probably present in every country where texting has become a feature of daily communication.

15   (In a logical world, text messaging should not have survived.) Imagine a pitch to a potential investor. "I have this great idea. A new way of person-to-person communication, using your phone. The users won't have a familiar keyboard. Their fingers will have trouble finding the keys. They will be able to send messages, but with no more than 160 characters at a time. The writing on the screens will be very small and difficult to read, especially if you have a visual handicap. The messages will arrive at any time, interrupting your daily

In Other Words

innovative linguistic phenomena creative
   language changes
impending upcoming
hugely exaggerated overstated
is incontrovertible clearly shows
condemning blaming

routine or your sleep. Oh, and every now and again you won't be able to send or receive anything because your battery will run out. Please invest in it." What would you have done?

16   But, it was direct, avoiding the problem of tracking down someone over the phone. It was quick, avoiding the waiting time associated with letters and emails. It was focused, avoiding time-wasting small-talk. It was portable, allowing messages to be sent from virtually anywhere. It could even be done with one hand, making it usable while holding on to a roof-strap in a crowded bus. It was personal, allowing **intimacy** and secrecy, reminiscent of classroom notes under the desk. It was unnoticed in public settings, if the user turned off the ringtone. It allowed young people to overcome the spatial boundary of the home, allowing communication with the outside world without the knowledge of parents and siblings. It hugely empowered the deaf, the shared writing system reducing the gap between them and hearing people. And it was relatively cheap (though, given the quantity of messaging, some parents still had an unpleasant shock when their phone bill arrived). It wasn't surprising, therefore, that it soon became the preferred method of communication among teenagers. Youngsters valued its role both as a badge of identity, like accents and dialects, and as **a ludic linguistic pastime**. And in due course adults too came to value its discreetness and convenience. The interruption caused by the arrival of a text message is disregarded. To those who text, the beep heralding a new message invariably thrills, not pains.

17   How long will it last? It is always difficult to predict the future, when it comes to technology. Perhaps it will remain as part of an increasingly sophisticated **battery** of communicative methods, to be used as circumstances require. Or perhaps in a generation's time texting will seem as **archaic** a method of communication as the typewriter or the telegram does today, and new styles will have emerged to replace it. For the moment, texting seems here to stay, though its linguistic character will undoubtedly alter as its use spreads among the older population.

18   Some people dislike texting. Some are **bemused** by it. Some love it. I am fascinated by it, for it is the latest **manifestation** of the human ability to be linguistically creative and to adapt language to suit the demands of diverse settings. In texting we are seeing, in a small way, language in evolution. ❖

How long will it last?

Reread and Analyze

12. Text Structure   Reread numbers 15 and 16. Circle a sentence that shows the main point in these two paragraphs. Highlight at least three details or reasons the author gives to show this point turned out to be false.

13. Text Structure   Reread the conclusion of the essay in numbers 17 and 18. Circle the statement that shows Crystal's thinking about texting. Then highlight the reasons he gives for this opinion.

14. Text Structure   Explain in your own words what Crystal thinks of texting and what he thinks will happen to it.

Possible response:

The author says

that the ability of

texting to encourage

linguistic creativity and

adaptability causes him

to be fascinated. The

author is unsure of the

future of texting.

In Other Words
intimacy a sense of closeness
a ludic linguistic pastime an activity
    that uses language and technology
    in simple ways
battery set

archaic old
bemused confused
manifestation expression

Discuss

15. **Synthesize** With the class, list some of the examples of the main idea and details structure that the author uses to make his argument that "texting benefits literacy skills." Discuss the part that each example plays in his argument. *Answers will vary. Possible responses are shown.*

Main Idea	Details
"a picture is emerging that texting does not harm writing ability and may even help it."	*"Finnish researchers found that the informal style of texting was an important motivating factor, especially among teenage boys"*

Then, with the class, discuss how the author uses this text structure to try to persuade his audience. Make notes.

Answers will vary but should show a recognition of the fact that by stating his ideas and then using details

to show the positive effects of texting, the author tries to persuade readers that rather than harm the

language, texting can help young people develop their understanding of language.

16. **Write** Use your notes from question 15 to write about the text structures that an author can use to make his or her ideas clear. Use the questions below to organize your thoughts.

> · **What is the viewpoint expressed in this essay?**
>
> · **What kind of text structure does David Crystal use?**
>
> · **Describe the structure. Give examples.**
>
> · **How does that structure help his argument in** *Txting: The Gr8 Db8?*

Answers will vary but should show how students have carried forward their thinking from item 16.

_____

_____

_____

_____

_____

_____

_____

Connect with the **EQ** What Does It Really Mean to Communicate?
Consider the role of technology in communication.

17. Viewpoint According to David Crystal, how is technology changing the way people communicate?

Answers will vary. Responses should include evidence from the text.

_____

_____

_____

_____

_____

18. Theme What is the author's message about communication?

Answers will vary. Responses should include evidence from the text.

_____

_____

_____

_____

_____

Unit 4

Key Vocabulary Review

A. Read each sentence. Circle the word that best fits into each sentence.

1. Sports fans can (**visualize** / **enumerate**) the names and statistics of their favorite players.

2. A good tailor makes clothing with (**ambience** / **precision**).

3. Children sometimes (**emulate** / **enhance**) their older siblings.

4. Your (**ambience** / **countenance**) can show others how you feel.

5. A (**competent** / **subtle**) person is able to perform a task well.

6. Making fun of others is (**intimidating** / **disrespectful**) behavior.

7. An (**abbreviated** / **articulate**) story might leave out important details.

8. A food critic must have a (**stimulating** / **discerning**) sense of taste.

B. Use your own words to write what each Key Vocabulary word means. Then write a synonym and an antonym for each word. *Answers will vary. Possible responses are shown.*

Key Word	My Definition	Synonym	Antonym
1. articulate	using words easily	well-spoken	stammering
2. enhance	to improve	increase	weaken
3. enlist	to win over or attract	recruit	fire
4. interminably	for a long time without stopping	endlessly	quickly
5. intimidating	frightening	terrifying	comforting
6. stimulating	exciting or arousing	challenging	uninteresting
7. surpass	to exceed or go beyond	beat	fall short
8. vary	to be different	change	be similar

Unit 4 Key Vocabulary

abbreviated	banish	disrespectful	enlist	intimidating	subtle
accentuate	competent	• emphasis	enumerate	obligation	surpass
ambience	countenance	emulate	humiliation	• precision	• vary
articulate	discerning	• enhance	interminably	stimulating	• visualize

• **Academic Vocabulary**

C. Answer the questions using complete sentences. *Answers will vary. Possible responses are shown.*

1. Describe the **ambience** of a place you enjoy.

   A place I enjoy plays popular music and has pictures of celebrities on the walls.

2. What do you **visualize** when you think about your future?

   I visualize having a family and a nice house.

3. Describe a time you experienced a great **humiliation**.

   I experienced humiliation when I tripped in the hall.

4. Why would a public speaker place **emphasis** on certain ideas?

   The speaker might want the audience to remember certain ideas.

5. Why might you **banish** someone from a public place?

   You might banish someone who harmed others or the property.

6. What might a person do to **accentuate** a physical feature?

   A woman might wear mascara to accentuate her eyes.

7. Why is it important for a chef to notice **subtle** differences in taste?

   A chef needs to be able to tell what spices foods need or do not need.

8. Describe an **obligation** you have.

   I have a responsibility to take care of my younger sister after school.

Prepare to Read

▶ **Say It with Flowers**
▶ **The Journey**

Key Vocabulary

A. How well do you know these words? Circle a rating for each word. Check your understanding of each word by choosing the correct synonym or antonym. Then write a definition. If you are unsure of a word's meaning, refer to the Vocabulary Glossary, page 926, in your student text.

Rating Scale	
1	I have never seen this word before.
2	I am not sure of the word's meaning.
3	I know this word and can teach the word's meaning to someone else.

Key Word	Check Your Understanding	Deepen Your Understanding
❶ disarm (dis-**ahrm**) *verb* **Rating:** 1 2 3	If you **disarm** people, you _____ them. discourage (charm)	My definition: _Answers will vary._
❷ ensuing (en-**sü**-ing) *adjective* **Rating:** 1 2 3	The opposite of an **ensuing** problem is a _____ problem. resulting (previous)	My definition: _Answers will vary._
❸ harmonize (**hahr**-mu-nīz) *verb* **Rating:** 1 2 3	If colors **harmonize**, they _____. (match) differ	My definition: _Answers will vary._
❹ inquisitive (in-**kwi**-zu-tiv) *adjective* **Rating:** 1 2 3	The opposite of **inquisitive** is _____. curious (uninterested)	My definition: _Answers will vary._

Key Word	Check Your Understanding	Deepen Your Understanding
5 integrity (in-**te**-gru-tē) *noun* Rating: 1 2 3	If a person has **integrity**, he or she is _____. (honest) dishonest	My definition: *Answers will vary.*
6 irritating (**ir**-u-tāt-ing) *adjective* Rating: 1 2 3	The opposite of **irritating** is _____. disturbing (agreeable)	My definition: *Answers will vary.*
7 melancholy (**me**-lun-kah-lē) *noun* Rating: 1 2 3	If a person is **melancholy**, he or she is _____. (sad) cheerful	My definition: *Answers will vary.*
8 transaction (tran-**zak**-shun) *noun* Rating: 1 2 3	An example of a business **transaction** is a _____. gift (purchase)	My definition: *Answers will vary.*

B. Use one of the Key Vocabulary words to write about a time you had a conflict with someone.

Answers will vary.

_____

Selection Review Say It with Flowers

 What Do People Discover in a Moment of Truth?
Find out how people's values differ.

A. In "Say It with Flowers," you found out how people's values can affect their actions. Complete the Plot Diagram below by writing the conflict, the climax, and the resolution.

Plot Diagram

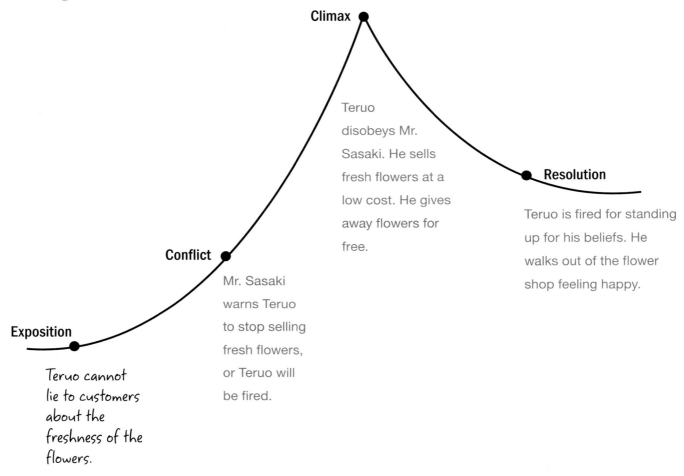

Climax

Teruo disobeys Mr. Sasaki. He sells fresh flowers at a low cost. He gives away flowers for free.

Resolution

Teruo is fired for standing up for his beliefs. He walks out of the flower shop feeling happy.

Conflict

Mr. Sasaki warns Teruo to stop selling fresh flowers, or Teruo will be fired.

Exposition

Teruo cannot lie to customers about the freshness of the flowers.

B. Use the information in the Plot Diagram to answer the questions.

1. What conflict does Teruo have with Mr. Sasaki? How does he resolve it?

Teruo sells fresh flowers to Mr. Sasaki's customers. Mr. Sasaki warns Teruo that if he doesn't stop, he will

be fired. Eventually, Teruo is fired.

2. How does Teruo behave on his last day of work? Why?

Teruo sells the freshest flowers and gives away flowers to make people happy. He does not think what Mr.

Sasaki is doing is right.

3. Why does Teruo show integrity after his moment of truth? Use **integrity** in your answer.

Possible response: Teruo shows integrity because he does not want to lie to customers. Teruo knows the

truth about the flowers, and he wants to keep his self-respect.

4. Do you think Teruo will make a good worker at a different place? Why or why not?

Possible response: Yes. I think Teruo will make a good worker because he is a good, honest person.

Customers like to buy things from honest people.

5. Write a paragraph about a time when you were asked to go against your values. What did you do? How does making this connection help you understand the plot?

Answers will vary.

Connect Across Texts

In "Say It with Flowers," Teruo's moment of truth leads him to decisive action. In this poem, the speaker also makes a decision.

The Journey
by Mary Oliver

The Ramble, 2005, Ross Penhall. Oil on canvas, courtesy of Caldwell Snyder Gallery, San Francisco, California.

Interact with the Text

1. Interpret
What do you think is the artist's message in *The Ramble*?

Possible response: The

artist may be trying to

show that journeys can

sometimes be dark, but

there are always good

things up ahead, too.

◀ Critical Viewing: Effect
What mood does *The Ramble* create? If you were walking along this path, how would you feel?

One day you finally knew
what you had to do, and began,
though the voices around you
kept shouting
5 their bad advice—
though the whole house
began to tremble
and you felt the old tug
at your ankles.
10 "Mend my life!"
each voice cried.
But you didn't stop.
You knew what you had to do,
though the wind pried
15 with its stiff fingers
at the very foundations—
though their melancholy
was terrible.

It was already late
20 enough, and a wild night,
and the road full of fallen
branches and stones.
But little by little,
as you left their voices behind,
25 the stars began to burn
through the sheets of clouds,
and there was a new voice,
which you slowly
recognized as your own,
30 that kept you company
as you strode deeper and deeper
into the world,
determined to do
the only thing you could do—
35 determined to save
the only life you could save.

In Other Words
"Mend my life!" "Rescue me!"

Interact with the Text

2. Make Connections
Underline the words and phrases in column 1 that suggest the difficulty of making changes. How does your personal experience with change help you understand the text?

Answers will vary.

3. Metaphor
Circle the words and phrases in column 2 that express ideas beyond the literal meaning. What effect does this language have on you?

Possible response:

This language creates a

mood of frustration and

excitement.

4. Interpret
Summarize in your own words what the speaker is trying to say.

Possible response: Taking

your own path in life is

difficult, but it can be a

positive experience.

Selection Review The Journey

A. A poet uses figurative language, such as metaphor and personification, to express ideas beyond the literal. Read the examples from "The Journey," and describe how each of these examples of figurative language helps you understand the poet's message.

Example 1:	**"the wind pried / with its stiff fingers"**
Example 2:	**"the stars began to burn / through the sheets of clouds"**

Possible response: In Example 1, the poet uses personification to describe how the wind shakes

the foundation of the house. The speaker says that even though she knows the path she has to

take, something or someone is trying to keep her from following it; Example 2: The speaker uses

metaphor (stars burning through sheets of clouds) to describe the inner knowledge she has from

listening to her own voice. Suddenly, the clouds give way to the stars, and she is no longer confused.

_____

_____

B. Answer the questions.

1. Choose one connection you made as you read the poem, and write how this connection helped make the poem clearer and more personal for you.

Answers will vary.

_____

_____

_____

_____

2. What leads the speaker to her "moment of truth"? In a paragraph, explain what the speaker does with this discovery.

Answers will vary.

_____

_____

_____

_____

_____

_____

_____

_____

_____

_____

Reflect and Assess

WRITING: Write About Literature

A. Plan your writing. Think about Teruo's values in "Say It with Flowers" and the speaker's values in "The Journey." Write how each expresses his or her values. *Answers will vary.*

Say It with Flowers	The Journey
Teruo wants to be fair to others, so he sells the freshest flowers.	The speaker counsels readers to listen to their own advice because other voices may give bad advice.

B. A mission statement expresses values. Think about the values you listed in the chart. Write two brief personal mission statements, one from Teruo's point of view and one from the speaker's point of view.

Students should support their answers with examples from both selections.

_____

_____

_____

_____

_____

_____

_____

_____

_____

Integrate the Language Arts

LITERARY ANALYSIS: Compare Characters' Motivations

Character motivation is the reason a character acts the way he or she does in a story. Over the course of a story, the characters' motivations can become more clear or can even change.

A. Write the motivations of the three characters from "Say It with Flowers." Some characters may have several different motivations. Then write the events that show the characters' motivations.

Character	Motivation	Events
Mr. Sasaki	to make money to have a good staff that follows his orders	hires Teruo so the shop is ready for the rush threatens to fire Teruo if he doesn't follow orders
Tommy	to keep his job to please his boss to earn money	warns Teruo not to sell the fresh flowers or let Mr. Sasaki see him tells Mr. Sasaki what Teruo has been doing
Teruo	to learn about the flower business to be honest with customers and make them happy	asks Tommy and the narrator to teach him about the business decides to sell only fresh flowers to customers

B. Answer the questions below.

1. Why do Teruo's motivations change over the course of the story?

Once he learns all about the flower business, Teruo realizes that he is cheating customers. He thinks that is wrong.

2. How do Mr. Sasaki and Teruo's different motivations affect the climax?

Possible response: Once Teruo's motivations change, the conflict becomes more intense because Teruo's actions keep Mr. Sasaki from making as much money as he wants (his motivation).

3. How could Teruo and Mr. Sasaki have resolved their differences differently?

Possible response: Mr. Sasaki could have made Teruo a delivery person. Teruo could have compromised and sold some fresh and some old flowers.

C. Think about a time when your motivations, or the motivations of someone you know, changed. Write a paragraph describing the motivations and the events that showed them.

Answers will vary.

VOCABULARY STUDY: Synonyms

A **synonym** is a word or phrase that means about the same thing as another word.

A. List at least three synonyms for each word in the chart below. Use a dictionary or a thesaurus if necessary. *Answers will vary.*

Word	Synonyms
diverse	
generous	
healthy	
hilarious	
idea	

B. Choose a synonym from each item in Activity A and write a sentence that contains the word. *Answers will vary.*

1. _____

2. _____

3. _____

4. _____

5. _____

C. Replace each underlined word with a synonym. Use a dictionary to confirm the word's meaning and to check to see if the sentence makes sense. *Answers will vary. Possible responses are shown.*

1. Teruo <u>wilted</u> in front of the customer.

   withered

2. On other occasions he would stand gaping speechless, without a <u>comeback</u>.

   response

3. "Gee, I feel <u>rotten</u>," he said to me. "Those flowers I sold won't last longer than <u>tomorrow</u>."

   awful

4. Mr. Sasaki was <u>furious</u> with Teruo for selling the fresh flowers.

   irate

5. One day when Teruo learned that I once had worked in the nursery and had experience in flower growing, he became <u>inquisitive</u>.

   curious

Prepare to Read

▶ Just Lather, That's All
▶ The Woman Who Was Death

Key Vocabulary

A. How well do you know these words? Circle a rating for each word. Check your understanding of each word by circling *yes* or *no*. Then provide an example. If you are unsure of a word's meaning, refer to the Vocabulary Glossary, page 926, in your student text.

Rating Scale	
1	I have never seen this word before.
2	I am not sure of the word's meaning.
3	I know this word and can teach the word's meaning to someone else.

Key Word	Check Your Understanding	Deepen Your Understanding
❶ destiny (**des**-tu-nē) *noun* **Rating:** 1 2 3	Your **destiny** is something that has happened in the past. Yes (**No**)	Example: _Possible response: a successful career or a_ bright future
❷ indelible (in-**de**-lu-bul) *adjective* **Rating:** 1 2 3	Grass can leave an **indelible** stain on a white shirt. (**Yes**) No	Example: _Possible response: an ink stain on a shirt_
❸ indifference (in-**di**-furns) *noun* **Rating:** 1 2 3	To show **indifference**, you should listen carefully and make eye contact. Yes (**No**)	Example: _Possible response: to not care about the_ outcome of a game
❹ inflexible (in-**flek**-su-bul) *adjective* **Rating:** 1 2 3	If a bench is **inflexible**, it will not bend when two people sit on it. (**Yes**) No	Example: _Possible response: a metal signpost_

Key Word	Check Your Understanding	Deepen Your Understanding
5 poised (**poizd**) *adjective* **Rating:** 1 2 3	Ballet dancers look very **poised**. (**Yes**) No	Example: _Possible response: a famous politician_ _giving a speech_
6 priority (prī-**or**-u-tē) *noun* **Rating:** 1 2 3	Watching television should be a **priority** over homework. Yes (**No**)	Example: _Possible response: family obligations_
7 regime (rā-**zhēm**) *noun* **Rating:** 1 2 3	A **regime** is usually powerless and ineffective. Yes (**No**)	Example: _Possible response: Hitler's Nazi party_ _during WWII_
8 virtue (**vur**-chü) *noun* **Rating:** 1 2 3	Spreading rumors is a **virtue**. Yes (**No**)	Example: _Possible response: honesty_

B. Use one of the Key Vocabulary words to write about an experience when you had to choose right from wrong.

Answers will vary.

Before Reading Just Lather, That's All

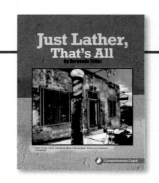

LITERARY ANALYSIS: Analyze Structure: Suspense

Suspense is the growing curiosity, tension, or excitement you feel as you read. Authors create suspense by putting characters in risky situations and by revealing important details slowly.

A. Read the passage below. Continue filling out the chart with examples from the text that build suspense.

> ### Look Into the Text
>
> He said nothing when he entered. I was passing the best of my razors back and forth on a leather strop. When I recognized him I started to tremble. But he didn't notice. Hoping to conceal my emotion, I continued sharpening the razor. I tested it on the meat of my thumb, and then held it up to the light. At that moment he took off the bullet-studded belt and the gun holster that dangled from it. He hung it up on a wall hook and placed his military cap over it. Then he turned to me, loosening the knot of his tie, and said, "It's hot as hell. Give me a shave." He sat in the chair.

Elements of Suspense	Text Examples
Putting characters in risky situations	*The narrator begins to tremble when the man enters.* The narrator sharpens a razor and hides his emotions. The man hangs up his gun and bullets and sits in the chair.
Revealing important details slowly	a razor, a bullet-studded belt, a gun holster, a military cap, a very hot day

B. Complete the sentence about the passage.

This passage is suspenseful because _Possible response: I do not know why the narrator is scared._ Both characters have weapons. The man hangs up his weapon. He is now defenseless. The narrator could kill him if he wanted to. The heat of the day adds to the tension.

FOCUS STRATEGY: Make Connections

> ## How to MAKE CONNECTIONS Focus Strategy
>
> 1. **Keep track** of important story details and events.
>
> 2. **Use what you know** to explain the events in your own words.

A. Read the passage. Use the strategies above to make connections as you read. Then answer the questions below.

Look Into the Text

> I got on with the job of lathering his beard. My hands started trembling again. The man could not possibly realize it, which was lucky for me. But I wished that he had never come. Chances were good that one of our men had seen him enter. And with an enemy under my own roof, I felt responsible.

Details and Events	My Explanation
"My hands started trembling again."	The narrator is very nervous.
Possible response: "But I wished that he had never come."	*Possible response:* The narrator does not want to be in this situation.

1. What causes the narrator to shake from nervousness?

   Possible response: The narrator is afraid of making a mistake because he is afraid of the man.

2. How does writing story details and explaining them in your own words help you understand the passage?

   Possible response: I had to think carefully about the important story details. This way, I made important connections that helped me understand the events.

B. Return to the chart above. What connection did you make about the narrator and his enemy?

   Possible response: The narrator is in a difficult situation. The man does not seem to know that the barber is his enemy. He is afraid his trembling hands will give him away.

Selection Review Just Lather, That's All

 What Do People Discover in a Moment of Truth?
See how people decide what is right.

A. In "Just Lather, That's All," you learn how a barber decides between right and wrong. Complete the Sequence Chart with events that make the story suspenseful.

Sequence Chart

First:	Next:	Last:
The barber becomes tense after seeing a man walk into his barber shop. The man hangs up his gun holster and asks for a shave.	The barber tries to decide if he should kill the man with his razor in order to defend his political beliefs.	The barber decides that he is not a murderer, but a barber. He shaves the man, and the man then tells him that he came to find out if the barber would kill him.

B. Use the information in the Sequence Chart to answer the questions.

1. What makes this story so suspenseful?

Possible response: The reader doesn't know why the man makes the barber nervous at first. Then, the reader is unsure whether the barber will kill the man or not. The author reveals the details of the story slowly to keep the reader guessing.

2. What is the barber's biggest priority? Use **priority** in your answer.

Possible response: The barber finally decides that his own personal sense of right and wrong is his first priority.

3. How might people in town react when they hear about this meeting between Captain Torres and the barber? Why?

Possible response: Some people might think that the barber is a traitor for not harming Torres. Not everyone knows whose side the barber is really on.

THE WOMAN WHO WAS DEATH

A Myth from India RETOLD BY JOSEPHA SHERMAN

Interactive

MYTH

Connect Across Texts

In *"Just Lather, That's All,"* the narrator must decide whether to take action. In this myth, a woman discovers the true purpose of her actions.

I n the day of the beginning, Lord Brahma created the earth and all that lived upon it: plant, animal, human.

One thing only did Brahma not create, and that was death. And so the <u>created ones lived</u> and thrived and multiplied till all the lands and seas were crowded. **Famine** came, and illness, yet there was no escape from pain. And **the earth itself groaned beneath the weight upon it**.

When Lord Brahma saw this suffering, he cried out in sorrow, and created from himself a woman, skin and hair

Lotus, 2000, Joel Nakamura. Acrylic on copper panel, private collection.

In Other Words

Famine An extreme scarcity of food
the earth itself groaned beneath the weight upon it nature struggled to support so many living things

Interact with the Text

1. Myth
Underline two details from the second paragraph that tell what happened after the world was made. Explain why these details are characteristics of a myth.

This story explains natural

events and the creation

of the world.

2. Make Connections
What connection can you make between the image on this page and the myth?

Possible response:

The text says that all

of nature is connected.

This image shows

how the sky and land

are connected with

plants, moons, and stars.

3. Make Connections

Underline the phrases that tell what the woman did in response to Lord Brahma's directions. What connections can you make to this detail?

Possible response: This part of the story makes me think of Lord Brahma and the woman as a parent and child arguing.

4. Myth

Circle the sentence that gives Lord Brahma's reason for creating the woman. Explain how his words reflect a cultural value, belief, or experience.

Possible response: His words reflect the universal experience of seeing death come to every living thing. The words also reflect a cultural belief that death is to be expected as part of the natural order of things.

and eyes dark and beautiful as night, and said to her:

"Your name is Death. And your task shall be to destroy life."

When the woman who was Death heard these words, <u>she wept</u> in horror. Not waiting to hear what else Lord Brahma might say, <u>she **fled**</u> from him.

But there was no escaping Lord Brahma. "You are Death," he told her. "The taking of life is your destiny."

Again she fled, weeping at these **bitter words**. Again Lord Brahma found her where she hid.

"I created you to be the destroyer of life," he told her. "It is as it must be."

A third time the woman who was Death fled, till she reached the very ends of creation. But there again, **on that very edge of emptiness**, Lord Brahma overtook her. And this time there was no place left to which Death could flee.

"O my lord, spare me!" she pleaded. "Why should I do this cruel thing? Why should I harm those who have done me no harm? I beg you, let me not be Death!"

"Daughter," Lord Brahma said gently, his great, wise eyes warm with pity, "you have not heard me out. If there is life, there must be an end to life."

"But how cruel to—"

Idol of the God Brahma, bronze, Dinodia Bombay, India/The Bridgeman Art Library.

▲ **Critical Viewing: Character** How does this sculpture of Brahma compare with your image of Lord Brahma in the myth?

In Other Words
fled ran away
bitter words harsh statements
on that very edge of emptiness in that empty, open space

Untitled, 2004, Dewashish Das. Tempera on handmade paper, courtesy of Kala Fine Art, Austin, Texas.

▲ **Critical Viewing: Character** What qualities might this woman have in common with the woman in the myth?

"Hush, daughter. Listen. Death shall not be evil, or cruel, or without **virtue**. Without death, there can be no peace, no rest for the suffering, the aged. Without death, there can be no rebirth. Daughter, death shall not be the destroyer of the world, but its protector."

Key Vocabulary
virtue *n.,* benefits

Cultural Background

Reincarnation, or rebirth, is a central idea in several Eastern religions. Some people believe that after death, a person takes on a new form of life determined by his or her behavior in the previous life.

5. Make Connections
Write details from the image that help you visualize the woman in the myth. How does this image help you make connections to the story?

Possible response:

The woman has a

big eye, large hands,

and jewelry. She

seems beautiful and

extraordinary, like

the mythological

characters I have seen

in books and movies.

6. Interpret
Underline a sentence that explains Death's virtue. Explain this idea in your own words, using the word **virtue**.

Possible response: The

virtue of death is that

it gives peace to those

who need it, and it

allows new life to grow

in the world.

7. Myth

Underline the sentences that tell the myth's life lesson. Explain the life lesson in your own words below.

Possible response:

Things live for a certain amount of time and then die, so that new life can begin. This helps keep order in the world.

When Death heard these words, she **pondered**. She dried her tears. And at last the woman called Death smiled a tender little smile, a mother's smile. She bowed low before Lord Brahma and went forth to **do his bidding**.

<u>And so all things came in time to die, and to be reborn. Order was restored to the earth.</u> ❖

In Other Words
pondered thought carefully
do his bidding follow his commands

Selection Review The Woman Who Was Death

A. Choose one of the details from the myth and make a connection using an experience you have had, another story you have read, or something you know about the world.

Detail 1:	Brahma follows the woman until she has no place to go.
Detail 2:	Brahma shows the woman that death can bring rest to the suffering.

Connection I made for Detail ___1___ :

Possible response: Sometimes in my life, people—like a parent or teacher—insist that I listen to their advice or knowledge and hear them out. At first, I usually don't want to listen, but usually I realize it's for my own good.

B. Answer the questions.

1. How did knowing the importance of myths to a culture help you understand this story?

Possible response: The interaction between Lord Brahma and Death helped me think about the way that this culture views the nature of life and death. This made me think about the life lesson in a way that I have not thought about before.

2. Why does the woman finally change her feelings about her responsibility?

Possible response: Death finally understands that her actions will create more life, even though she has to take life, too.

Reflect and Assess

WRITING: Write About Literature

A. Plan your writing. Read the statements below. Mark an *X* next to the statement that you agree with. Then list examples from each text to support your opinion. *Answers will vary.*

□ A person's fate is fixed and unable to change.
□ People can influence their own destiny.

Just Lather, That's All	The Woman Who Was Death

B. What is your opinion? Write an opinion statement. Support your answer with evidence from both texts.

Students should support their answers with examples from both selections.

_____

_____

_____

_____

_____

_____

_____

_____

_____

Integrate the Language Arts

▶ Just Lather, That's All
▶ The Woman Who Was Death

LITERARY ANALYSIS: Understand Irony

Irony is a contrast between appearance and reality. In verbal irony, a contrast exists between what is said and what is meant. In situational irony, the contrast is between what we expect and what actually happens.

A. Brainstorm an example of verbal irony and situational irony you have encountered in your own life, in books, or in TV or film. Write the examples in the chart.

Answers will vary. Possible responses are shown.

Verbal Irony	Situational Irony
Someone says, "I love this beautiful weather" when it's storming outside.	Death is portrayed as a beautiful woman in "The Woman Who Was Death."
My father says, "Looks delicious!" when the dinner is burned and the kitchen is full of smoke.	The flowers get rain when they need sun, and get sun when they need rain.

B. Decide if each story detail is an example of verbal irony or situational irony. Write what makes it one or the other in the correct column.

Detail	Verbal	Situational
Captain Torres asks a known enemy for a shave.		The captain willingly puts himself in danger.
Torres says, "They told me that you would kill me. I came to find out."	Torres admits to taking a risk that a person would not normally take.	
Lord Brahma sees suffering and creates Death to solve the problem.		Something as sad as death is supposed to keep people from suffering.
Lord Brahma says, "Daughter, death shall not be the destroyer of the world, but its protector."	Death is defined as a protector and not a destroyer of life.	

C. Write a short explanation of how verbal and situational irony affect you as a reader. Give specific examples from each text.

Answers will vary.

_____

_____

_____

204 Unit 5: Moment of Truth

VOCABULARY STUDY: Synonyms and Antonyms in Analogies

A **synonym** is a word or phrase that means the same thing as another word.
An **antonym** is the opposite.

A. Write a synonym and an antonym for each Key Vocabulary word below.
Use a dictionary or thesaurus if necessary. *Answers will vary. Possible responses are shown.*

Key Word	Synonym	Antonym
indelible	permanent	temporary
indifference	disinterest	interested
inflexible	firm	bendable
poised	prepared	unprepared
virtue	merit	disadvantage

B. The chart below contains words from the selections. Complete the chart
by giving a definition, synonym, and antonym for each word. The first one
has been done for you.

Word	Definition	Synonym	Antonym
enemy	a person from an opposing group	rival	partner, friend
protective	willing to defend someone	caring	unfeeling
responsible	accountable to someone	answerable	unaccountable
suffer	to feel pain	endure	recover
thrive	to grow well	flourish	deteriorate

C. Use the words from both of the charts above to complete each
analogy below.

1. *Protective* is to *unfeeling* as *interested* is to _____indifference_____.
2. *Enemy* is to *rival* as *merit* is to _____virtue_____.
3. *Thrive* is to *deteriorate* as *recover* is to _____suffer_____.
4. *Indelible* is to *permanent* as *firm* is to _____inflexible_____.
5. *Poised* is to *unprepared* as *destiny* is to _____accident_____.

Prepare to Read

▶ Be-ers and Doers
▶ My Moment of Truth

Key Vocabulary

A. How well do you know these words? Circle a rating for each word. Check your understanding of each word by marking an *X* next to the correct definition. Then complete the sentences. If you are unsure of a word's meaning, refer to the Vocabulary Glossary, page 926, in your student text.

Rating Scale

1	I have never seen this word before.
2	I am not sure of the word's meaning.
3	I know this word and can teach the word's meaning to someone else.

Key Word	Check Your Understanding	Deepen Your Understanding
❶ accelerate (ik-**se**-lu-rāt) *verb* **Rating:** 1 2 3	☐ to be helpful ☒ to move faster	Machines that accelerate are *Possible response:* cars and airplanes ____.
❷ commentary (**kahm**-un-tair-ē) *noun* **Rating:** 1 2 3	☐ a certain way of doing something ☒ an explanation of someone's opinion	You might hear a commentary on *Possible response:* the news ____.
❸ conformist (kun-**for**-mist) *noun* **Rating:** 1 2 3	☐ a person who is sick ☒ a person who follows	A person can be a conformist by *Possible response:* doing exactly what his or her friends do ____.
❹ contrary (**kahn**-trair-ē) *adjective* **Rating:** 1 2 3	☐ dangerous ☒ opposite	Ideas that are contrary to what I think are right are ____ *Possible response:* prejudice and intolerance ____.

Key Word	Check Your Understanding	Deepen Your Understanding
5 malleable (**mal**-ē-uh-bul) *adjective* **Rating:** **1 2 3**	[X] easily shaped [ ] easily persuaded	Materials that are malleable include _Possible_ _response:_ gold, wax, and clay _____ _____ _____ .
6 revelation (re-vu-**lā**-shun) *noun* **Rating:** **1 2 3**	[ ] an invention [X] a discovery	A person can experience a revelation by _Possible_ _response:_ reading a book or having an unusual experience _____ _____ .
7 saturate (**sa**-chu-rāt) *verb* **Rating:** **1 2 3**	[ ] to do something repeatedly [X] to soak or satisfy	I saturate my friends with _Possible response:_ love and affection _____ _____ _____ .
8 temporary (**tem**-puh-rair-ē) *adjective* **Rating:** **1 2 3**	[X] not permanent [ ] not effective	Things in my life that are temporary are _Possible_ _response:_ bad skin and braces on my teeth _____ _____ _____ .

B. Use one of the Key Vocabulary words to write about a time you discovered the truth.

Answers will vary. _____

_____

Before Reading Be-ers and Doers

LITERARY ANALYSIS: Analyze Structure: Foreshadowing

Foreshadowing is an author's use of clues or hints about events that will happen later in a story. Foreshadowing creates **suspense**. An author may use dialogue, details, or a character's actions to foreshadow events.

A. Read the passage below. Continue to find the clues in the text that show foreshadowing. Write them in the chart below.

> ### Look Into the Text
>
> Dad stirred uneasily in his chair. "Aw, Dorothy," he mumbled. "Leave him be. He's a good kid."
>
> "Or could be. *Maybe*," she threw back at him. "What he seems like to me is rock-bottom lazy. He sure is slow-moving, and could be he's slow in the head, too. Dumb."
>
> Albert's eyes flickered at that word, but that's all. He just stood there and watched, eyes level.
>
> "But I love him a lot," continued Mom, "and unlike you, I don't plan t'just sit around and watch him grow dumber. If it's the last thing I do, I'm gonna light a fire under his feet."

Elements of Foreshadowing	Text Clues
Dialogue	Mom tells dad that she thinks Albert is dumb. Mom accuses Dad of being passive. Mom says that she is going to light a fire under Albert.
Details	Albert may or may not be slow-moving. Albert is a good kid.
Characters' actions	Albert's eyes flicker at the word "dumb." Dad does nothing when Mom complains about Albert.

B. Use the information in the chart to complete the sentence about Albert.

Later in the story, Albert will probably *Possible response:* respond to his mother's insults and prove to his mother that he is not dumb

FOCUS STRATEGY: Make Connections

HOW TO MAKE CONNECTIONS Focus Strategy

1. **Track details** from the text.

2. **Think about** how you can relate to the event or the character.

3. **Determine** if the connection you made was helpful.

A. Read the passage. Use the strategies above to make connections as you read. Then answer the questions below.

> **Look Into the Text**
>
> . . . He was white now, like death, and he made a low and terrible sound. He didn't exactly pull his lips back from his teeth and growl, but the result was similar. It was like the sound a dog makes before he leaps for the throat. And what he said was *"You jest leave me be, woman!"*
>
> We'd never heard words like this coming out of Albert, and the parlor was as still as night as we all listened.
>
> "You ain't proud o' me, Mom," he whispered, all his beautiful grammar gone. "Yer jest proud o' what you want me t'be. And I got some news for you. Things I shoulda tole you years gone by. *I ain't gonna be what you want."* His voice was starting to quaver now, and he was trembling all over. *"I'm gonna be me.* And it seems like if that's ever gonna happen, it'll have t'be in some other place. And I plan t'do somethin' about that before the day is out."

1. What personal connection can you make to a detail in the text? Why?

Possible response: I can connect to Albert's speech to his mother. I know sometimes parents push too hard.

2. Was making this connection helpful to you? Why or why not?

Possible responses: Yes, sometimes I think my parents expect too much out of me; No, I've never felt that way before, so I don't really understand his strong emotions.

B. Return to the passage above. Circle the words or sentences that helped you answer question 1.

Selection Review Be-ers and Doers

 What Do People Discover in a Moment of Truth?
Learn how a moment of truth can change your life.

A. In "Be-ers and Doers," you found out how a moment of truth changes Albert's life. Write three clues from the text that hint that the author is foreshadowing the final conflict in the story.

Examples of Foreshadowing	What This Example Foreshadows
Albert's eyes flicker when Mom says he's dumb.	Albert is hurt by this insult. He will eventually have to rebel.
Possible response: Albert's mother decides that Albert will be a doer, not a be-er.	*Possible response:* Albert shows her that he is not who she thinks he is.
Possible response: Albert is content and not making waves.	*Possible response:* Albert has made a decision about his life.

B. Use the information in the chart to answer the questions.

1. How does the author build suspense by foreshadowing that Albert will eventually turn against his mother?

   Possible response: The author hints at the final conflict between Albert and his mother several times. Her character helps build the suspense by showing how Albert is hurt by his mother's insults, how increasingly controlling she is, and how calm Albert becomes right before the final conflict.

2. How might Albert's life have been different if he had chosen to be a conformist rather than to rebel? Use **conformist** in your answer.

   Possible response: Albert may have continued to be a conformist and let his mother bully him into becoming a lawyer or teacher. He would have been very unhappy.

3. How might the story have been different if Albert had not saved the house and the family from the fire?

   Possible response: The mother may have finally realized that Albert was more like his father than her. She may have accepted it if she hadn't seen that "sign that he was alive."

My Moment of Truth

By Caroline V. Clarke, Sonja D. Brown, *Black Enterprise* magazine

Connect Across Texts

*In "Be-ers and Doers," we see how a young man changes his life.
The following article describes turning points in the lives of real people.*

We all have them. Those moments that fundamentally change us. We may not always recognize them as they're happening, but we look back and they are crystal clear—the turning points that shape our lives, alter our direction, offer us a deeper understanding of who we are or want to become. Moments of truth often come **in the guise of** a challenge or even a crisis. Sometimes **no great strife** is involved at all. **Revelation** comes in all forms. But the result is always the same: We are molded by specific events and experiences. The lessons they teach help and heal us. They provide answers to questions we may not have even known we had.

DOMINIQUE DAWES
The Night I Found My Path

Dominique Dawes's young life has been a series of dazzling, dramatic highlights. She began taking gymnastics at age six and was competing by age ten. Just five years later, she burst onto the international scene in 1992, becoming the first African American gymnast to ever qualify and compete in the Olympic Games in Barcelona.

By the time she retired, following the 2000 Olympic Games in Sydney, Australia . . . she had

Dominique Dawes
Olympic Gold Medalist, Motivational Speaker

Key Vocabulary
revelation *n.*, sudden insight, discovery

In Other Words
in the guise of concealed as
no great strife no hardship

1. Author's Purpose
Underline the details on page 211 that are clues to the author's reason for writing. What is the author's purpose: to inform, entertain, inspire, reflect, or persuade? Why do you think so?

Possible response:

To inspire. The author

wants to inspire readers

to see moments of truth

in their own lives.

2. Make Connections
Underline the realizations that caused Dawes's turning point. How is this similar to something you or someone you know has experienced? How does this connection help you understand Dawes's thinking?

Answers will vary.

won more national championship medals than any other athlete—male or female—as well as four world championship medals, two Olympic bronze medals, and one gold. Perhaps because Dawes was **saturated** by the spotlight for so many years, her moment of truth came at a quiet time, **devoid of** drama, cameras, coaches, or fans. "There was no real single experience that brought me to that moment . . . I was working on my degree in communications from the University of Maryland, and I was doing a lot of [public] speaking, some gymnastics **commentary**, and some acting . . . I had been doing all of the things everyone around me kept telling me I'd be good at. But I was **somewhat on autopilot**. I was doing things to please other people, not because I really had a passion for them. I was almost a robot. Whatever people said was good for me, I'd just say, 'Okay. Fine. I'll do it.'"

But one night, at home alone in Maryland, Dawes confronted a critical question for the first time. "I asked myself what I really wanted to do. I felt almost like I was dreaming, I had never asked myself that. From the time I was young, I was guided in a very structured way. That was good for my gymnastics career. I needed it then. But when I retired, I kept waiting for someone to tell me what to do—like they always had. And they did. But a wonderful friend sat me down one day and made me realize that I wasn't happy doing those things. At home alone that night, I finally realized, this is my life and I need to pave my own path. I also came to the realization that the key to failure is trying to please everyone. I needed to figure out for myself what Dominique loves to do, wants to do, and is really good at. That was the beginning of my changing the way I thought about my life. . . .

"When I finally retired (in 2000)—from gymnastics and from living for other people—I felt like I had a 1,000 pound weight lifted off me," she says. "That's how I feel now—like I have been totally freed! I'm free to do what I like, and what I want. This is the life that I want."

Key Vocabulary
saturate *v.*, to fill completely, to soak
commentary *n.*, series of interpretations, explanations, or opinions

In Other Words
devoid of free from, empty of any
somewhat on autopilot acting without careful thought, going through routines

WYNTON MARSALIS
The Summer I Discovered Coltrane

Listening to Wynton Marsalis play, one would think this Juilliard-trained, nine-time Grammy award-winning jazz and classical musician has loved jazz and classical music from the time he was able to hold a trumpet. Not so. "Mama took us to see classical orchestras play a few times, but I didn't know anything about classical music. I couldn't get into it. Daddy always played jazz, but I didn't like that either. I liked them [the musicians his father played with] but I didn't like the music. And I didn't understand his dedication to it. The funk bands I knew used to **pack the house**; I played in a funk band when I was a teenager. But whenever daddy played, there would only be ten or fifteen people around.

"Jazz musicians were strange to me. I liked Earth, Wind & Fire, and Parliament; I was used to people in shiny suits and costumes and stuff. The people on the covers of my daddy's jazz albums looked funny to me. They were dressed normal and looked all serious."

Wynton
Marsalis
Jazz Musician, Artistic Director of "Jazz At Lincoln Center"

Then one day when Marsalis was twelve years old, he came home from his summer job and decided to try something. "I came home from work one day and put on one of my daddy's John Coltrane records. I didn't like it." And for most of us, that would have been the end of it. Went there, tried that, didn't like it. But something was happening that Marsalis didn't quite understand. "I played it again. I still didn't like it, but I kept playing it. There was something about it, something about the sound that I couldn't get away from, something that compelled me to keep playing it and playing it and playing it. And then I started listening to other people. That's when I started to realize I wanted to be a jazz musician. I had always played,

In Other Words
pack the house play to large audiences

Cultural Background
Saxophonist **John Coltrane** (1926–1967) and trumpeter **Miles Davis** (1926–1991) were two of the most influential jazz musicians of the mid-1900s.

3. Interpret
Underline the words and phrases on page 213 and on this page that show how Marsalis felt about jazz at first. How did this change?

Possible response:

Marsalis didn't always

like jazz, but now he

loves it. Jazz helped him

understand life.

but <u>now I wanted to be good</u>. I wanted to play like 'trane, like Miles [Davis], and everybody else I was listening to.

"<u>[Jazz] helped me understand life and my place in it</u>. Music is like that, it's spiritual. It goes beyond emotion; music can take you to a whole different **consciousness**. My whole approach to everything changed, not just playing."

Now, almost thirty years and one Pulitzer Prize in Music later, Marsalis is jazz. He plays it, composes it, teaches it, and it's always in his head—at any moment he's liable to surprise you with a **riff** on his trumpet.... "I just want people to be aware of jazz, to make the music available through recordings and broadcasts ... " ❖

In Other Words
consciousness understanding of the relationship between one's self and the world
riff short tune

Selection Review My Moment of Truth

A. The authors include two different turning points in two individuals' lives. What was the authors' purpose for doing this? Use evidence in the text to support your answer.

Possible response: In the first paragraph of the article, the authors state that moments of truth

often come with a challenge. Others come gradually, over a period of time. The authors show that

Dawes's turning point didn't come suddenly, but evolved gradually. On the other hand, Marsalis

wanted to understand jazz music and to understand why his father loved it so much. His turning

point came after listening to a Coltrane record several times and finally understanding it.

B. Answer the questions.

1. Choose either Dawes or Marsalis and explain how you can relate to their stories in some way.

Possible response: I am like Dawes because I always try to please others first. I need to start

making decisions based on what I want and not what others want me to do.

2. What do you think the lives of Dawes and Marsalis would be like today if they hadn't both experienced a moment of truth?

Possible response: Dawes would still be involved in activities that she is not passionate about,

and she would not be happy. Marsalis would probably still be playing funk music. He may never

have become famous or inspired and entertained so many people.

Reflect and Assess

WRITING: Write About Literature

A. Plan your writing. Write details from the selections that argue whether or not it's better to be a "doer" or a "be-er." *Answers will vary.*

	Be-ers and Doers	My Moment of Truth
Be-er		
Doer		

B. Imagine that you want to convince people that it is more important to be a "doer" or a "be-er." Write a speech. Be sure that the first sentence of your speech captures the attention of your listeners. Use details from both texts.

Students should support their speeches with examples from both selections. Encourage students to read

their speeches aloud.

_____

_____

_____

_____

_____

LITERARY ANALYSIS: Dialect

Dialect is a unique form of language spoken by people in the same region or group. Writers use dialect to reveal things about their characters and to establish the setting of a story.

> Example: "Couldn't understand why y' can't go on feedin' an animal that'll never produce milk."

A. Find at least two examples from "Be-ers and Doers" for each aspect of dialect. *Answers will vary. Possible responses are shown.*

Aspect of Dialect	Examples from Text
Pronunciation	"Nothin' I need t'hear" "Aw, c'mon now, Dorothy"
Vocabulary	"What he seems like to me is rock-bottom lazy." "Maybe even a lick more alive than the rest of us."
The spelling of words and the structure of sentences	"Fold that laundry, now, Adie, and don't let no grass grow under your feet." "Let's just be happy and forget all them plans . . ."

B. Read the two examples of dialect from "Be-ers and Doers" below. Identify the speaker, write what he or she means in your own words, and then explain what the dialect tells you about the character.

Dialect	Spoken By	Meaning	Characterization
"What he seems like to me is rock-bottom lazy."	Mrs. Horton	He is really lazy.	*Possible response:* She is very judgmental. She uses phrases unique to the region she lives in.
"Let's just be happy and forget all them plans . . ."	Mr. Horton	We should be happy and forget the plans.	*Possible response:* Mr. Horton is not educated. His grammar is incorrect.

C. Describe an event or experience you have had. Write a brief paragraph using dialect that is unique to your region or group.

Answers will vary.

_____

_____

VOCABULARY STUDY: Synonyms and Antonyms in Analogies

A **synonym** is a word or phrase that means the same thing as another word.
An **antonym** is a word that has the opposite meaning. *Answers will vary. Possible responses are shown.*

Example: *Bad* is to *good* as *rotten* is to *wonderful.*

A. Complete each analogy with the appropriate synonym or antonym.

1. *Large* is to *small* as *huge* is to _____miniature_____.
2. *Beautiful* is to *hideous* as *pretty* is to _____ugly_____.
3. *Hot* is to *cold* as *warm* is to _____cool_____.
4. *Pointed* is to *blunt* as *sharp* is to _____dull_____.
5. *Careless* is to *reckless* as *careful* is to _____cautious_____.

B. List synonyms and antonyms for each word in the chart below. Use a dictionary and a thesaurus to help you.

Word	Synonym	Antonym
clean	spotless	filthy
complicated	difficult	easy
create	construct	destroy
generous	giving	stingy
inexpensive	cheap	expensive
rich	wealthy	poor

C. Write analogies using the words in the chart above.

Example: *Spotless* is to *filthy* as *clean* is to *dirty.*

1. *Complicated* is to *simple* as *difficult* is to *easy.*
2. *Create* is to *destroy* as *construct* is to *demolish.*
3. *Generous* is to *stingy* as *giving* is to *taking.*
4. *Inexpensive* is to *expensive* as *cheap* is to *costly.*
5. *Rich* is to *poor* as *wealthy* is to *broke.*

Read for Understanding

1. Genre What kind of text is this passage? How do you know?

The text comes from an

autobiography (nonfiction).

The author shares an

event from his life.

2. Topic Write a topic sentence to tell what the text is mostly about.

The text mostly tells

about an incident and

how Wright responded

boldly to it.

Reread and Summarize

3. Key Ideas Circle three words or phrases that best express the key ideas in each section. Note why each word or phrase is important in the section.

- Section 1: paragraphs 1–24
- Section 2: paragraphs 25–49

4. Summary Use your topic sentence and notes from item 3 to write a summary of the selection.

Possible response:

Wright's principal writes

a valedictory speech for

Wright, but Wright wants

to read the one he has

written. Everyone agrees

with the principal, but

Wright stands his ground.

from

Black Boy

by Richard Wright

Lynford, 1969, Karen Armitage. Oil on canvas, private collection, The Bridgeman Art Library.

▲ **Critical Viewing: Subject** What can you know about this person, based on the details you see? What can you not know about him?

1   The school term ended. I was selected as **valedictorian** of my class and assigned to write a paper to be delivered at one of the public auditoriums. One morning the principal **summoned** me to his office.

2   "Well, Richard Wright, here's your speech," he said with smooth bluntness and shoved a stack of stapled sheets across his desk.

3   "What speech?" I asked as I picked up the papers.

4   "The speech you're to say the night of graduation," he said.

5   "But, professor, I've written my speech already," I said.

6   He laughed confidently, indulgently.

7   "Listen, boy, you're going to speak to both *white* and colored people that night. <u>What can you alone think of saying to them? You have no experience . . .</u>"

8   I burned.

9   "I know that I'm not educated, professor," I said. "But the people are coming to hear the students, and I won't make a speech that you've written."

 Possible response to Critical Viewing: You can tell that he is a young African American, possibly from an earlier era. You cannot know his interests or why he looks so reflective.

In Other Words
valedictorian the highest-ranking student
summoned called

Historical Background
Richard Wright wrote about society's poor treatment of African Americans. In his autobiography, *Black Boy,* he describes his experiences growing up in the U.S. in the 1910s and 20s.

10　He leaned back in his chair and looked at me in surprise.

11　"You're just a young, hotheaded fool," he said. He toyed with a pencil and looked up at me. "Suppose you don't graduate?"

12　"But I passed my examinations," I said.

13　"Look, mister," he shot at me, "I'm the man who says who passes at this school."

14　I was so astonished that my body **jerked**. I had gone to this school for two years and I had never suspected what kind of man the principal was; it simply had never occurred to me to wonder about him.

15　"Then I don't graduate," I said flatly.

16　I turned to leave.

17　"Say, you. Come here," he called.

18　I turned and faced him; he was smiling at me in a remote, superior sort of way.

19　"You know, I'm glad I talked to you," he said. "I was seriously thinking of placing you in the school system, teaching. But, now, I don't think that you'll fit."

20　He was tempting me, baiting me; this was the technique that **snared** black young minds into supporting the southern way of life.

21　"Look, professor, I may never get a chance to go to school again," I said. "But I like to do things right."

22　I went home, hurt but determined. I had been talking to **a "bought" man** and he had tried to "buy" me. I felt that I had been dealing with something unclean. That night Griggs, a boy who had gone through many classes with me, came to the house.

23　"Look, Dick, you're throwing away your future here in Jackson," he said. "Go to the principal, talk to him, take his speech and say it. I'm saying the one he wrote. So why can't you? What the hell? What can you lose?"

24　"No," I said.

> **I felt that I had been dealing with something unclean.**

In Other Words
jerked shook
snared tricked
a "bought" man someone who did things because others told him to

Reread and Analyze

5. Author's Purpose What is the author's purpose for writing this selection?

Possible response: to inform readers about a past experience

6. Text Structure Reread paragraphs 1–8. Describe the conflict.

Possible response: The author and the principal disagree about which valedictory speech the author should present.

7. Text Structure Reread section 1. Underline at least three comments that increase the conflict that the author feels.

8. Text Structure How does the author use the conflict in this section of the narrative to create suspense?

Possible response: The author shows the conflict by presenting two conversations. At their end, the conflict is still not resolved, which builds suspense about how the conflict will be resolved.

9. Text Structure Reread paragraphs 31–43. Highlight Wright's main argument in his conversation with his uncle. Then review Wright's conversation with Griggs and highlight Wright's main argument in that conversation.

10. Text Structure Discuss and write about how the conversations are similar and how they might foreshadow what Wright will do at the valedictory service.

Responses should

recognize that in both

conversations, Wright

shows determined

independence; and

unless something

unexpected happens,

Wright probably will

give the speech he

has written, not the

principal's speech.

25   "Why?"

26   "I know only a hell of a little, but my speech is going to reflect that," I said.

27   "Then you're going to be **blacklisted for** teaching jobs," he said.

28   "Who the hell said I was going to teach?" I asked.

29   "God, but you've got a will," he said.

30   "It's not will. I just don't want to do things that way," I said.

31   He left. Two days later Uncle Tom came to me. I knew that the principal had called him in.

32   "I hear that the principal wants you to say a speech which you've rejected," he said.

> "I just don't want to do things that way."

33   "Yes, sir. That's right," I said.

34   "May I read the speech you've written?" he asked.

35   "Certainly," I said, giving him my manuscript.

36   "And may I see the one that the principal wrote?"

37   I gave him the principal's speech too. He went to his room and read them. I sat quiet, waiting. He returned.

38   "The principal's speech is the better speech," he said.

39   "I don't doubt it," I replied. "But why did they ask me to write a speech if I can't deliver it?"

40   "Would you let me work on your speech?" he asked.

41   "No, sir."

42   "Now, look, Richard, this is your future . . ."

43   "Uncle Tom, I don't care to discuss this with you," I said.

44   He stared at me, then left. The principal's speech was simpler and clearer than mine, but it did not say anything; mine was cloudy, but it said what I wanted to say. What could I do? I had **half a mind** not to show up at the graduation exercises. I was hating my environment more each day. As soon as school was over, I would get a job, save money, and leave.

In Other Words
blacklisted for not able to get
half a mind an idea

45   Griggs, who had accepted a speech written by the principal, came to my house each day and we went off into the woods to practice **orating**; day in and day out we spoke to the trees, to the creeks, frightening the birds, making the cows in the pastures stare at us in fear. I memorized my speech so thoroughly that I could have recited it in my sleep.

46   The news of my clash with the principal had spread through the class and the students became openly critical of me.

47   "Richard, you're a (fool.) You're throwing away every chance you've got. If they had known the kind of (fool) boy you are, they would never have made you valedictorian," they said.

48   I gritted my teeth and kept my mouth shut, but my **rage was mounting** by the hour. My classmates, motivated by a desire to "save" me, pestered me until I all but reached the breaking point. In the end the principal had to caution them to let me alone, for fear I would **throw up the sponge** and walk out.

49   <u>On the night of graduation I was nervous and tense; I rose and faced the audience and my speech rolled out.</u> When my voice stopped there was some applause. I did not care if they liked it or not; I was through. Immediately, even before I left the platform I tried to **shunt** all memory of the event from me. A few of my classmates managed to shake my hand as I pushed toward the door, seeking the street. Somebody invited me to a party and I did not accept. I did not want to see any of them again. I walked home saying to myself: The hell with it! With almost seventeen years of **baffled** living behind me, I faced the world in 1925. ❖

Graduation, 1948, Jacob Lawrence. Brush and black ink © 2013 The Jacob and Gwendolyn Lawrence Foundation, Seattle / Artists Rights Society (ARS), New York.

⚠ Critical Viewing: Design How does the artist use shape to differentiate the groups of people in this painting? What effect does this have?

⚠ *Possible response to Critical Viewing:* The angled shape of the graduation caps distinguish the students from the audience. This makes the graduates seem superior to the audience.

In Other Words
orating speaking
rage was mounting anger was growing
throw up the sponge give up suddenly
shunt remove
baffled confused

Reread and Analyze

11. Text Structure Reread paragraphs 46–48. Circle the name that Wright's classmates use to describe him. Explain how what Wright says in paragraph 48 shows another complication in the narrative.

Possible response:

The fact that Wright's

classmates oppose

him, even with good

intentions, complicates

the conflict by making

it seem that the whole

world is against Wright. It

also raises the question

of whether Wright will

change his mind to

show his friends that

he understands their

concern.

12. Text Structure Reread the final paragraph. Underline the sentence that shows how the conflict is resolved. Discuss and write about how Wright responds to the principal's demand.

Possible response:

Wright boldly gives his

own speech and then

turns his back on this

chapter in his life.

Discuss

13. **Synthesize** With the class, revisit the conflict and the key events in this narrative. Discuss how the author uses each event to build suspense and add to the conflict. *Answers will vary. Possible responses are shown.*

Event	How Event Affects the Conflict
Wright says that he does not want to read the principal's speech at the graduation ceremony.	This action establishes the conflict that will create suspense and shape the narrative.

Then, with the class, discuss how the author uses details to keep the attention of his readers. Make notes.

Answers will vary but should show a recognition of the importance of conflict and suspense in this narrative.

By showing that one person after another tries to persuade Wright to use the principal's speech instead

of the one that he himself has written, Wright builds tension and holds readers' attention by making them

wonder whether his younger self can withstand the pressure to conform.

14. **Write** Use your notes from question 13 to write about how the author develops his ideas to show conflict and create suspense. Use the questions below to organize your thoughts.

> · Analyze the author's text structure: How does Wright structure this selection?
>
> · Analyze the author's use of suspense and foreshadowing: Why do these elements encourage readers to continue reading to the end of the narrative?
>
> · Evaluate the author's effectiveness: How does Wright's text structure and use of suspense and foreshadowing help him make a point that readers will remember?

Answers will vary but should show how students have carried forward their thinking from item 13.

Connect with the **EQ** — What Do People Discover in a Moment of Truth?

Consider how social pressure can affect your decisions.

15. Viewpoint Think about the selection as a whole and the "moments of truth" that the teenage Wright faces. As the older Wright looks back at and writes about this experience, does he agree with the view that people make discoveries at such moments? How do you know?

Answers will vary. Responses should include evidence from the text.

16. Theme What is the author's message about making discoveries in a moment of truth?

Answers will vary. Responses should include evidence from the text.

Key Vocabulary Review

A. Use these words to complete the paragraph.

accelerate	**destiny**	**indifference**	**regime**
contrary	**ensuing**	**priority**	**virtue**

Some people believe it is their _____ destiny _____ to challenge a _____ regime _____ that
                                              (1)   (2)

lacks _____ virtue _____ and treats its citizens with disrespect. However, many citizens show
               (3)

_____ indifference _____ and have not made human rights a _____ priority _____. Activists believe they can
               (4)   (5)

_____ accelerate _____ progress in the _____ ensuing _____ years by sharing their _____ contrary _____ ideas
               (6)   (7)   (8)

about the government.

B. Use your own words to write what each Key Vocabulary word means.
Then write an example of the word. *Answers will vary. Possible responses are shown.*

Key Word	My Definition	Example
1. commentary	an expression of an opinion	the interpretations of sports announcers after a game
2. indelible	lasting and unforgettable	words written in permanent marker
3. inflexible	rigid and firm	a metal rod
4. integrity	honesty and fairness	not cheating on a test
5. irritating	annoying and provoking	a buzzing insect
6. revelation	something that is revealed or exposed	a scientific discovery
7. temporary	not permanent	the twenty-four-hour flu
8. transaction	an exchange of goods or services	depositing money at the bank

Unit 5 Key Vocabulary

accelerate	destiny	indelible	• integrity	poised	saturate
commentary	disarm	indifference	irritating	• priority	• temporary
• conformist	ensuing	inflexible	malleable	• regime	transaction
• contrary	harmonize	inquisitive	melancholy	revelation	virtue

• **Academic Vocabulary**

C. Complete the sentences. *Answers will vary. Possible responses are shown.*

1. I am most **inquisitive** when I'm learning something new
   _____ .

2. If I wanted to **disarm** someone I just met, I would compliment him or her
   _____ .

3. An example of a historical figure who was not a **conformist** is Gandhi
   _____ .

4. Two **malleable** substances that I have used are clay and cookie dough
   _____ .

5. I sometimes get **melancholy** when I do not do well on a test
   _____ .

6. You can tell two people **harmonize** well if they are almost always in agreement
   _____ .

7. After high school, I am **poised** to start college
   _____ .

8. Something you should **saturate** with water is a very dry yard
   _____ .

Prepare to Read

▶ Too Young to Drive?
▶ Rules of the Road

Key Vocabulary

A. How well do you know these words? Circle a rating for each word. Check your understanding of each word by circling the correct synonym or antonym. Then complete the sentences. If you are unsure of a word's meaning, refer to the Vocabulary Glossary, page 926, in your student text.

Rating Scale	
1	I have never seen this word before.
2	I am not sure of the word's meaning.
3	I know this word and can teach the word's meaning to someone else.

Key Word	Check Your Understanding	Deepen Your Understanding
❶ consistently (kun-**sis**-tent-lē) *adverb* **Rating:** 1 2 3	The opposite of **consistently** is _____. (**irregularly**) evenly	One thing I do consistently is _Possible response:_ exercise _____ .
❷ excessive (ik-**se**-siv) *adjective* **Rating:** 1 2 3	If there is an **excessive** amount of something, there is _____ of it. not enough (**too much**)	I think people spend an excessive amount of money on _Possible response:_ their cars _____ .
❸ intrusion (in-**trü**-zhun) *noun* **Rating:** 1 2 3	If something is an **intrusion**, it is an _____. (**invasion**) invitation	It is an intrusion when _Possible response:_ my brother enters my room without knocking first _____ .
❹ precaution (pri-**kaw**-shun) *noun* **Rating:** 1 2 3	If you bring an umbrella as a **precaution** against rain, you are taking a _____ against getting wet. (**safety measure**) wasted step	Something I do as a precaution is _Possible response:_ wear a seat belt in the car _____ .

Key Word	Check Your Understanding	Deepen Your Understanding
5 **proficiency** (pru-**fi**-shun-sē) *noun* **Rating:** 1 2 3	The opposite of **proficiency** is _____. (inability) talent	I have a proficiency in *Possible response:* Spanish _____ _____ _____ _____ _____ .
6 **restrict** (ri-**strikt**) *verb* **Rating:** 1 2 3	If your parents **restrict** how much TV you watch, they _____ the time you spend watching TV. increase (limit)	Two things that my parents restrict are *Possible* _____ *response:* eating a lot of junk food and watching _____ late-night TV _____ _____ _____ .
7 **transform** (trans-**form**) *verb* **Rating:** 1 2 3	When you **transform** yourself, you _____ something about yourself. (change) question	If I could transform something about myself, it would be *Possible response:* my haircut _____ _____ _____ _____ .
8 **violate** (**vī**-u-lāt) *verb* **Rating:** 1 2 3	The opposite of **violate** is _____. disobey (follow)	If I violate the rules at home, I *Possible response:* get extra chores _____ _____ _____ _____ .

B. Use one of the Key Vocabulary words to write about a privilege you enjoy.

Answers will vary. _____

_____

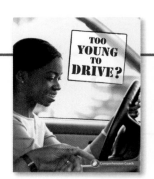

LITERARY ANALYSIS: Evaluate Argument

In **persuasive nonfiction**, a writer presents an **argument** and supports it with **evidence**. A writer who supports an issue takes the **pro** side, and a writer who is against an issue takes the **con** side.

A. Read the passage below. Find the arguments and evidence used to support or discourage raising the driving age. Write the details in the chart. *Answers will vary. Possible responses are shown.*

Look Into the Text

Should the Driving Age Be Raised?

Author 1: NO! Driver's ed, not age, is key to road safety. Although the state requires that teens under 18 take driving classes before getting their licenses, it sets no specific curriculum standards.

Author 2: YES! Because immaturity fuels fatal crashes, Georgia should raise the driving age to 17 and permit age to 16. Sixteen-year-old drivers account for the highest percentages of crashes involving speeding, single vehicles, and driver error.

Con Side	Pro Side
Argument: *Driver's ed, not age, is the key to road safety.*	**Argument:** Immaturity is the reason so many teens get into car crashes.
Evidence: State law requires teens under 18 to take driver's ed, but many of the courses are poorly designed.	**Evidence:** Sixteen-year-old drivers cause the most crashes involving speeding, single vehicles, and driver error.

B. Answer the question about the writers' arguments.

How do the writers explain and support their arguments?

Possible response: Both writers clearly state their arguments at the beginning and then support their arguments with factual evidence.

FOCUS STRATEGY: Draw Conclusions

How to DRAW CONCLUSIONS

1. **Look for facts** or details the author provides.

2. **Use logical reasoning** and what you already know to develop a judgment, or opinion, about the facts.

3. **Rethink your conclusions** if you need to by checking for additional details as you read.

A. Read the passage. Use the strategies above to draw conclusions as you read. Then answer the questions below.

Look Into the Text

> A visit to one busy metro area school found some <u>students asleep during class</u>. Others stayed awake by <u>text-messaging friends or reading magazines</u>. Teens at other schools and concerned driving instructors confirm this was not unusual. Some schools, they say, are <u>assembly lines that fill the required thirty hours of instruction</u> with <u>30-year-old safety videos</u> and <u>simple recitation of the Registry's rules-of-the-road</u>.

1. What conclusion can you make about driving schools from the details in the text?

   Possible response: Many driving schools do not have good driver's education programs. Driver's education is a requirement, so the students are not very interested in doing well. In addition, the educational materials are outdated.

2. What do you already know about driver's education? Put this information together with your answer to question 1 to form a new conclusion.

   Possible response: Many driving schools do care about the students, but many students do not pay attention in class because the classes are not interesting. I think that young people need more driving practice before they get their license.

B. Return to the passage above. Underline the words or phrases that helped you find the answer to question 1.

EQ ## How Can We Balance Everyone's Rights?
Examine personal rights and privileges.

A. In "Too Young to Drive?" you read two writers' arguments about changing the driving age. Complete the chart to compare the evidence each writer uses to support his or her argument. *Answers will vary. Possible responses are shown.*

T Chart

Fred Bayles	Maureen Downey
There are no specific curriculum standards for driving classes.	Sixteen-year-old drivers account for the highest percentage of crashes.
Thirty-five percent of high school seniors said they were tested on seven or fewer of the twelve driving skills.	Evidence suggests that growing up is the only thing that transforms a teenager into a good driver.
Fifty-six percent said their driver's test lasted ten minutes or less.	Limiting how early and how much teens can drive and how many passengers they can transport has reduced teen crashes.
Twenty-one percent said their driving school was either "fair" or "poor."	Sixty-two percent of teenage passengers killed in crashes were traveling in cars driven by other teens.
Students sleep or text-message each other during class.	Drivers age 15 to 20 were involved in 7,898 fatalities.
Teachers show 30-year-old safety videos or recite the rules-of-the-road.	Risk assessment skills do not develop until age 25.

B. Use the information in the chart to answer the questions.

1. Based on the evidence each writer uses, what conclusions can you draw about teens and driving? Which writer do you agree with? Why?

Possible response: Teens need more experience and instruction to be good drivers. I agree that schools need to do a better job teaching students and testing them.

2. How does experience transform teens into better drivers? Use **transform** in your answer.

Possible response: Experience transforms teens into better drivers because it helps them become more responsible drivers. Teen drivers learn to judge distance, speed, and time more accurately.

3. How do you think parents can help their teens become responsible drivers?

Possible response: Parents can help their teens become responsible drivers if they supervise driving, limit driving time, and make sure their teen does not use a cell phone while driving or drive with friends.

Connect Across Texts

In "Too Young to Drive?" you read about different solutions to the problem of unsafe driving among teens. Now read the following how-to article for tips on safe driving.

Rules of the Road

by Lynn Lucia

So, you've mastered left-hand turns, parallel parking, and merging onto the freeway. Now all you need are the keys to the family car and you'll be fully able to take advantage of your vehicular independence . . .

Not so fast! Passing the driving test is only half the challenge. Becoming an experienced, safe driver is the other. Remember, driving isn't a right. It's a privilege that can be easily revoked if you don't play it safe.

In Other Words
your vehicular independence the freedom of being able to drive a car
revoked taken away, removed

1. Predict

Read the title and the introduction, and look at the photo on page 231. What kind of how-to information will you find in this article?

Possible response: I will

find information about

the rules of safe driving.

The day Eddie Angert got his driver's license, he was **on top of the world**. "Getting my license was huge," says the 18-year-old senior from Oceanside, New York. "Now I don't have to depend on my parents, or my friends' parents, to drive me anywhere." But within a year after getting his license, Eddie found out there's more to driving than turning on the ignition and stepping on the accelerator. "I got three traffic tickets at once," Eddie says. "I lost control of my car on a turn and a cop gave me tickets for **imprudent speed**, failure to keep right, and making an unsafe turn."

Eddie isn't alone in making mistakes behind the wheel. Teens ages 16 and 17 represent only about 2 percent of all drivers in the United States, but they are involved in nearly 11 percent of all motor-vehicle crashes.

Why are teen drivers so unreliable? They're inexperienced drivers, say transportation and driving safety experts. It takes at least five years of driving to make someone an experienced driver, says Edwin Bailey, a safety education officer in Amherst, New York. "You're not going to become proficient in driving unless you do it," Bailey says. "Get your parents to take you out to get that driving experience."

2. Draw Conclusions

Underline the words and phrases that tell what Eddie learned about the responsibility of driving. What conclusions can you draw about his experience?

Possible response: Many

teens like Eddie put

themselves and others

in danger because they

get caught up in the

excitement of driving.

> **It takes at least five years of driving to make someone an experienced driver.**

Of course, getting that experience isn't easy. There's plenty to be concerned about while driving: your car, other cars on the road, traffic lights, road conditions, and bad weather. Below are tips from driving-school teachers, police officers, and department of motor vehicle officials on how to **steer clear of** trouble on the road.

In Other Words
on top of the world really happy
imprudent not wise, not sensible
steer clear of avoid

How to Be a Safe Driver

Obey laws. Wear your seat belt. Seat belts save 9,500 lives per year according to the National Highway Traffic Safety Administration. Don't drink and drive. Do obey the posted speed limit.

Cut down on distractions. Say your favorite tune is playing on the radio so you reach over and **blast the volume.** Bad idea. The noise reduces your ability to hear sirens coming from police cars, fire trucks, or ambulances, and honking horns from other cars and trucks. Don't chat on a cell phone while driving either; people who talk on phones while driving are four times more likely to have an accident.

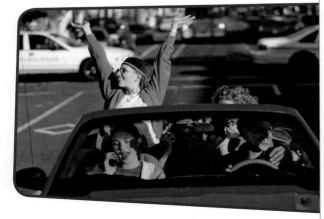

Distractions such as loud music, cell phones, and rowdy friends are dangerous for the driver.

At a green light, accelerate gradually.

If your car is the first vehicle at a red light, wait a few seconds after the light turns green before proceeding. Often, cars try to make it through an intersection during a yellow light. If you **gun your vehicle** immediately when a light turns green, you run the risk of crashing into an oncoming car.

In Other Words
blast the volume turn the sound up very loud
gun your vehicle make your car go very fast

3. Analyze Development of Ideas
Highlight the words and phrases in the first paragraph that give instructions about how to be a safe driver. Why do you think the writer starts with this information?

Possible response:

These are the most

basic driving rules.

These rules can save

your life if you follow

them.

4. Draw Conclusions
Circle the words and phrases that tell what can distract drivers. Think about what you know. What can you conclude about how sound affects drivers?

Possible response:

Drivers need to

concentrate, and

sounds and talking on

cell phones distract

drivers. Drivers also

will not be able to hear

sounds around them.

5. Analyze Development of Ideas

Underline the words and phrases that instruct drivers what to do before making a right-hand turn. Why is this step so important?

Possible response:

Drivers need to be aware

of pedestrians and other

cars. If drivers don't look

right, they could hit a

pedestrian.

6. Interpret

Circle a sentence that tells why an experienced driver should help a less experienced driver make left turns. Explain why this precaution is necessary.

Possible response: An

experienced driver acts

as a safety precaution

because he or she can

help teens judge how

fast or slow other cars

are going and when it is

safe to make a left turn.

Go slow near schools. Watch for kids getting on and off school buses. When a bus stops in front of you and flashes its lights, you MUST stop. The flashing lights mean that students are getting on and off the bus and may be crossing the street.

Look both ways before making a right-hand turn. You may think you only have to look to the left to watch for oncoming cars before you make a right-hand turn. But if you don't look to the right, you risk hitting **a pedestrian** who's crossing the street and who has the **right of way**.

Many schools have crossing guards stationed nearby to warn drivers and protect pedestrians.

Turn left at a light only when there's a green arrow. Sure it's legal to turn left at a green light that doesn't have a green arrow. But it's a dangerous move if **traffic is heavy**. A green arrow guarantees that you have the right of way. If you want to practice turning left at lights that don't have green arrows, make sure an experienced driver is with you. He or she can help you judge the flow of traffic.

Don't rely only on mirrors when changing lanes. Looking in your car's rearview and sideview mirrors isn't enough to make sure that a car isn't too close to your vehicle. Those mirrors have blind spots—areas where cars are hidden from your vision. The only way to know for sure if it's safe to change lanes is to turn your head and see for yourself.

In Other Words

a pedestrian someone walking
right of way right to cross a street or intersection first
traffic is heavy there is a lot of traffic

Be careful in parking lots. Believe it or not, many accidents occur in parking lots. A common **collision** happens when cars parked across from each other are both backing out. Always back out slowly and check for cars and pedestrians crossing into your path.

Don't assume what other drivers will do. Just because you're paying attention to the road and driving safely doesn't mean that other drivers are doing the same. For example, a car with a flashing turn signal may not, in fact, turn at all. The driver may change his or her mind about turning, or may not realize that the turn signal is on.

Be cautious in bad weather. Rain, snow, and ice make streets harder to drive on, so when roads are wet, slow down. A good rule is to double the space between you and the vehicle in front of you. This will give you more space to stop if you have to hit the brakes. Turn your headlights on anytime you need to turn your windshield wipers on. This will help you see other cars and other cars see you. Some states require that all vehicles turn on their lights during bad weather. ❖

Bad weather can seriously affect a driver's ability to see and to react.

In Other Words
collision crash

7. Analyze Development of Ideas
Underline the words and phrases that show how other drivers can cause traffic accidents. Summarize the writer's instructions about why it is important to watch other drivers.

Possible response:

Drivers do not always look behind them when they are backing out of parking spaces. They can change their minds about making a turn. It is important to not assume other drivers are paying attention and driving safely.

8. Draw Conclusions
Highlight the words and phrases that instruct drivers what to do in bad weather. Draw a conclusion about why drivers should take these precautions.

Possible response:

Drivers need more space to stop when the roads are wet. Other drivers may slide on the road. Headlights help drivers see in the dark and help other drivers see other cars.

Selection Review Rules of the Road

A. Choose a topic and write five driving tips from the article that support it. Then explain why each instruction was given.

> **Topic 1:** **Good Driving Practices**
> **Topic 2:** **Important Things for Drivers to Avoid**

I chose topic *Possible response: 2*

1. Tip: _Do not drink and drive._

Explanation: *Possible response:* Drinking and driving can cause serious accidents and death.

2. Tip: _Do not assume what drivers around you are going to do._

Explanation: *Possible response:* Drivers do not always follow the signals and the laws.

3. Tip: _Do not speed up quickly when the light turns green._

Explanation: *Possible response:* Some drivers try to make yellow lights, but the light might turn red.

4. Tip: _Do not play loud music or talk on the phone._

Explanation: *Possible response:* Noise distracts drivers and makes it hard to hear sirens and horns.

5. Tip: _Do not only use your mirrors when changing lanes._

Explanation: *Possible response:* All cars have blind spots, and drivers cannot see other cars.

B. Answer the questions.

1. Put the ideas from the article together. Then draw a conclusion about what you've learned about driving.

Possible response: Driving is not easy, and it takes a lot of practice to become a good driver. There are many things to think about when you drive.

2. Do you think the tips in "Rules of the Road" apply to drivers in general or to teen drivers in particular? Why?

Possible response: I think the tips apply to all drivers because teen drivers are not the only drivers who need to learn this information. It is important for all drivers to know how to be safe, regardless of their age.

Reflect and Assess

WRITING: Write About Literature

A. Plan your writing. The authors of "Too Young to Drive?" and "Rules of the Road" try to convince readers that teens may be too young or too inexperienced to drive. In the chart, list the important evidence each author gives to support his or her claim. *Answers will vary.*

Too Young to Drive?	Rules of the Road
Some states require the instructor to have only a safe driving record.	Teens ages 16 and 17 represent only about 2 percent of all drivers in the United States, but they are involved in nearly 11 percent of all motor-vehicle crashes.

B. Choose two types of supporting evidence from each selection. Write two paragraphs to analyze the evidence. Evaluate how these types of evidence are important.

Students should support their answers with evidence from both selections.

_____

_____

_____

_____

_____

_____

_____

_____

_____

_____

_____

LITERARY ANALYSIS: Bias

Bias is a strong opinion that reveals an author's viewpoint. It can sometimes be unreasonable or emotional and can encourage stereotypes. Bias can prevent a reader from looking fairly at both sides of an issue.

A. Read examples from Bayles's column that reveal the author's bias. Then explain why each example is biased. *Answers will vary. Possible responses are shown.*

Example of Bias	Why I Think So
"Driver's education is poor."	Bayles explains only one side of his argument.
"The state driver's exam is little more than a formality."	Bayles uses language like "little more than a formality" to express his low opinion of the exam.
"A harsh fine pales in comparison to the life sentence of grief faced by the parent of a dead teen."	Bayles shows his simplified beliefs about all parents whose teens have died in car accidents.

B. Read the examples from Downey's column that reveal the author's bias. Then explain why you think each example is biased. *Answers will vary. Possible responses are shown.*

Example of Bias	Why I Think So
"Parents often overestimate their children's proficiency behind the wheel."	Downey is sharing her simplified beliefs about parents.
"What does seem to work is limiting how early and how much teens can drive . . ."	Downey is explaining only one side of her argument.
"Teen drivers should not be allowed to carry nonfamily members in the car during their first year."	Downey is sharing her simplified beliefs about teen drivers.
"Parents have to start treating a driver's license as a first step in their child's driving education, not a final destination."	Downey is using words like "have to" that show she feels strongly that parents must do this.

C. Describe something you have read or written that showed clear bias. How do you know it was biased? How might the bias change if a different author wrote the text?

Answers will vary.

VOCABULARY STUDY: Denotation and Connotation

Denotation is a word's direct meaning. **Connotation** is the feeling or attitude a word conveys. Connotations can be positive, negative, or neutral.

A. Determine the denotation and connotation for each word in the chart below. *Answers will vary. Possible responses are shown.*

Word	Denotation	Connotation
disgust	to arouse distaste	negative
organize	to bring structure	positive
pure	innocent or naive	positive
stupid	slow of mind or senseless	negative

B. Write a synonym with a negative connotation and a positive connotation for each word in the chart below. *Answers will vary. Possible responses are shown.*

Word	Negative	Positive
confident	cocky	poised
explore	probe	investigate
fire	sack	let go
reject	refuse	decline

C. Rewrite each sentence. Replace the underlined word with a new word that has the same denotation, but a different connotation.
Answers will vary. Possible responses are shown.

1. The line to buy concert tickets moved at a <u>sluggish</u> pace.

The line to buy concert tickets moved at a leisurely pace.

2. I do not want to see that movie because it is <u>revolting</u>.

I do not want to see that movie because it is distasteful.

3. Some people think that he is <u>brash</u>.

Some people think that he is frank.

Prepare to Read

▶ Piracy Bites!
▶ Doonesbury on Downloading

Key Vocabulary

A. How well do you know these words? Circle a rating for each word. Check your understanding of each word by circling *yes* or *no*. Then provide an example. If you are unsure of a word's meaning, refer to the Vocabulary Glossary, page 926, in your student text.

Rating Scale	
1	I have never seen this word before.
2	I am not sure of the word's meaning.
3	I know this word and can teach the word's meaning to someone else.

Key Word	Check Your Understanding	Deepen Your Understanding
❶ access (**ak**-ses) *verb* **Rating:** 1 2 3	You have to get special permission to **access** the rare books in a library. (**Yes**) No	Example: _*Possible response:* looking up the weather forecast on the Internet_
❷ counterfeit (**kown**-tur-fit) *adjective* **Rating:** 1 2 3	When you work in a bank, you have to watch for **counterfeit** bills. (**Yes**) No	Example: _*Possible response:* a fake $100 bill_
❸ facilitate (fu-**si**-lu-tāt) *verb* **Rating:** 1 2 3	Schools **facilitate** how parents receive information by having meetings and using e-mail. (**Yes**) No	Example: _*Possible response:* my teacher guiding discussion in class_
❹ fundamental (fun-du-**men**-tul) *adjective* **Rating:** 1 2 3	Sugar, oil, and chemicals are the **fundamental** ingredients of a healthful meal. Yes (**No**)	Example: _*Possible response:* needs like food and water_

Key Word	Check Your Understanding	Deepen Your Understanding
5 **impact** (**im**-pakt) *noun* **Rating:** 1 2 3	Good role models make a big **impact** on young children. (Yes) No	Example: *Possible response:* influential advice from a coach or teacher
6 **merit** (**mer**-it) *noun* **Rating:** 1 2 3	The new computers in the classrooms have **merit** because students use them once a month. Yes (No)	Example: *Possible response:* an award-winning book
7 **repercussion** (rē-pur-**ku**-shun) *noun* **Rating:** 1 2 3	A **repercussion** for speeding on the freeway is a speeding ticket. (Yes) No	Example: *Possible response:* failing a test because you didn't study
8 **verify** (**ver**-i-fī) *verb* **Rating:** 1 2 3	When you write a research paper, you don't have to **verify** your sources. Yes (No)	Example: *Possible response:* confirming the definition of a word in a dictionary

B. Use one of the Key Vocabulary words to tell about a personal right you want to protect.

Answers will vary.

Before Reading Piracy Bites!

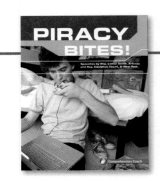

LITERARY ANALYSIS: Evaluate Argument

Writers use evidence and effective reasons to support their arguments. Readers must **evaluate** an argument to see if the evidence is valid and persuasive enough to support the claim.

A. Read the passages below. Find the evidence in both arguments and list it in the T Chart.

> ### Look Into the Text
>
> ### Piracy in Cyberspace
> by Rep. Lamar Smith
>
>   Pirates still exist, but they aren't like the pirates of the past. The modern day thieves are engaged in the theft of intellectual property. . . .
>
>   Intellectual property represents the largest single sector of the American economy, employing 4.3 million Americans.
>
> ### Piracy Hurts Everyone Both Online and Offline
> by Rep. Edolphus Towns
>
>   . . . The rush to make all content available online . . . has real world consequences. These consequences . . . affect small urban record stores, rural used booksellers, and other retailers. . . . These are small businesses that provide jobs in my community, . . . and theft . . . affects the ability of these small business owners to exist. I have a serious problem with that.

T Chart

Piracy in Cyberspace	Piracy Hurts Everyone Both Online and Offline
Intellectual property represents the largest part of the American economy—4.3 million Americans work in the field.	Small businesses are affected, as well as people who work for them.

B. State the arguments using the information in the T Chart. Evaluate the authors' evidence. Whose argument is more effective?

Both of these authors feel   *Possible response:* that sharing files is stealing and affects many people. I

think that the first author's argument is more effective because he uses a statistic that helps me understand

the seriousness of the problem.

FOCUS STRATEGY: Compare Evidence

HOW TO COMPARE EVIDENCE

1. **Write examples** of effective evidence as you read.

2. **Determine your own understanding** based on your evaluation of both texts.

A. Read the passages. Use the strategies above to compare evidence from both texts as you read. Then answer the questions below.

Look Into the Text

Piracy in Cyberspace

by Rep. Lamar Smith

Just because material is available in cyberspace doesn't make it legal to access it. Downloading a copyrighted song, video game, or movie from the Internet is the same as shoplifting a CD or DVD from a local store.

Piracy Hurts Everyone Both Online and Offline

by Rep. Edolphus Towns

There are class issues in play here, too. If someone in a low-income community—who has no Internet or computer access—goes to a record store and steals a CD or DVD, he is fined and/or put in jail. If an affluent child with broadband access downloads (i.e., steals) ten CDs from online sharing services, there are no visible repercussions and parents often praise that child for being tech savvy.

1. What evidence does each writer use to support his claim?

   Smith gives an ethical reason. He claims downloading a copyrighted song is like shoplifting. Towns uses a

   comparison to say that children from different backgrounds are treated differently for the same crime.

2. Do you agree or disagree with the writers' claims? Explain.

   Possible response: Illegal downloading seems to be a serious crime. Many people do not seem to

   understand the consequences.

B. Return to the passages above. Circle the phrases or sentences that helped you answer the questions.

Selection Review Piracy Bites!

 How Can We Balance Everyone's Rights?
Decide how best to protect individual and public rights.

A. In "Piracy Bites!" you found out how lawmakers feel about people sharing and copying files from the Internet. Complete the diagram below with the evidence each writer uses to support the argument. *Answers will vary. Possible responses are shown.*

Argument-Evidence Diagram

> **Argument:**
> Copying and sharing music and other intellectual property is wrong.

Smith's Evidence:

The music industry estimates that 2 billion illegal CDs are sold every year and are worth $4 to 5 billion.

One in three recordings is a pirated copy.

One million movie files are illegally downloaded every day.

Software makers suffer a loss of $2.6 billion dollars a year.

Towns's Evidence:

Piracy affects the profits of companies and small stores.

Illegal downloads hurt small businesses and their employees.

Piracy teaches kids that things online are free.

Piracy teaches that stealing other people's hard work is OK.

People from different social classes are treated differently for a similar crime.

B. Use the information in the diagram to answer the questions.

1. What differences do you see in the kinds of evidence each representative presents? Which evidence is more credible? Why?

Possible response: Smith presents statistics about business losses. Towns discusses ethical issues. Smith's evidence is more credible because it can be proven.

2. How can prohibiting counterfeit materials protect the public's rights? Use **counterfeit** in your answer.

Possible response: If we prohibit counterfeit materials, the consumer will get the best possible product and the creator of the product will make money. Small businesses can also benefit because they won't lose business to pirates.

3. How do you think piracy can be stopped?

Possible response: More laws need to be passed, and more articles should be written about piracy and its effects so people understand the crime and its repercussions.

Connect Across Texts

In "Piracy Bites!" two Congressmen use persuasive language to argue against Internet piracy. Now see how a cartoonist uses a different method to present the same argument.

Doonesbury on Downloading

by Garry Trudeau

Over the years, readers have seen comic strip character Mike Doonesbury develop from a college student into a middle-aged parent. He and Alex, his daughter, disagree on many issues, including pirated music.

1. Central Idea

Mark an *X* in the frame that shows the characters' feelings. What does this panel help you understand about the characters and their conversation?

Possible response: I can

tell the characters are

frustrated with each

other. Their expressions

show that this is a

serious conversation

and that they do not

agree on the issue.

2. Interpret

Underline the statements that show the characters' opinions. Summarize their opinions. Why do you think they have different opinions?

Possible response:

The daughter doesn't

understand the problem.

She is trying to be

thoughtful. The father

thinks what she has

done is stealing. The

differences in their ages

could be one reason

they see downloading

music so differently.

Cultural Background

Beggars Banquet (1968) is an album by the Rolling Stones, one of the world's longest running, most popular rock bands.

In Other Words

a looter's logic the way a thief thinks
set me straight on warn me about

3. Compare Evidence

Underline the father's argument. How does it compare to the arguments in "Piracy Bites!"?

Alex's father and Smith

and Towns feel that

downloading music

without paying for it is

stealing.

4. Central Idea

Mark an X in the frame that is visually different from the others. What do you think the cartoonist wanted to show by drawing it this way?

Possible response:

The cartoonist wanted

the reader to focus on

the dialogue. It shows

how they have had this

argument many times.

The cartoonist might

have wanted to show how

important this issue is and

that many groups have

argued about it.

5. Compare Evidence

Circle Alex's statement that shows her views on piracy. What do you think the representatives in "Piracy Bites!" would say about Alex's idea of sharing?

Possible response: I think they would argue that just because something is on the Internet does not mean it is free. It would only be sharing if the artist gave Alex permission to download the music.

6. Central Idea

Underline the dialogue that is meant to be humorous. Why do you think the cartoonist uses humor?

Possible response: He uses humor to make a point about piracy. If Alex's father takes her computer, she can't steal anymore. Taking away her computer is the only way to stop her.

In Other Words
impounding taking away

In Other Words
picking up sensing
Frankly Honestly

7. Compare Evidence
Underline Alex's claims in the second and third frames. Compare her arguments to the arguments in "Piracy Bites!"

Possible response:

Alex's arguments are

based on emotions,

while Smith and Towns

used facts and statistics

to support their claims.

8. Central Idea
How does the cartoonist use humor in the last frame? Do you think this cartoon is more or less effective than the articles on piracy? Why or why not?

Possible response:

The cartoonist shows a

teenager using emotion

to get around the issue.

It also shows her side of

the issue. The cartoon

expresses a central idea,

but it can't provide all

the facts that an article

can.

Doonesbury

9. Interpret

How does the prize Trudeau won in 1975 affect your views about the impact of cartoons on readers?

Possible response:

I never realized

that cartoons were

considered journalism

and could be so

effective.

About the Cartoonist

Garry Trudeau (1948–) created Doonesbury when he was a college student. So far, his Doonesbury collections have sold over 7 million copies worldwide, and the cartoon appears in almost 1,400 newspapers. In 1975, he became the first comic strip artist to win a Pulitzer Prize for editorial cartooning. The Pulitzer Prize is considered the highest honor in the field of print journalism.

Selection Review   Doonesbury on Downloading

A. Compare the opinions from the entertainers in "Piracy Bites!" and the ideas in "Doonesbury on Downloading." Synthesize the information and then describe how it helps you have a new understanding of the issue.

Opinion 1:	**Piracy drives up the price of legitimate recordings.**
Opinion 2:	**When you make an illegal copy, you are stealing from the artist.**
Opinion 3:	**Copying files is a form of stealing.**
Opinion 4:	**It's just file-sharing. Everybody does it.**

My new understanding: *Possible response:* There needs to be some compromise between consumers and the music industry. Maybe if CD prices were lower, people wouldn't be so willing to pirate their favorite music. Then again, piracy affects everyone negatively.

B. Answer the questions.

1. How did reading a cartoon help you understand the issues about piracy better?

Possible response: It showed me what a real argument might look like between someone who illegally downloads and someone who disagrees with this practice. It showed how humor can be used to support an argument.

2. What do you think Trudeau's personal views are about the illegal downloading of music?

Possible response: I think he believes that entertainers have the right to make money and not have their work stolen. He also understands each generation's point of view very clearly.

WRITING: Write About Literature

A. Plan your writing. What do the writers of "Piracy Bites!" and "Doonesbury on Downloading" think about the topic of file sharing? Use the information in the selections to list the pros and cons.

Answers will vary. Possible responses are shown.

	Piracy Bites!	**Doonesbury on Downloading**
Pros	none listed	People are sharing. People shouldn't have to pay for entertainment.
Cons	It supports terrorism. It hurts small businesses. It's stealing.	It's stealing from others.

B. Elected officials seek ideas from the public when considering new laws. Write a letter to a local representative. Express your opinions about file sharing. Support your opinions with evidence from both selections.

Students should support their answers with examples from both selections, if possible.

_____

_____

_____

_____

_____

_____

_____

_____

_____

_____

_____

LITERARY ANALYSIS: Faulty Persuasive Techniques

Persuasive writers use techniques to support their opinions and persuade readers. **Faulty persuasive techniques** are unsupported by facts, not related to the issue, or simply not true.

A. Read the explanation of each faulty persuasive technique listed below. Write your own example of each. *Answers will vary. Possible responses are shown.*

Ad hominem: Avoid discussion of the issue by attacking someone personally instead.

Teachers who don't want pep rallies don't care about students.

Circular reasoning: Argue something is true by simply restating what you're arguing about.

Dieting is popular because many people do it.

Bandwagon appeals: Argue that someone should do something because everyone else is doing it.

Everyone goes to the football games, so you should too.

B. The author of "Doonesbury on Downloading" used all three of the techniques listed above. Write examples of each from the selection. *Possible responses are shown.*

Ad Hominem	Circular Reasoning	Bandwagon Appeals
"I'm picking up a lot of jealousy here!"; "It's not my fault that your generation had to pay for entertainment and mine doesn't."	"I don't see what the big deal is—it's just file-sharing."	"And everyone does it!"; "The only ones who think [it is stealing] are giant corporations and greedy musicians!"

C. Write an advertisement for an imaginary product that prevents file-sharing. Use at least one faulty persuasive technique. *Answers will vary.*

VOCABULARY STUDY: Connotation

Connotations are the feelings conveyed by words. For example, the word *touchy* can connote a negative feeling, whereas the word *sensitive* connotes a more neutral feeling.

A. Read the synonym pairs below. Circle the word that has the negative connotation. Then provide a word with a positive or neutral connotation.
Answers will vary. Possible responses are shown.

Synonym Pair	Neutral or Positive
ask / (interrogate)	question
(immature) / young	inexperienced
(escape) / leave	go
uninteresting / (dull)	bland

B. Read the sentences. Write *positive* to identify an underlined word with a positive connotation. Write *negative* to identify an underlined word with a negative connotation.

1. The park attendant began <u>ordering</u> people to leave at midnight. _____ negative

2. The sun was <u>sweltering</u> yesterday afternoon while we were at the beach. _____ negative

3. Sheila was <u>courteous</u> to her parents' friends at the dinner party last night. _____ positive

4. The <u>pleasant</u> weather made for a perfect picnic. _____ positive

C. Write two brief paragraphs. In the first, use words from Activity A with all positive connotations. Then write it again using synonyms with negative connotations. Compare the paragraphs. *Answers will vary.*

_____

_____

_____

_____

_____

_____

_____

_____

_____

_____

_____

_____

_____

_____

_____

_____

Prepare to Read

▶ Long Walk to Freedom
▶ We Hold These Truths

Key Vocabulary

A. How well do you know these words? Circle a rating for each word. Check your understanding by marking an *X* next to the correct definition. Then complete the sentences. If you are unsure of a word's meaning, refer to the Vocabulary Glossary, page 926, in your student text.

Rating Scale

1	I have never seen this word before.
2	I am not sure of the word's meaning.
3	I know this word and can teach the word's meaning to someone else.

Key Word	Check Your Understanding	Deepen Your Understanding
❶ apathetic (a-pu-**the**-tik) *adjective* **Rating:** 1 2 3	[X] indifferent [ ] interested	I know some people who are apathetic about ___ *Possible* *response:* politics _____ _____ .
❷ distinction (di-**stink**-shun) *noun* **Rating:** 1 2 3	[ ] a similarity [X] a difference	The main distinction between CDs and DVDs is _____ *Possible response:* CDs are used for music or photographs, and DVDs are used for movies _____ .
❸ emancipation (i-man-su-**pā**-shun) *noun* **Rating:** 1 2 3	[ ] permission [X] freedom	If someone says that washing machines are a form of emancipation, he means that *Possible response:* the machines free people from some work _____ .
❹ exploitation (ek-sploi-**tā**-shun) *noun* **Rating:** 1 2 3	[X] taking advantage of [ ] respect of people	Having a person help you is exploitation when _____ *Possible response:* you do not pay him or her for the work _____ .

Key Word	Check Your Understanding	Deepen Your Understanding
⑤ inclination (in-klu-**nā**-shun) *noun* **Rating:** **1 2 3**	[X] preference [ ] refusal	Sometimes I have an inclination to *Possible response:* ride my bike in the rain .
⑥ liberate (**li**-bu-rāt) *verb* **Rating:** **1 2 3**	[X] to release [ ] to trap	I would like to liberate *Possible response:* animals that are being used for experiments .
⑦ motivated (**mō**-tu-vā-tid) *verb* **Rating:** **1 2 3**	[ ] discouraged [X] determined	I am motivated to play sports when *Possible* *response:* I watch the Olympics on TV .
⑧ oppression (u-**pre**-shun) *noun* **Rating:** **1 2 3**	[X] unfair treatment [ ] kindness	There is oppression in a country when *Possible* *response:* people cannot practice their religious or political beliefs .

B. Use one of the Key Vocabulary words to describe some rights you have in this country that people in other countries do not enjoy.

Answers will vary.

Before Reading Long Walk to Freedom

LITERARY ANALYSIS: Analyze Viewpoint: Word Choice

Authors who write to persuade make careful word choices to appeal to the reader's feelings, to emphasize key points, to clarify their own viewpoint, and to emphasize the need for action. These word choices include **emotion-filled words**, **repetition of words**, and **signal words** like *should* and *must*.

A. Read the passage below. Write examples of the author's word choices in the chart.

> ### Look Into the Text
>
> . . . We thank all of our distinguished international guests for having come to take possession with the people of our country of what is, after all, a common victory for justice, for peace, for human dignity.
>
> . . . Never, never, and never again shall it be that this beautiful land will again experience the oppression of one by another. . . . The sun shall never set on so glorious a human achievement.

Word Choices	Examples from Passage
Emotion-filled words	"victory for justice" *peace, human dignity, beautiful land,* *oppression, glorious*
Repetition of words	*for justice, for peace, for human dignity, never*
Signal words	*shall never*

B. Answer the questions.

What word choices does the author make to persuade readers and appeal to feelings? What is the speaker trying to do? _Possible response:_ The speaker uses emotion-filled words and repeats words and phrases to emphasize that people will never allow oppression again.

FOCUS STRATEGY: Synthesize

How to FORM GENERALIZATIONS

1. **Take note of statements** that tie ideas together.

2. **Add examples** from your own knowledge and experience.

3. **Construct a sentence** from the author's statements and your own examples.

A. Read the passage. Use the strategies above to form a generalization as you read. Complete the chart below.

Look Into the Text

It was this desire for the freedom of my people to live their lives with dignity and self-respect that animated my life, that transformed a frightened young man into a bold one, that drove a law-abiding attorney to become a criminal, that turned a family-loving husband into a man without a home, that forced a life-loving man to live like a monk. I am no more virtuous or self-sacrificing than the next man, but I found that I could not even enjoy the poor and limited freedoms I was allowed when I knew my people were not free.

Notes from Text	My Knowledge and Experience
Mandela wanted his people to live their lives with dignity and self-respect.	*Possible response:* Sometimes people break the law to stand up for their beliefs. I have been
Mandela could not enjoy his limited freedoms knowing his people were not free.	frightened to defend my beliefs, but I respect others for doing it.

Using the information in the chart, construct a sentence that seems true for both the author's statements and your own experience.

Possible response: Mandela was brave for standing up for the rights of his people.

B. Explain how using the strategies helped you form a generalization.

Possible response: Using the strategies made me stop and think about what I read and what I already know that I can add to it. It would have been difficult to make a generalization if I had just read the passage.

Selection Review Long Walk to Freedom

 EQ **How Can We Balance Everyone's Rights?**
Explore the struggle for human rights around the world.

A. In "The Long Walk to Freedom," you learned how Mandela fought apartheid in South Africa. List the statements of persuasion Mandela gives to support his message of freedom. *Answers will vary. Possible responses are shown.*

Details Web

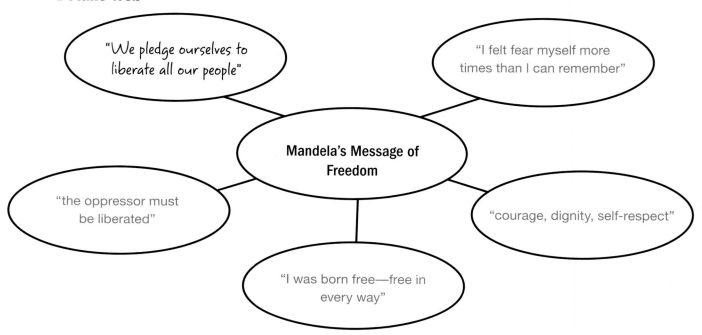

"We pledge ourselves to liberate all our people"

"I felt fear myself more times than I can remember"

Mandela's Message of Freedom

"the oppressor must be liberated"

"courage, dignity, self-respect"

"I was born free—free in every way"

B. Use the information in the web to answer the questions.

1. How do these persuasive statements help make Mandela's autobiography effective? Which word choices persuaded you the most?

Possible response: The persuasive statements appeal to readers' emotions and emphasize the need to

protect everyone's rights. His words emphasize achievement but demand more progress. The emotion-filled

words affected me the most because they made me realize how people in South Africa felt.

2. How was Mandela motivated to change the rights of the people of South Africa? Use **motivated** in your answer.

Possible response: Mandela was motivated to fight for the rights of the people in his country because he

saw how people who looked like him were not free.

3. Mandela spent 27 years in jail for a cause he deeply believed in. Is there a cause you would sacrifice for? Explain your answer.

Possible response: Yes. I would sacrifice my freedom to call attention to the mistreatment of animals for

medical research.

Connect Across Texts

In *"Long Walk to Freedom,"* you read about how South Africans overcame **exploitation** and **oppression** and demanded equal rights. Now travel to the United States and read how two other groups declared their rights.

WE HOLD THESE TRUTHS

In 1776, a group of men representing Great Britain's 13 North American colonies wrote one of history's most famous persuasive texts. In it, they <u>outlined the British king's exploitation of the Colonies and declared their freedom from the oppression of his rule.</u>

Seventy years later, another group made a similar declaration, this time <u>demanding women's equality and rights, including the right to vote.</u>

John Parrot/Stocktrek Images, after the painting by J.L.G. Ferris.

▲ Ben Franklin (left), John Adams, and Thomas Jefferson (standing) study a draft of the Declaration of Independence.

▲ Elizabeth Cady Stanton (seated) and Susan B. Anthony (standing) were leaders and partners in the fight for women's rights.

Key Vocabulary
- **exploitation** *n.*, selfish use of others for personal gain
- **oppression** *n.*, the act of preventing people from having equal rights

Interact with the Text

1. Declarations

Underline the statements in this introduction that tell you the purpose of each declaration. Then restate each purpose in your own words.

Possible response:

The Declaration of Independence—to explain how Britain's king had hurt the Colonies and announce that the Colonies were breaking way from his authority;

The Declaration of Sentiments—to require the government to treat women as equal to men and to grant women the vote.

2. Form Generalizations
Highlight the specific complaints listed in this excerpt from the Declaration of Independence. Then write a generalization about how the authors of this declaration felt about being ruled by Great Britain.

Possible response: The

authors felt that being

ruled by Great Britain

meant not being able

to create and live under

their own government

and laws.

3. Relate Arguments
Reread the final sentence in the introductory paragraph of each declaration. Circle the phrases in the Declaration of Sentiments that make the sentence different from the related sentence in the Declaration of Independence.

from THE DECLARATION OF INDEPENDENCE, 1776

…We hold these truths to be self-evident, that all men are created equal, that they are **endowed** by their Creator with certain **unalienable** Rights, that among these are Life, Liberty and the pursuit of Happiness.—That to secure these rights, Governments are instituted among Men, deriving their just powers from the **consent of** the governed, —That whenever any Form of Government becomes destructive of these ends, it is the Right of the People to alter or to **abolish** it, and to institute new Government, laying its foundation on such principles and organizing its powers in such form, as to them shall seem most likely to effect their Safety and Happiness.…—Such has been the patient sufferance of these Colonies; and such is now the necessity which constrains them to alter their former Systems of Government.

The history of the present King of Great Britain is a history of repeated injuries and **usurpations**, all having in direct object the establishment of **an absolute Tyranny** over these States. To prove this, let Facts be submitted to a candid world.…

—He has kept among us, in times of peace, Standing Armies without the Consent of our legislatures.…

—He has combined with others to subject us to a jurisdiction foreign to our constitution, and unacknowledged by our laws…

—For cutting off our Trade with all parts of the world…

—For depriving us in many cases, of the benefits of Trial by Jury…

—For taking away our Charters, abolishing our most valuable Laws, and altering fundamentally the Forms of our Governments…

We, therefore…solemnly publish and declare, That these United Colonies are, and of Right ought to be Free and Independent States…

In Other Words
endowed given
unalienable guaranteed
consent of agreement by
abolish end
usurpations takeovers
an absolute Tyranny complete power

Historical Background
The authors used a writing style typical of the 1700s, which included capitalizing important nouns. The Declaration contained the first formal statement by a whole people of their right to a government of their choosing.

from THE DECLARATION OF SENTIMENTS, 1848

...We hold these truths to be self-evident: that all men and women are created equal; that they are endowed by their Creator with certain inalienable rights; that among these are life, liberty, and the pursuit of happiness; that to secure these rights governments are instituted, deriving their just powers from the consent of the governed. Whenever any form of government becomes destructive of these ends, it is the right of those who suffer from it to refuse **allegiance** to it, and to insist upon the institution of a new government, laying its foundation on such principles, and organizing its powers in such form, as to them shall seem most likely to effect their safety and happiness....Such has been the patient sufferance of the women under this government, and such is now the necessity which constrains them to demand the equal station to which they are entitled.

The history of mankind is a history of repeated injuries and usurpations on the part of man toward woman, having in direct object the establishment of an absolute tyranny over her. To prove this, let facts be submitted to a candid world....

He has **compelled** her to submit to laws, in the formation of which she had no voice....

He has denied her the **facilities** for obtaining a thorough education, all colleges being closed against her....

He has endeavored, in every way that he could, to destroy her confidence in her own powers, to lessen her self-respect, and to make her willing to lead a dependent and **abject** life.

Now,...because women do feel themselves aggrieved, oppressed, and **fraudulently deprived of their most sacred** rights, we insist that they have immediate admission to all the rights and privileges which belong to them as citizens of the United States.... ❖

4. Relate Arguments
Compare the final sentence in the introductory paragraph of each declaration. How does the wording in the Declaration of Sentiments show a difference in the arguments?

Possible response:

The wording shows an

argument for a part of

the population. It also

argues for change.

5. Relate Arguments
Highlight the three specific "injuries and usurpations" in this declaration. How do they differ from the "injuries and usurpations" in the Declaration of Independence?

Possible response: Those

in this declaration relate to

the denial of opportunities

to women as individuals.

Those in the Declaration of

Independence relate to the

violation of existing laws

that govern all the people.

Key Vocabulary
- **distinction** *n.*, difference
  apathetic *adj.*, indifferent, uninterested

In Other Words
allegiance loyalty
compelled forced
facilities opportunities
abject horrible
**fraudulently deprived of
  their most sacred** without
  their most important

Historical Background
In 1848, the U.S. drew big **distinctions** between men and women, and many were **apathetic** about women's rights. Women's rights activists held a meeting in Seneca Falls, New York. There they signed the **Declaration of Sentiments**.

Selection Review We Hold These Truths

A. Write a generalization about one of these topics, based on the text of the appropriate declaration.

> **Topic 1:** American colonists' desire to create an independent nation
> **Topic 2:** American women's desire for equality under the law

Possible response: 1: The writers believed that Britain had abused its purpose as a government.

2: The writers believed that the United States was following the historical tradition of intimidating and oppressing women.

B. Answer the questions.

1. How does the organization of these declarations help you understand both arguments?

Possible response: Both declarations follow the same organization: an introduction that presents the right to protest; a listing of grievances; and an announcement of or call to action. This organization—basically, first stating a WHY and then stating a WHAT—is easy to follow and understand.

2. Do you agree with the viewpoints that these declarations express about changing existing governments?

Possible response: I agree that people who are oppressed should campaign for change.

I do not think, however, that breaking away from an existing government is always right.

Reflect and Assess

WRITING: Write About Literature

A. Plan your writing. List examples from the selections that show the use of techniques such as repetition and emotional reasons to support an argument. *Answers will vary.*

Nelson Mandela	The Declaration of Independence *and* The Declaration of Sentiments
"Never, never, and never again shall it be that this beautiful land will again experience the oppression of one by another."	"The history of the present King of Great Britain is a history of repeated injuries and usurpations, all having in direct object the establishment of an absolute Tryanny over these States." (the Declaration of Independence)

B. Share your opinion about a local or national issue that involves human rights, such as prisoner rights or immigrant rights. Write a letter to the editor of a newspaper. Use the techniques you listed in the chart to convince readers they should support your point of view.

Students should support their answers with examples from both selections.

_____

_____

_____

_____

_____

_____

_____

_____

_____

LITERARY ANALYSIS: Rhetorical Devices

A **rhetorical device** is a tool writers use to bring about an emotional response from the reader. **Parallelism** pairs words or phrases of equal importance and similar sound. **Repetition** repeats a concept, phrase, or word in order to emphasize it. **Alliteration** is the repetition of consonant sounds in two or more words in the same sentence.

A. Read the examples of rhetorical devices in the chart. Then write which type of rhetorical device each example illustrates.

Example from "Long Walk to Freedom"	Rhetorical Device
"It was during those long and lonely years that my hunger for the freedom of my own people became a hunger for the freedom of all people, white and black."	alliteration
"Freedom is indivisible; the chains on any one of my people were the chains on all of them, the chains on all of my people were the chains on me."	repetition
"In life, every man has twin obligations—obligations to his family, to his parents, to his wife and children; and he has an obligation to his people, his community, his country."	parallelism

B. Write example sentences about your own life for each rhetorical device. *Answers will vary.*

1. _____

2. _____

3. _____

C. Use one of the rhetorical devices above to make a point about something that matters to you. Write your point in the form of dialogue. Think about the emotional response you want from readers.

Answers will vary.

_____

_____

_____

_____

_____

_____

_____

_____

VOCABULARY STUDY: Denotation and Connotation

Denotations are words' direct meanings. **Connotations** are the feelings that words convey. Words can have the same denotation but very different connotations.

A. Use a dictionary to write the denotation of each word in the chart below. Then write a synonym with a different connotation. Use a thesaurus if necessary. *Answers will vary. Possible responses are shown.*

Key Word	Denotation	Synonym
achievement	accomplishment	conquest
glorious	magnificent	great
outlaws	criminals	bandits
privilege	honor	birthright

B. Imagine that you borrowed your aunt's car and got into a minor accident. The body of the car is not badly damaged, but you do not want her to be angry with you. List words that might describe damage to a car. Make sure the words have different connotations.

Positive Words	
1. nick	**4.** dent
2. scratch	**5.** chip
3. ding	**6.** break

C. Write an e-mail to your aunt to tell her about the damage. Use words from the list in Activity B.

Dear Aunt,

I'm fine, but I have news about your car. *Answers will vary.*

_____

_____

_____

_____

_____

_____

_____

Read for Understanding

1. Genre What kind of text is this passage? How do you know?

It is a speech, as seen in

the use of direct address.

2. Topic Write a topic sentence to tell what the text is mostly about.

The text mostly tells about

celebrating the Fourth of

July and how the holiday

is an offense to enslaved

African Americans.

Reread and Summarize

3. Key Ideas Circle three words or phrases that best express the key ideas in each section. Note why each word or phrase is important in the section.

· Section 1: paragraphs 1–8
· Section 2: paragraphs 9–15

4. Summary Use your topic sentence and notes from item 3 to write a summary of the selection.

Possible response:

Douglass says that

enslaved African

Americans see the

Fourth of July as a grim

reminder of the injustice

that keeps them in

chains. He hopes that

slavery will soon end.

FROM

What to the Slave Is the Fourth of July?

by Frederick Douglass
JULY 5, 1852

Frederick Douglass (1818–1895). Photograph ©Bettmann/CORBIS.

1 **M**r. President, Friends and Fellow Citizens:

2 The papers and placards say that I am to deliver a Fourth [of] July oration. . . .

3 The fact is, ladies and gentlemen, the distance between this platform and the slave plantation, from which I escaped, is considerable—and the difficulties to be overcome in getting from **the latter to the former**, are by no means slight. . . .

4 So, fellow-citizens, pardon me, allow me to ask, why am I called upon to speak here to-day? What have I, or those I represent, to do with your national independence? Are the great principles of political freedom and of natural justice, embodied in that Declaration of Independence, extended to us? And am I, therefore, called upon to bring our humble offering to the national altar, and to confess the benefits and express **devout** gratitude for the blessings resulting from your independence to us?

5 Would to God, both for your sakes and ours, that an affirmative answer could be truthfully returned to these questions! Then would my task be light, and my burden easy and delightful. . . .

In Other Words
the latter to the former the slave plantation to the platform
devout sincere

Historical Background
Frederick Douglass was one of the most important human rights leaders of the 1800s. A former slave, Douglass wrote and spoke powerfully for the liberation of enslaved people, for women's rights, and for equal rights for all people.

6   But, such is not the state of the case. I say it with a sad sense of the disparity between us. I am not included within the **pale** of this glorious anniversary! Your high independence only reveals the immeasurable distance between us. The blessings in which you, this day, rejoice, are not enjoyed in common. The rich inheritance of justice, liberty, prosperity and independence, **bequeathed** by your fathers, is shared by you, not by me. The sunlight that brought life and healing to you, has brought stripes and death to me. This Fourth [of] July is yours, not mine. You may rejoice, I must mourn. To drag a man in **fetters** into the grand illuminated temple of liberty, and call upon him to join you in joyous anthems, **were inhuman mockery** and sacrilegious irony. Do you mean, citizens, to mock me, by asking me to speak to-day? . . .

7   Fellow-citizens, above your national, tumultuous joy, I hear the **mournful wail** of millions! Whose chains, heavy and grievous yesterday, are, to-day, rendered more intolerable by the **jubilee** shouts that reach them. If I do forget, if I do not faithfully remember those bleeding children of sorrow this day, "may my right hand forget her cunning, and may my tongue cleave to the roof of my mouth!" To forget them, to pass lightly over their wrongs, and to chime in with the popular theme, would be **treason** most scandalous and shocking, and would make me a **reproach** before God and the world. My subject, then, fellow-citizens, is American slavery. I shall see this day and its popular characteristics from the slave's point of view. Standing there identified with the American **bondman**, making his wrongs mine, I do not hesitate to declare, with all my soul, that the character and conduct of this nation never looked blacker to me than on this Fourth of July! . . .

8   But I **fancy** I hear some one of my audience say, "It is just in this circumstance that you and **your brother abolitionists** fail to make a favorable impression on the public mind. Would you argue more, and denounce less; would you persuade more, and rebuke less; your cause would be much more likely to succeed." But, I submit, where all is plain there is nothing to be argued. . . .

In Other Words

pale light	**treason** disloyalty
bequeathed given	**reproach** disgrace
fetters chains	**bondman** slave
were inhuman mockery is cruel teasing	**fancy** think
mournful wail sad cry	**your brother abolitionists** others who wish
jubilee joyful	to free enslaved people

5. Claim Reread paragraphs 1–8. What claim does Douglass make? Write his claim in your own words.

Possible response:

Celebrating the Fourth

of July mocks the

Americans who live in

slavery.

Circle the two paragraphs that introduce the specific claim.

6. Emotive Language Reread paragraphs 6 and 7. Underline statements that contrast the audience with the slaves.

7. Evaluate Argument How well does the author's use of contrast develop his argument?

Possible response: The

contrasting statements

and images are effective

in helping Douglass

make it clear that his

audience is intentionally

blind to the issue of

slavery.

8. Counterclaim Put a box around Douglass's counterclaim in paragraph 8. Think about how he refutes it in the following text.

9. Argument Go back to page 266 and highlight the name of the historical document that Douglass refers to. Then highlight details in paragraphs 9–11 that appear to be references to the text of that document.

10. Allusion Discuss and write about ways in which Douglass's argument relates to earlier arguments in the Declaration of Independence about freedom and human rights.

Responses should

recognize that both

arguments speak of

natural and God-given

rights to freedom.

Furthermore, Douglass's

list of ways in which

slaves have been

mistreated (paragraph

10) is similar to

the Declaration of

Independence's list of

"repeated injuries and

usurpations."

9   Would you have me argue that man is entitled to liberty? That he is the rightful owner of his own body? You have already declared it. Must I argue the wrongfulness of slavery? Is that a question for Republicans? Is it to be settled by the rules of logic and argumentation, as a matter **beset with** great difficulty, involving a doubtful application of the principle of justice, hard to be understood? How should I look to-day, in the presence of Americans, dividing and subdividing **a discourse**, to show that men have a natural right to freedom? Speaking of it relatively, and positively, negatively, and affirmatively. To do so, would be to make myself ridiculous, and to offer an insult to your understanding. There is not a man beneath the canopy of heaven, that does not know that slavery is wrong *for him*.

10   What, am I to argue that it is wrong to make men **brutes**, to rob them of their liberty, to work them without wages, to keep them **ignorant** of their relations to their fellow men, to beat them with sticks, to flay their flesh with the lash, to load their limbs with irons, to hunt them with dogs, to sell them at auction, to **sunder** their families, to knock out their teeth, to burn their flesh, to starve them into obedience and submission to their masters? Must I argue that a system thus marked with blood, and stained with pollution, is *wrong*? No! I will not. I have better employments for my time and strength than such arguments would imply.

11   What, then, remains to be argued? Is it that slavery is not divine; that God did not establish it; that our doctors of divinity are mistaken? There is **blasphemy** in the thought. That which is inhuman, cannot be **divine**! *Who* can reason on such a proposition? They that can, may; I cannot. The time for such argument is past.

12   At a time like this, **scorching irony**, not convincing argument, is needed. . . .

> **What, then, remains to be argued?**

13   What, to the American slave, is your Fourth of July? I answer: a day that reveals to him, more than all other days in the year, the gross injustice and cruelty to which he is the constant victim. To him, your celebration is a **sham**; your boasted liberty, an unholy license; your national greatness, swelling **vanity**; your sounds of rejoicing are empty and heartless; your

In Other Words
beset with of
a discourse an argument
brutes animals
ignorant unaware
sunder separate
blasphemy wickedness

divine godlike
scorching irony angry words
sham fake
vanity pride

denunciations of tyrants, **brass fronted impudence**; your shouts of liberty and equality, <u>hollow mockery</u>; your prayers and hymns, your sermons and thanksgivings, with all your religious parade and solemnity are, to him, <u>mere bombast, fraud, deception, impiety, and hypocrisy—a thin veil to cover up crimes which would disgrace a nation of savages.</u> There is not a nation on the earth <u>guilty of practices more shocking and bloody</u> than are the people of these United States, at this very hour. . . .

14   Allow me to say, in conclusion, notwithstanding the dark picture I have this day presented of the state of the nation, I do not **despair of** this country. There are forces in operation which must inevitably work the downfall of slavery. "The arm of the Lord is not shortened," and the doom of slavery is certain. I, therefore, leave off where I began, with hope. While drawing encouragement from <u>the Declaration of Independence</u>, the great principles it contains, and the genius of American Institutions, my spirit is also cheered by the obvious tendencies of the age. Nations do not now stand in the same relation to each other that they did ages ago. No nation can now shut itself up from the surrounding world, and trot round in the same old path of its fathers without interference. . . . No abuse, no outrage whether in taste, sport, or **avarice**, can now hide itself from the **all-pervading light**. . . . ❖

▶ **Critical Viewing: Effect** What effect does a life-size sculpture have that a painting does not?

Frederick Douglass statue, Harlem, New York City, Randy Duchaine. Photograph ©Randy Duchaine/Alamy.

In Other Words
denunciations criticisms
brass fronted impudence showy confidence
despair of lose hope in
avarice greed
all-pervading light light that is everywhere

Reread and Analyze

▼ **11. Argument** Reread paragraphs 13 and 14. Underline five emotion-filled phrases. Also underline another reference to a historical document. Explain how Douglass develops his argument in these paragraphs.

Possible response:

Douglass again chooses

words with negative

connotations to make

his opinon of slavery

clear. His reference

to the Declaration of

Independence expresses

hope that things can

change and connects his

argument about slavery

to his listeners' feelings

of patriotism.

12. Conclusion Circle the sentences in paragraph 14 that express a call to action. Discuss and write about the action and what Douglass says will make it happen.

Possible response:

Douglass indicates that

pressure from other

nations and the work of

God will move the United

States to end slavery.

Discuss

13. **Synthesize** With the class, revisit this speech. Discuss the author's
word choices, his reference to an authoritative text, and the impact that
they are intended to have upon the audience. *Answers will vary. Possible responses are shown.*

Word Choice	Reference to an Authoritative Text	Impact Upon the Audience
stripes and death (paragraph 4)	entitled to liberty, natural right to freedom, liberty and equality	makes listeners feel the horror of life as a slave

Then, with the class, discuss how the author uses word choices and
allusion to encourage his audience to accept his ideas. Make notes.

Answers will vary but should recognize the impact of word connotations and literary allusions. Douglass's

word choices create powerful mental images and arouse strong emotions to help his audience better grasp

the wrongs of slavery. His few words that allude to the Declaration of Independence pass on extra authority

to what he is saying.

14. **Write** Use your notes from question 13 to write about how the author
develops his argument so that his audience will be persuaded about
the need to end slavery. Use the questions below to organize your
thoughts.

> · Analyze the author's argument: What is Douglass's central idea?
>
> · Analyze the author's word choices: Why does Douglass choose certain words to
>   describe the celebration and the lives of slaves?
>
> · Analyze the author's relating of ideas: What is the purpose of the references to the
>   Declaration of Independence?
>
> · Evaluate the author's effectiveness: How well does this speech express Douglass's
>   ideas? How persuasive is it?

Answers will vary but should show how students have carried forward their thinking from item 13.

_____

_____

_____

_____

_____

_____

_____

Connect with the **EQ** How Can We Balance Everyone's Rights?

Explore the struggle for human rights in the United States.

15. Viewpoint Think about the time in American history during which Douglass gave this speech. What do you think was his audience's viewpoint regarding human rights? What do you think his listeners believed about their responsibilities to others? How do you know?

Answers will vary. Responses should include evidence from the text.

_____

_____

_____

_____

_____

16. Theme What is the author's message about the balance between rights and responsibilities?

Answers will vary. Responses should include evidence from the text.

_____

_____

_____

_____

_____

Key Vocabulary Review

A. Read each sentence. Circle the word that best fits into each sentence.

1. You can (**liberate** /(**facilitate**)) a party by sending invitations.

2. Receiving a speeding ticket is one possible ((**repercussion**)/ **precaution**) of driving too fast.

3. Someone with an ((**inclination**)/ **emancipation**) for the outdoors likes to hike and go camping.

4. Becoming friends with people to get them to do your homework is an act of (**oppression** /(**exploitation**)).

5. You need a key to (**violate** /(**access**)) the contents of the locked cupboard.

6. Tadpoles (**restrict** /(**transform**)) into frogs.

7. Opening a door without knocking is an act of (**impact** /(**intrusion**)).

8. Eating dessert after every meal is ((**excessive**)/ **motivated**).

B. Use your own words to write what each Key Vocabulary word means. Then write a synonym and an antonym for each word. *Answers will vary. Possible responses are shown.*

Key Word	My Definition	Synonym	Antonym
1. **counterfeit**	not real; forged	fake	genuine
2. **distinction**	a distinguished difference	contrast	similarity
3. **emancipation**	the act of giving someone or something freedom	freedom	enslavement
4. **fundamental**	basic or deep-rooted	essential	minor
5. **liberate**	to set free	free	imprison
6. **merit**	someone or something's value	worth	inferiority
7. **proficiency**	ability or adeptness	skillfulness	inability
8. **violate**	to disregard	break	follow

Unit 6 Key Vocabulary

• access	• distinction	• facilitate	intrusion	oppression	• restrict
apathetic	emancipation	• fundamental	liberate	precaution	• transform
• consistently	excessive	• impact	merit	proficiency	verify
• counterfeit	• exploitation	inclination	• motivated	repercussion	• violate

• **Academic Vocabulary**

C. Answer the questions using complete sentences. *Answers will vary. Possible responses are shown.*

1. What **precaution** might you take if you need to get up early?

   I would set my alarm clock.

2. How can you show someone that you are **motivated**?

   You can work hard and take on more responsibility.

3. Describe an issue that you are not **apathetic** about.

   I feel very strongly about human rights issues.

4. Who has had the greatest **impact** on your life? Why?

   My father has had the greatest impact on me because he has always been supportive of my goals.

5. Describe one way you can **verify** the meaning of a word.

   You can verify the meaning of a word by looking it up in the dictionary.

6. How would you feel if someone tried to **restrict** your freedom?

   I would feel angry about that restriction, unless it was meant to keep me safe.

7. Name one historical example of **oppression**.

   One historical example of oppression is apartheid in South Africa.

8. Explain why laws should be applied **consistently** to all citizens.

   Laws should be applied consistently to all citizens because people should be treated equally.

Prepare to Read

▶ The Jewels of the Shrine
▶ Remembered

Key Vocabulary

A. How well do you know these words? Circle a rating for each word. Check your understanding of each word by circling *yes* or *no*. Then complete the sentences. If you are unsure of a word's meaning, refer to the Vocabulary Glossary, page 926, in your student text.

Rating Scale	
1	I have never seen this word before.
2	I am not sure of the word's meaning.
3	I know this word and can teach the word's meaning to someone else.

Key Word	Check Your Understanding	Deepen Your Understanding
❶ compensate (**kahm**-pun-sāt) *verb* Rating: 1 2 3	To pay people for their work is to **compensate** them. (**Yes**) No	My parents compensate me when *Possible response:* I mow the lawn _____ _____ _____ .
❷ destitute (**des**-tah-tüt) *adjective* Rating: 1 2 3	A **destitute** person might own a large house and fancy cars. Yes (**No**)	A destitute person cannot *Possible response:* buy food and clothes _____ _____ _____ .
❸ impudently (**im**-pyu-dunt-lē) *adverb* Rating: 1 2 3	If you behave **impudently** toward people, you show them respect. Yes (**No**)	A student would act impudently if she *Possible* *response:* made fun of her teacher _____ _____ _____ .
❹ infuriate (in-**fyur**-ē-āt) *verb* Rating: 1 2 3	You might **infuriate** your best friend if you lie to him or her. (**Yes**) No	It is easy to infuriate *Possible response:* my little brother when I beat him at games _____ _____ _____ .

Key Word	Check Your Understanding	Deepen Your Understanding
5 **prophecy** (**prah**-fu-sē) *noun* **Rating:** 1 2 3	Everybody believes that a **prophecy** will come true. **Yes** (**No**)	One prophecy that I have heard is *Possible response:* <u>the world will end on a certain date</u> _____ _____ _____ .
6 **respectably** (ri-**spek**-tah-blē) *adverb* **Rating:** 1 2 3	People who behave **respectably** at a play might talk loudly to each other in the audience. **Yes** (**No**)	I like to act respectably at *Possible response:* <u>weddings and family celebrations</u> _____ _____ _____ .
7 **traditional** (tru-**di**-shu-nul) *adjective* **Rating:** 1 2 3	A **traditional** dance is one that has just been created. **Yes** (**No**)	A traditional event I celebrate with my family is _____ *Possible response:* our holiday dinner _____ _____ _____ .

B. Use one of the Key Vocabulary words to write about how you show respect to someone you care about.

Answers will vary. _____

_____

_____

Before Reading The Jewels of the Shrine

LITERARY ANALYSIS: Analyze Structure: Script

A writer chooses dramatic elements and presents them in a **script**, or the text of a play. **Acts** are divided into **scenes**. **Stage directions** give instructions. A **cast of characters** provides the characters' names and descriptions. **Dialogue**, or conversation, provides information about characters and conflicts.

A. Read the passage below. Write examples of dramatic elements in the chart. The first one has been done for you.

> ### Look Into the Text
>
> **Scene I.** *The furniture consists of a wide bamboo bed, on which is spread a mat; a wooden chair; a low table; and a few odds and ends.* OKORIE, *an old man, is sitting at the edge of the bed. . . . On the wooden chair near the bed sits a* STRANGER, *a man of about forty-five years of age. It is evening.*
>
> **OKORIE.** I need help, Stranger, for although I have two grandsons, I am lonely and unhappy because they do not care for me. . . .
>
> [*Exit* STRANGER. BASSI, *a beautiful woman of about thirty years, enters.*]

Dramatic Element	Example
Scene	In the evening in OKorie's bedroom
Stage directions	OKORIE, an old man, is sitting at the edge of the bed; near the bed sits a STRANGER. Exit STRANGER. BASSI enters.
Characters	OKORIE, STRANGER, BASSI
Dialogue	"I need help, Stranger, for although I have two grandsons, I am lonely and unhappy because they do not care for me. . . ."

B. Complete the sentence about dramatic elements.

The dramatic elements in this passage reveal that Okorie is   *Possible response:* an old man who is
unhappy because his grandsons do not take care of him. He asks a stranger to help him.

FOCUS STRATEGY: Identify Emotional Responses

HOW TO IDENTIFY EMOTIONAL RESPONSES

1. **Take notes** on the dialogue and stage directions that help you re-create the scene.

2. **Describe** what you "see" and "hear" in your mind.

3. **Combine the mental images** with your personal experience to identify how you feel.

A. Read the scene from the play. Use the strategies above to identify emotional responses as you read. Complete the chart below.

Look Into the Text

> **OKORIE.** [*calling from offstage*] Bassi! Bassi! Where is that woman?
>
> **OJIMA.** The old man is coming. Let us hide ourselves. [*Both rush under the bed.*]
>
> **OKORIE.** [*comes in, limping on his stick as usual*] Bassi, where are you? Haven't I told that girl never—
>
> **BASSI.** [*entering*] Don't shout so. It's not good for you.
>
> **OKORIE.** Where are the two people?
>
> **BASSI.** You mean your grandsons? They are not here. They must have gone into their room.
>
> **OKORIE.** Bassi, I have a secret for you. [*He narrows his eyes.*] A big secret. [*His hands tremble.*] Can you keep a secret?

Words or Phrases	I Visualize	I Feel
"Both rush under the bed."	two grandsons hiding under the bed	I feel a little angry. I don't trust the grandsons.
"He narrows his eyes." "His hands tremble."	an excited old man who can't wait to share his secret	I wonder what the old man's secret is.

B. How does using the strategies help you to identify your emotional response to this scene?

Possible response: The strategies help me visualize what is happening. Visualizing helps me think about how I would feel in this situation.

Selection Review The Jewels of the Shrine

 What Deserves Our Care and Respect?
See how people show what they respect.

A. In "The Jewels of the Shrine," Okorie teaches his grandsons a lesson about respect. Complete the Main-Idea Diagram with examples of dialogue that support the play's main message.

Main-Idea Diagram

> **Main Message:**
> Young people should respect their elders and not expect something in return.
>
> > **Dialogue:** OJIMA. If we can only get the jewels, we can go and live in town and let the old man manage as he can.
> >
> > **Dialogue:** OKORIE. My grandsons, they thought I would die in disgrace . . . But those wicked children must change, or when I die, I shall not leave a penny for them.
> >
> > **Dialogue:** OJIMA. Well, he is now a rich man, and we must treat him with care. AROB. We have no choice. He says that unless we change, he will not leave a penny to us.
> >
> > **Dialogue:** OKORIE. These are my wishes. Make my burial the best you can. Spend as much as is required, for you will be compensated.
> >
> > **Dialogue:** OKORIE . . . Shame on you, young men, who believe that because you can read and write, you need not respect old age . . .

B. Use the information in the chart to answer the questions.

1. What does the dialogue reveal about the plot and characters? How does this information help you understand the play's message?

Possible response: The dialogue reveals the characters' feelings and how they are lying to each other to get what they want. It helps me understand how Okorie views respect and tradition.

2. Do the grandsons deserve to be compensated when their grandfather dies? Use **compensate** in your answer.

Possible response: No, because they are selfish. The grandsons change their attitudes only when they think they are going to be compensated with jewels.

3. Do you agree with Okorie's actions? Why or why not?

Possible response: No, I would not trick someone just to get respect. I want people to respect me because I deserve it. People don't deserve respect if they lie.

Connect Across Texts
In "The Jewels of the Shrine," an old man worries that his wishes have been forgotten. In this poem, a man hopes to be remembered.

Remembered
by Naomi Shihab Nye

Creative Lifeline, 2005, Laura Lein-Svencner. Assemblage, collection of the artist.

▲ **Critical Viewing: Design** What kind of person might have such objects? Does this assemblage, or grouping of objects, seem like art to you? Why or why not?

1. Interpret

Look at the assemblage on page 279. Why are objects important to people?

Possible response:

Objects represent the

people who gave them

to us or the places

where we have found

them. They remind us of

the past.

2. Identify Emotional Responses

What do you think the poet wants you to feel? Explain.

Possible response: The

poet wants me to feel

respect for the man

because he treated

everything with respect.

3. Word Choice

Circle a phrase in the third stanza that uses words in an unconventional way. What images do the words create?

Possible response: The

words create an image

of a fire that sounds like

music. It is a comforting

image.

He wanted to be remembered so he gave people things
they would remember him by. A large trunk, handmade of
ash and cedar. A tool box with initials shaped of scraps.
A tea kettle that would sing every morning,
5 antique glass jars to fill with crackers, noodles, beans.
A whole family of jams he made himself from the figs and berries
that purpled his land.

He gave these things unexpectedly. You went to see him
and came home loaded. You said "Thank you" till your lips
10 grew heavy with gratitude and swelled shut.
Walking with him across the acres of piney forest,
you noticed the way he talked to everything, a puddle, a stump,
the same way he talked to you.
"I declare you do look purty sittin' there in that field
15 reflectin' the light like some kind of mirror, you know what?"
As if objects could listen.
As if earth had a memory too.

At night we propped our feet by the fireplace
and laughed and showed photographs and the fire remembered
20 all the crackling music it knew. The night remembered
how to be dark and the forest remembered how to be mysterious
and in bed, the quilts remembered how to tuck up under our chins.
Sleeping in that house was like falling down a deep well,
rocking in a bucket all night long.

In Other Words

A whole family Different kinds
loaded carrying a lot of gifts

25   In the mornings we'd stagger away from an unforgettable breakfast

of biscuits—he'd lead us into the next room

ready to show us something or curl another story into our ear.

He scrawled the episodes out in elaborate longhand

and gave them to a farmer's wife to type.

30   Stories about a little boy and a grandfather,

chickens and prayer tents, butter beans and lightning.

He was the little boy.

Some days his brain could travel backwards easier than it could

sit in a chair, right there.

35   When we left he'd say "Don't forget me! You won't forget me now,

will you?" as if our remembering could lengthen his life.

I wanted to assure him, there will always be a cabin in our blood

only you live in. But the need for remembrance silenced me,

a ringing rising up out of the soil's centuries, the ones

40   who plowed this land, whose names we do not know.

In Other Words

stagger away walk slowly, feeling full

could travel backwards would remember things

cabin in our blood place in our memory

plowed farmed

4. Identify Emotional Responses

Highlight the words and phrases that show what the man does to be remembered. What does the poet want you to feel about the man?

Possible response: The poet wants the reader to feel sympathy for the man's need to be remembered and loved.

5. Word Choice

Circle the phrases that show what stories the man told. What do you picture?

Possible response: I see the old man as a little boy and growing up on a farm. The chosen details create an image of a simple but happy childhood.

6. Interpret

Reread the poem. Then describe the man in your own words.

Possible response: The man is kind, generous, and respectful.

Selection Review Remembered

A. Read the excerpts from the text. Choose one and complete the chart below. *Answers will vary. Possible responses are shown.*

Excerpt 1: Sleeping in that house was like falling down a deep well, / rocking in a bucket all night long.

Excerpt 2: At night we propped our feet by the fireplace / and laughed and showed photographs and the fire remembered . . .

What do you visualize?	What words and phrases help you visualize?	What do you feel? What does the poet want you to feel?	Does the poet succeed? Why or why not?
Excerpt __1__ I visualize a dark, narrow house that lulls me to sleep.	deep well, rocking in a bucket	I feel comforted, like a baby. The poet wants me to feel calm.	Yes. I can understand how a place I loved might make me feel calm.

B. Answer the questions.

1. How does the poet's imagery help you understand the poem? Support your answer by listing one example from the poem for each sense.

I am able to picture and feel what the speaker experienced.

_____

a. I saw: _a tool box with initials shaped of scraps_

b. I heard: _a tea kettle that sings_

c. I smelled: _a piney forest_

d. I tasted: _an unforgettable breakfast of biscuits_

e. I felt: _quilts under my chin_

2. Explain what you think the speaker cares about and respects most in life. How do you know?

The speaker cares about the older people in her life. She respects memories and thinks they are important. The objects she talks about are representations of the memories she has about the old man.

_____

Reflect and Assess

WRITING: Write About Literature

A. Plan your writing. Find examples from both texts that illustrate the saying "actions speak louder than words." *Answers will vary.*

The Jewels of the Shrine	Remembered
Okorie's grandsons do not take care of him until they discover he is rich.	The man gives people gifts so they will remember him.

B. How does the saying apply to the two selections? Write an analysis in a paragraph. Support it with examples from both texts.

Students should support their answers with examples from both texts.

_____

_____

_____

_____

_____

_____

_____

_____

_____

_____

_____

LITERARY ANALYSIS: Dialogue, Character Traits, and Character Foils

Dialogue is conversation between two or more characters. You learn the characters' traits by what they say.

A **character foil** is a character whose traits contrast with those of the main character. A character foil is a static character, which means he or she does not change during the story. *Answers will vary. Possible responses are shown.*

A. Read Okorie's dialogue in the chart below. Then write what the dialogue tells you about Okorie.

Okorie's Dialogue	Okorie's Traits
"Farewell, Stranger. If you call again and I am alive, I will welcome you back."	welcoming and friendly
"You know, woman, when I worshipped at our forefathers' shrine, I was happy."	respectful of tradition
"Woman, I cannot eat. When happiness fills your heart, you cannot eat."	joyful

B. Answer the questions below.

1. Which character is a foil to Okorie? Why?

Arob; he never changes, and his traits contrast with Okorie's traits.

2. What are the traits of this character foil? Give two examples of dialogue that support your answer.

He is rude, disrespectful, and bitter. Arob says, "The old cheat! He cheated us to the last. To think that I scratched his back only to be treated like this!" and "The old fogy is asleep."

3. How do the traits of the character foil help you understand Okorie?

I understand Okorie better because Arob's disrespectful comments make Okorie seem even more respectful. The contrast makes each trait stand out.

C. Imagine that you are writing a play about yourself. Describe your traits and write a line of dialogue. Then describe the traits of the character foil and give an example of his or her dialogue.

1. My traits: I am quiet, timid, and afraid to try new things.

Dialogue: "Do we have to keep walking? Let's just sit and enjoy the sun."

2. Character foil traits: The character foil is loud, bold, and curious.

Dialogue: "Stop walking so slowly. Look! Footprints! Let's follow them!"

VOCABULARY STUDY: Idioms

Idioms are common phrases or expressions that do not have a literal meaning. Writers use idioms in dialogue to make characters more realistic or to express a character's personality. *Answers will vary. Possible responses are shown.*

A. In the chart below are some common idioms. Determine what each underlined idiom means and write the meaning in the chart below.

Idiom	Meaning
I was nervous about singing in front of the entire school, but Allison was <u>cool as a cucumber.</u>	not nervous
Jim wants to <u>take a crack at</u> the most difficult jigsaw puzzle we have.	try to do something
It's time to <u>cut to the chase</u>, because I'm leaving in five minutes.	get to the point
I'm going to go <u>out on a limb</u> and suggest that we change the way we work.	take a risk

B. Underline the idioms in the sentences below. Rewrite each sentence with the intended meaning.

1. We have <u>a lot of ground to cover</u> before Tuesday, so let's get started on the project right now.

We have a lot of material to complete before Tuesday, so let's get started on the project right now.

_____

2. Will you please <u>hold your tongue</u> while I make my own decision?

Will you please be quiet while I make my own decision?

_____

C. Read each idiom and its meaning below. Then write a sentence using the idiom.

1. Idiom: break a leg
Meaning: good luck

Break a leg tonight at the choir concert!

_____

2. Idiom: take a seat
Meaning: sit down

Once you enter the room, take a seat next to the window.

_____

Prepare to Read

▶ **Romeo and Juliet**
▶ **West Side Story**

Key Vocabulary

A. How well do you know these words? Circle a rating for each word. Check your understanding by circling the correct synonym or antonym. Then write a definition in your own words. If you are unsure of a word's meaning, refer to the Vocabulary Glossary, page 926, in your student text.

	Rating Scale
1	I have never seen this word before.
2	I am not sure of the word's meaning.
3	I know this word and can teach the word's meaning to someone else.

Key Word	Check Your Understanding	Deepen Your Understanding
❶ attitude (**a**-tu-tüd) *noun* **Rating:** 1 2 3	Someone who has an upbeat **attitude** has an optimistic _____ on life. (**outlook**) story	My definition: *Answers will vary.*
❷ dense (**dens**) *adjective* **Rating:** 1 2 3	The opposite of **dense** is _____. crowded (**sparse**)	My definition: *Answers will vary.*
❸ envious (**en**-vē-us) *adjective* **Rating:** 1 2 3	If you are **envious** of someone, you are _____ of him or her. (**jealous**) proud	My definition: *Answers will vary.*
❹ feud (**fyūd**) *noun* **Rating:** 1 2 3	If two people are having a **feud**, they are in a _____. (**battle**) friendship	My definition: *Answers will vary.*

Key Word	Check Your Understanding	Deepen Your Understanding
5 **fractured** (**frak**-churd) *adjective* **Rating:** 1 2 3	When something is **fractured**, it is _____. whole (**broken**)	My definition: *Answers will vary.*
6 **mature** (mu-**choor**) *adjective* **Rating:** 1 2 3	The opposite of **mature** is _____. (**childish**) grown-up	My definition: *Answers will vary.*
7 **perfection** (pur-**fek**-shun) *noun* **Rating:** 1 2 3	The opposite of **perfection** is _____. (**fault**) flawlessness	My definition: *Answers will vary.*
8 **resolution** (re-zu-**lü**-shun) *noun* **Rating:** 1 2 3	If you make a **resolution**, you make a _____. bet (**promise**)	My definition: *Answers will vary.*

B. Use one of the Key Vocabulary words to write about someone you love.

Answers will vary.

_____

_____

LITERARY ANALYSIS: Analyze Structure: Blank Verse

Blank verse is unrhymed poetry. Shakespeare and other sixteenth-century playwrights used blank verse to show that a character was of high rank.

In blank verse, every line has ten syllables and five stressed beats. Every second syllable is stressed. This **meter** is called iambic pentameter. Read the example aloud to hear the stress and rhythm.

> Example: See **how** she **leans** her **cheek** up**on** her **hand**?
>   **1**   **2**   **3**   **4**   **5**

Remember that in blank verse, an idea can continue past the end of the line.

A. Read the passage below aloud. Look for the imagery, stress and rhythm as you read. Then answer the questions.

> ### Look Into the Text
>
> *Capulet's orchard. Enter* Romeo.
> **ROMEO.** He jests at scars that never felt a wound.
>   1   2   3   4   5
> But soft, what light through yonder window breaks?
> It is the East, and Juliet is the sun.
> Arise, fair sun, and kill the envious moon,
> Who is already sick and pale with grief
> That thou, her maid, art far more fair than she.

B. Return to the passage above. Choose a line and number the stressed syllables. Then read the line aloud to confirm that you marked the stress and rhythm correctly.

1. When read aloud, what do these lines sound like?

Possible response: The lines sound like music. The lines have a very rhythmic beat, like a song.

2. Why does Romeo compare Juliet to the sun?

Possible response: He thinks she is bright and beautiful like the sun. It is becoming daylight, so he says that the moon is jealous of Juliet's beauty, or brightness.

FOCUS STRATEGY: Form Mental Images

HOW TO FORM MENTAL IMAGES

1. Look for Clues Picture the details and descriptions that appeal to your senses.

2. Draw What You See Make a sketch of how you visualize the scene.

A. Read the passage. Use the strategies above to form mental images as you read. Then answer the questions below.

Look Into the Text

JULIET. My (ears have yet not drunk) a hundred (words)
   Of thy tongue's uttering, yet I know the sound.
   Art thou not Romeo, and a Montague?

ROMEO. Neither, fair maid, if either thee dislike.

JULIET. How cam'st thou hither, tell me, and wherefore?
   The (orchard walls are high) and (hard to climb,)
   And the place death, considering who thou art,
   If any of my kinsmen find thee here.

ROMEO. With (love's light wings) did I (o'erperch these walls,)
   For (stony limits) cannot hold love out,
   And what love can do, that dares love attempt.
   Therefore thy (kinsmen are no stop to me.)

---

1. What do you visualize when you read Juliet's lines?

   Possible response: I visualize Juliet leaning over to get closer to Romeo, and Romeo whispering in her ear.

   I also visualize a tall cement wall in a grove of trees.

2. What do you picture when you read Romeo's lines?

   Possible response: I picture someone with wings soaring over a wall made of stones. He is brave and ready

   to battle anyone who tries to stop him.

B. Return to the passage above. Circle the words and phrases that helped you answer the questions.

Selection Review Romeo and Juliet

EQ **What Deserves Our Care and Respect?**
Consider love's importance to people.

A. In "Romeo and Juliet," two young lovers take great risks to be together. Complete the chart with examples of dialogue that help you understand each character.

Character	What the Character Says	What This Reveals About the Character
Romeo	*"Call me but love, and I'll be new baptized. / Henceforth I never will be Romeo."*	Romeo is willing to give up his family to be with Juliet.
	"Alack, there lies more peril in thine eye / Than twenty of their swords."	Romeo is willing to risk violence for the chance to speak to Juliet.
Juliet	"Or, if thou wilt not, be but sworn my love, / And I'll no longer be a Capulet."	Juliet will give up her family to be with Romeo.
	"I would not for the world they saw thee here."	Juliet would protect Romeo and risk her family's rejection.

B. Use the information in the chart to answer the questions.

1. What does the dialogue reveal about Romeo and Juliet? How important do you think love is to them?

Possible response: The dialogue reveals that they will give up their families and risk death to be together. To them, love is more important than their families or their lives.

2. How does the feud between Romeo and Juliet's families influence the characters' actions? Use **feud** in your answer.

Possible response: The feud makes Juliet fear for Romeo's safety. Romeo has to visit her in secret, during the night, so no one will know of their love for each other.

3. How is love important in your life? What does love mean to you? Explain.

Possible response: Love is important to me because the people who love me give me support and encouragement. To me, love means generosity, kindness, and support.

West Side Story is a musical based on Shakespeare's play *Romeo and Juliet*.

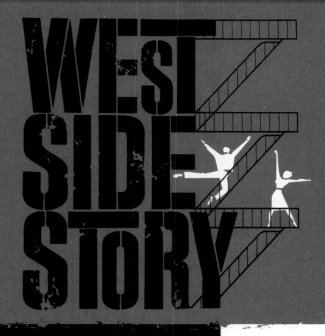

WEST SIDE STORY

by Ernest Lehman

Film logo, 1961. Saul Bass. © Pictorial Press Ltd / Alamy.

In ***West Side Story***, Maria is the sister of gang leader Bernardo. She falls in love with Tony, who is from a rival gang. Tony and Maria's **resolution** to be together causes both gangs to hate each other even more, so Maria and Tony are forced to make a **mature** decision. They must try to heal the **fractured** relationship between the gangs and bring peace before it is too late. Instead of a balcony, this scene takes place on a fire escape among **dense** apartment buildings.

[*Maria HEARS A VOICE calling to her from outside her open window, which leads to a fire escape.*]

54. EXT. BACK ALLEY AND FIRE ESCAPE

[*Tony is standing in the alley, looking about, not sure which window is Maria's.*]

TONY. [*calling*] Maria …

[*She appears on the fire escape, moves forward, sees Tony.*]

Interact with the Text

1. Screenplay
The script for a screenplay is similar to the script for a stage play. On this page, circle a stage direction that tells how a character should move and a stage direction that tells how a character should speak. What do you see on this page that identifies this as the script for a screenplay?

Possible response: The reference 54. EXT. BACK ALLEY AND FIRE ESCAPE identifies this as a camera shot in a movie scene.

2. Relate to Source
Reread the text to the left of the script. In a sentence or two, summarize how the plots of *West Side Story* and *Romeo and Juliet* are similar.

Possible response: Both stories tell of young people who come from enemy groups and yet, at great risk, fall in love.

Key Vocabulary

resolution *n.*, strong decision to do or not do something
- **mature** *adj.*, fully developed, grown-up, adult
fractured *adj.*, broken
dense *adj.*, closely crowded together, thick

Technical Background
Screenplays are scripts for movies. Like scripts for plays, screenplays include dialogue, stage directions, and scenes. Each new scene begins with a number and a description of the scene's location. "EXT." stands for "EXTERIOR," meaning that the scene takes place outdoors.

Interact with the Text

3. Interpret

Highlight three words in the dialogue, before Maria's father speaks, that refer to time. What do these words suggest about the love that Tony and Maria feel?

Possible response: It is a

love that will never end.

4. Form Mental Images

How do the stage directions help you form a mental image of Tony's movements? Underline the stage directions that help you form this mental image.

Possible response: I

picture Tony climbing

the fire escape to reach

Maria.

MARIA. Quiet! If Bernardo—

TONY. Come down.

MARIA. [*turning*] My father and mother will wake up—

TONY. Just for a minute.

MARIA. [*smiles*] A minute is not enough.

TONY. [*smiles*] For an hour, then.

MARIA. I cannot.

TONY. Forever.

MARIA'S FATHER'S VOICE. [*from the apartment*] Maria?

MARIA. [*turning*] ***Momentito***, Papa… [*to Tony*] Now see what you've done …

TONY. [*climbing up*] ***Momentito***, Maria.

55. CLOSER ANGLE - THE FIRE ESCAPE

MARIA. ***Callate!*** [*She reaches out her hand to stop him.*]

TONY. [*grabbing her hand*] [*He is at her side now.*]

MARIA. It is dangerous. If Bernardo knew—

TONY. We'll *let* him know. I am not "one of them," Maria.

MARIA. But you are not one of *us*, and I am not one of you.

TONY. To me, you're all the beautiful—

From the film West Side Story, 1961. Getty Images

In Other Words
Momentito One moment (in Spanish)
Callate! Be quiet! (in Spanish)

Historical Background
West Side Story had its first success in 1957 as a Broadway musical play. In 1961, it was released as a film starring Richard Beymar (as Tony) and Natalie Wood (as Maria). This excerpt is illustrated with images from that film.

[*She covers his mouth with her hand as:*]

MARIA'S FATHER'S VOICE. *Maruca!*

MARIA. *Si, yo vengo*, Papa.

[*They move towards the farther side of the fire escape, away from the window.*]

TONY. *Maruca?*

MARIA. His pet name for me.

TONY. I like him. He'll like me.

MARIA. No. He is like Bernardo: afraid. [*suddenly laughing*] Imagine being afraid of you!

TONY. Ya see?

From the film *West Side Story*, 1961. © John Springer Collection/ CORBIS

MARIA. [*touching his face*] I see you.

TONY. See only me.

MARIA. [*sings*] Only you, you're
the only thing I'll see forever.
In my eyes, in my words and
in everything I do,
Nothing else but you
Ever!

TONY. [*sings*] And there's
nothing for me but Maria,
Every sight that I see is Maria.
Always you, every thought
I'll ever know,
Everywhere I go, you'll be.

MARIA. All the world is only you
and me!

[*And now, through "special effects," the buildings, the sky, the very night seems to take on a magical quality.*]

TONY. Tonight, tonight,
It all began tonight,
I saw you and the world
went away.

MARIA. Tonight, tonight,
There's only you tonight,
What you are, what you do,
what you say.

In Other Words
Si, yo vengo Yes, I'm coming (in Spanish)

7. Relate to Source

Highlight Tony's response to Maria's warning that he should leave. How does this response remind you of Romeo?

Possible response: Both

characters feel that their

love drives away any fear.

TONY. Today, all day I had the feeling
A miracle would happen—
I know now I was right.

BOTH. For here you are
And what was just a
world is a star
Tonight!

[*As the scene fades back to "reality":*]

MARIA'S FATHER'S VOICE. [*from inside*] Maruca!

MARIA. I cannot stay. Go quickly!

TONY. I'm not afraid.

MARIA. Please.

TONY. [*kissing her*] Good night.

MARIA. *Buenas noches.*

TONY. I love you.

MARIA. Yes, yes. Hurry. ❖

Selection Review West Side Story

A. Find an example of a mental image in one of the texts. Write the example. Then complete the chart. *Answers will vary. Possible responses are shown.*

Detail:	Tony and Maria sing that their world has become "a star / Tonight."
Similar detail in other source:	Romeo says that "Juliet is the sun" and that her eyes are like stars.
How details are related:	In both relationships, love is described in terms of the heavens.
Idea that the details express:	Love has the power to make the loved one—and the world—seem more glorious than real life.

B. Answer the questions.

1. How did mental images help you understand some of the ideas in *West Side Story*?

The mental images helped me understand how Tony and Maria feel about each other. Because of that, I had a better understanding of what the screenplay is expressing about the power of love.

2. What do these characters from *West Side Story* care about and respect?

It seems that Tony and Maria care about and respect each other more than anything else. Maria shows some respect for her father, but it is not as important to her as is her sudden love for Tony.

Reflect and Assess

▶ **Romeo and Juliet**
▶ **West Side Story**

WRITING: Write About Literature

A. Plan your writing. The play and the screenplay are both written as scripts, but they have distinct and different styles. Find three examples of each selection's style, focusing on lines about love.   *Answers will vary.*

Romeo and Juliet	West Side Story
1. "Or, if thou wilt not, be but sworn my love, / And I'll no longer be a Capulet."	1. "Only you, you're the only thing I'll see forever. / In my eyes, in my words and in everything I do, / Nothing else but you / Ever!"

B. Which style speaks more clearly and sincerely of love to you? Write a brief literary response. Evaluate the distinct styles of the selections. Use text details to explain your reasoning.

Students should support their answers with examples from both selections.

_____

_____

_____

_____

_____

_____

_____

_____

_____

LITERARY ANALYSIS: Parody

A **parody** is a humorous work that imitates a more serious work. The words
and images in a parody mock the style of the original.

A. Read the texts below. Then answer the question.

Text 1: And there's nothing for me but Maria,
     Every sight that I see is Maria.
     Always you, every thought I'll ever know,
     Everywhere I go, you'll be.

Text 2: And there's nothing I love more than pizza,
     Every meal that I eat could be pizza.
     It has cheese, and red sauce on hearth-baked dough—
     When it's there, I know—I'll eat!

Why is the second text a parody of the first text?

The second text is a humorous imitation of the first one. Both have a similar style, but the second one alters

words and images to poke fun at the meaning of "true love."

B. Many writers have written parodies of the balcony scene in "Romeo and
Juliet." Change each element in the chart below to make it a parody.

Element	Parody
Title	"Ben and Nancy"
Balcony	Diving board
Rival families	Rival schools
Dialogue: "O Romeo, Romeo, wherefore art thou, Romeo?"	"Ben, Ben, where are you, Ben?"

C. Write a short parody of the balcony scene in "Romeo and Juliet." Use the
parodied elements from the chart above in your parody.

Answers will vary.

_____

_____

_____

_____

VOCABULARY STUDY: Figurative Language (Simile)

One kind of figurative language is called a **simile**. A simile compares two unlike things using the words *like* or *as*. *Answers will vary. Possible responses are shown.*

   Example: She was as cold as ice.

A. Determine the meaning of the simile in each sentence.

Sentence	Meaning of Simile
His smile was as wide as the ocean.	His smile was very large.
The wind roared like an express train.	The wind was loud and powerful.
These jewels shine like drops of dew.	The jewels are shiny and clear.
Her new dog is as dark as night.	The woman's dog is very dark in color.

B. Complete each simile with an appropriate word or phrase.

   1. My new pajamas are as soft as a bunny's fur.

   2. The Olympic athlete swam like a fish.

   3. At the parade, the confetti came down like rain.

   4. This lawn is as scratchy as a wool blanket.

   5. The dog's barking is like nails on a chalkboard.

C. Write a sentence that contains a simile about each topic below.

   1. Topic: homework

   Homework is as painful as getting a shot at the doctor's office.

   2. Topic: the month of May

   The month of May is like a pillow of roses.

   3. Topic: the Sahara Desert

   The Sahara Desert is as hot as the sun.

   4. Topic: biting into a crisp, green apple

   Biting into a crisp, green apple is like tasting heaven.

   5. Topic: yourself

   I am as friendly as a python.

Prepare to Read

▶ **Poems for the Earth**
▶ **I Was Born Today/Touching the Earth**

Key Vocabulary

A. How well do you know these words? Circle a rating for each word. Check your understanding of each word by circling *yes* or *no*. Then provide an example for each word. If you are unsure of a word's meaning, refer to the Vocabulary Glossary, page 926, in your student text.

Rating Scale

1	I have never seen this word before.
2	I am not sure of the word's meaning.
3	I know this word and can teach the word's meaning to someone else.

Key Word	Check Your Understanding	Deepen Your Understanding
1 commercial (ku-**mur**-shul) *adjective* **Rating:** 1 2 3	**Commercial** buildings are usually warm and inviting. Yes (**No**)	Example: _Possible response: an office building_
2 endure (in-**dyūr**) *verb* **Rating:** 1 2 3	People who explore the North Pole must **endure** extremely cold weather. (**Yes**) No	Example: _Possible response: a serious illness_
3 essence (**e**-sens) *noun* **Rating:** 1 2 3	The seeds are the **essence** of a good orange. Yes (**No**)	Example: _Possible response: the most important part of a book_
4 industrial (in-**dus**-trē-ul) *adjective* **Rating:** 1 2 3	Many large companies manufacture their products in **industrial** buildings. (**Yes**) No	Example: _Possible response: factories and power plants_

Key Word	Check Your Understanding	Deepen Your Understanding
5 perish (**pair**-ish) *verb* **Rating:** 1 2 3	Water pollution can cause fish to **perish**. (Yes) No	Example: _Possible response: flowers dying after a_ frost
6 resolve (ri-**zolv**) *noun* **Rating:** 1 2 3	If you have **resolve**, you give up easily. Yes (No)	Example: _Possible response: deciding to exercise_ more regularly
7 suffice (su-**fīs**) *verb* **Rating:** 1 2 3	If you are very hungry, a small amount of food will **suffice**. Yes (No)	Example: _Possible response: be enough to satisfy_ or meet a need
8 tremulous (**trem**-yu-lus) *adjective* **Rating:** 1 2 3	A **tremulous** animal is mean and dangerous. Yes (No)	Example: _Possible response: a stray puppy_

B. Use one of the Key Vocabulary words to write about a way you take care of the earth.

Answers will vary.

Before Reading Poems for the Earth

LITERARY ANALYSIS: Compare Representations: Poetry and Art

Poets and other writers represent subjects through the **medium of words**, but painters and other artists represent subjects through **visual media**. Poets and painters make choices about which details to include and how to present them. As a result, even when representing the same subject, the work of a poet and the work of a painter may have very different effects.

A. Read the passage below and study the painting. Circle one detail from the poem that also is represented in the painting. *Answers will vary. Possible responses are shown.*

> **Look Into the Text**
>
> I say feed me.
> She serves (red prickly pear) on a
> spiked cactus.
> I say tease me.
> She sprinkles raindrops in my face.

Orange Light on the Four Peaks, 2003, Stephen Morath. Acrylic on canvas, collection of the artist.

B. Answer the questions.

1. The painter represents many varieties of cacti. Why do you think the poet includes only one?

The poet wants to represent many things that she gets from the desert; fruit of the cactus is only one of those

things. The painter may find the cacti more important than anything else in the scene.

2. In these lines, the poet represents the desert as if it were a person. Later, she ends the poem by calling the desert "strong mother." Do you think that the painter represents the desert in that way? Why or why not?

The painter represents the desert differently. He includes images that suggest beauty (such as the sunset),

richness (such as the many colors and the abundant plant life), and strength or age (such as the mountains),

but the scene does not suggest that the desert has a human-like personality or wants to interact with humans.

FOCUS STRATEGY: Form Sensory Images

HOW TO FORM SENSORY IMAGES

Focus Strategy

1. **Look for details** that appeal to your senses.

2. **Use your imagination** and your own experience to create sensory images.

A. Read the passage. Use the strategies above to form sensory images as you read. Then respond to the text and complete the chart.

Look Into the Text

> I say feed me.
> She serves red (prickly pear) on a (spiked cactus.)
>
> I say tease me.
> She sprinkles (raindrops) in my face.
>
> I say frighten me.
> She (shouts thunder, flashes lightning.)

My Response to the Text	
I see... red prickly pear, flashes of lightning	**I taste...** prickly pear, raindrops
I hear... thunder	**I feel...** spiked cactus, raindrops on my face
I smell... prickly pear, wet ground	

1. What do you visualize as you read?

   Possible response: I see the earth giving the poet fruit, rain, and lightning. I picture a loud thunderstorm. I feel the rain on my face.

2. How does forming sensory images help you understand the poem?

   Possible response: The sensory images I create help me feel what the poet feels. I know what rain feels like and what thunder sounds like, so I can relate to the poet's ideas.

B. Return to the passage above. Circle the words or phrases that helped you answer the first question.

Selection Review Poems for the Earth

EQ **What Deserves Our Care and Respect?**
Examine how well people treat the earth.

A. In "Poems for the Earth," four poets describe the relationship between nature and humans. Complete the chart with examples of sensory images that helped you understand this relationship.

Mi Madre	Hard Questions
"She strokes my skin with her warm breath."	"Mark out the land / into neat rectangles / squares and clover leafs?"
"She endures: glaring heat / numbing cold / frightening dryness."	Does not the thought need / something / to rest upon / not self-made by man, / a bosom / not his own?

There Will Come Soft Rains	Fire and Ice
"Robins will wear their feathery fire"	"Some say the world will end in fire, / Some say in ice."
"And Spring herself, when she woke at dawn, / Would scarcely know that we were gone."	"But if it had to perish twice, / I think I know enough of hate"

B. Use the information in the chart to answer the questions.

1. How do the sensory images help you understand the poems? How do the poets think humans treat the earth?

   Possible response: The images help me see and feel how people treat the earth and how the earth treats people. People do not always treat the earth with respect. They pollute it and destroy it to build houses and roads.

2. Based upon what you have read, what is the essence of nature? Use **essence** in your answer.

   Possible response: The essence of nature is that it nourishes and provides for itself and for us.

3. What do these poems help you realize about the earth?

   Possible response: "Mi Madre" and "Hard Questions" help me realize the earth's beauty and how much we need it, while the other two poems make me think of nature's power over us.

Connect Across Texts

In the last section, four poets commented on the tension between humankind and nature. Read the following poem and the essay passage to see another side of the bond between Earth and us.

I Was Born Today

by Amado Nervo

Every day that dawns, you must say to
    yourself,
"I was born today!
The world is new to me.
5 This light that I behold
Strikes my unclouded eyes for the
    first time;
The rain that scatters its crystal drops
Is my baptism!

10 "Then let us live a pure life,
A shining life!
Already, yesterday is lost. Was it bad?
    Was it beautiful?
. . . Let it be forgotten.
15 And of that yesterday let there remain
    only the essence,
The precious gold of what I loved
    and suffered
As I walk along the road . . .

Light Spark, 2003, Johannes Seewald. Photography, collection of the artist.

▲ Critical Viewing: Design In what sense does this photograph represent an idea in the first two stanzas of the poem?

Key Vocabulary
essence *n.*, quality that determines someone or something's character

In Other Words
my baptism a new beginning

1. Structure and Style
Underline two lines on page 303 that reveal the form of the poem. Why do you think the poet uses this form?

Possible response: The

poet sees each day as

fresh and new as if he were

just born. The form mimics

this idea because it is

informal and unstructured.

2. Form Sensory Images
Underline the words in lines 20–27 that help you form sensory images. What images do you picture in your mind?

Possible response: I think

of how I feel during holidays

and how happy I am to be

with my family and friends.

I imagine eating and

drinking and laughing as

we share stories.

3. Structure and Style
Circle the words or phrases in lines 28–36 that repeat. How does this repetition add to the meaning of the poem?

Possible response:

With repetition, the poet

emphasizes what people

give to the world and

what they take from it.

20 "Today, every moment shall bring
   feelings of well being and cheer.
And the reason for my existence.
My most urgent resolve
Will be to spread happiness all over
25   the world,
To pour the wine of goodness into the
   eager mouths around me . . .

"My only peace will be the peace of others;
Their dreams, my dreams;
30 Their joy, my joy;
My crystal tear,
The tear that trembles on the eyelash
   of another;
My heartbeat,
35 The beat of every heart that throbs
Throughout worlds without end!"

Every day that dawns, you must say to
   yourself,
"I was born today!"

About the Poet

Amado Nervo (1870–1919) is considered one of Mexico's most important and influential poets of the 19th and 20th centuries. Although he left the priesthood to become a writer, his poems are often spiritual and focus on living in a changing world. His wife's death inspired his most famous work, *La Amada Inmóvil (The Motionless One),* which was published in 1922.

Key Vocabulary
• **resolve** *n.,* determination to do something

In Other Words
for my existence that I am alive

Touching the Earth

by bell hooks

When we love the earth, we are able to love ourselves more fully. I believe this. The ancestors taught me it was so.

As a child I loved playing in dirt, in that rich Kentucky soil, that was a source of life. Before I understood anything about the pain and **exploitation** of the southern system of sharecropping, I understood that grown-up black folks loved the land. I could stand with my grandfather Daddy Jerry and look out at fields of growing vegetables, tomatoes, corn, collards, and know that this was his handiwork. I could see the look of pride on his face as I expressed wonder and awe at the magic of growing things.

I knew that my grandmother Baba's backyard garden would yield beans, sweet potatoes, cabbage, and yellow squash, that she too would walk with pride among the rows and rows of growing vegetables showing us what the earth will give when tended lovingly. ❖

Preparing Broad Beans, Felicity House. Pastel on paper, private collection, The Bridgeman Art Library.

▲ Critical Viewing: Design How do you think Baba would respond to this painting? Explain.

In Other Words
exploitation abuse

Historical Background
The system of **sharecropping** developed in the southern U.S. after the Civil War. Freed slaves farmed their former owners' land in exchange for a share of the crops. Many sharecroppers were treated poorly, and most lived in poverty, unable to buy their own land.

Interact with the Text

4. Interpret
The writer believes that when you love the earth, you can love yourself. Underline phrases that support her belief and explain how her grandfather loved the land and himself.

Possible response: Her grandfather nurtured his crops and was proud of the work he did. His pride and care show how much he loved and respected the land, himself, and his family.

5. Form Sensory Images
Circle the words that appeal to your senses. What do you see, hear, smell, taste, and feel? How do these images help you understand the essay?

Possible response: I see, smell, and taste the growing vegetables. I feel the woman's exhaustion and feel the hot sun on my face. I hear the wind rustling the leaves. I understand her satisfaction and pride.

6. Interpret
Underline the information that tells you why bell hooks decided to spell her pen name with lowercase letters. What can you conclude about how she sees her work?

Possible response: It

shows that she believes

her ideas are more

important than who

wrote them.

About the Writer

bell hooks's (1952–   ) real name is Gloria Watkins, but when she writes, she uses her great-grandmother's name. The author doesn't capitalize her pen name, hooks, because she <u>believes the ideas in her work are what are most important</u>. She is a poet, professor, and activist who explores how society views and treats African American women.

Selection Review   I Was Born Today/Touching the Earth

A. Choose one line from "I Was Born Today" or "Touching the Earth," and complete the chart.   *Answers will vary. Possible responses are shown.*

Line	Sensory Images
"As a child I loved playing in dirt, in that rich Kentucky soil, that was a source of life."	A child draws pictures in the dirt with a branch. I can smell the fresh dirt and see the brown color of the dirt. In the dirt I can see the colors of flowers and vegetables growing.

B. Answer the questions.

1. How did recognizing form or style help you understand what each writer was trying to say?

Nervo used free verse to express all his feelings in a way that would not fit a strict pattern. Hooks

wrote an essay to express her voice in an informal way, as if she were telling a friend about memories

of her family.

2. Now that you have read the selections, what do you think deserves your care and respect?

We need to protect the earth so it will continue to give us what we need.

Reflect and Assess

WRITING: Write About Literature

A. Plan your writing. Write quotes from the selections that illustrate how human beings treat the earth. *Answers will vary.*

Poems for the Earth	I Was Born Today/ Touching the Earth
"I say heal me. / She gives me manzanilla, orégano, dormilón."	"Already, yesterday is lost. Was it bad? / Was it beautiful?"

B. How important is the earth to human beings? Do we treat it with care and respect? Write a short essay analyzing human beings' treatment of the earth. Use quotations from the poems or the essay to illustrate your ideas.

Students should support their answers with examples from both selections.

_____

_____

_____

_____

_____

_____

_____

_____

_____

Integrate the Language Arts

LITERARY ANALYSIS: Rhythm and Line Length

A poem's **rhythm** comes from the pattern of strong and weak beats in each line, the **length of the line**, and how the line breaks. For example, "There Will Come Soft Rains" is written as a series of rhyming **couplets**, or pairs of lines.

A. Read the lines from "There Will Come Soft Rains" below. Underline the strongest beats in each line. Then answer the questions. *Answers will vary. Possible responses are shown.*

> Not <u>one</u> would <u>mind</u>, neither <u>bird</u> nor <u>tree</u>
> If <u>mankind</u> <u>perished</u> <u>utterly</u>;
>
> And <u>Spring</u> herself, when she <u>woke</u> at <u>dawn</u>,
> Would <u>scarcely</u> <u>know</u> that <u>we</u> were <u>gone</u>.

1. How do the beats you underlined reinforce the poem's meaning?

The beats emphasize important words. For example, many of the strong beats are on words that describe

nature. That reminds readers of nature's power, which is the point of the poem.

2. How would you describe the line breaks?

The line breaks seem natural, as if the poet is speaking.

B. Look at the same rhyming couplets that appear in Activity A. Write a one-sentence summary of each couplet in the chart below. *Answers will vary. Possible responses are shown.*

Couplet	Summary
1	The plants or the animals would not care if every human being vanished forever.
2	In fact, Spring wouldn't even know that anything had changed, because mankind does not matter compared to nature and the passing of the seasons.

C. Use what you wrote in Activity B to help you rewrite the rhyming couplets in free verse. (Remember that in free verse, line lengths vary and lines do not have to rhyme.) You can add, change, or delete words.

Answers will vary.

VOCABULARY STUDY: Figurative Language (Metaphor)

A **metaphor** is a kind of figurative language that compares two things without using *like* or *as*. Authors use metaphors to suggest how two unlike things are similar.

A. Mark an *X* in the chart to indicate whether or not the sentence is a metaphor.

Sentence	Metaphor	Not a Metaphor
I always tell my friend she has a heart of gold.	X	
Today the sun is bright and shining.		X
The trapeze artists soared through the air like a flock of birds.		X
This chocolate cake is heaven.	X	
His writing is a beam of light in the darkness.	X	

B. Identify the metaphor used in each sentence by listing each object compared in the chart.

Metaphor	Object 1	Object 2
The dirt of the earth is a bed to lie on.	the earth	a bed
The hallways are a maze.	hallways	maze
My love is a burning flame.	my love	a burning flame
That girl is a cool breeze.	girl	cool breeze

C. Rewrite each sentence from the chart above. Replace the metaphor with its literal meaning. *Answers will vary.*

1. _____

2. _____

3. _____

4. _____

Read for Understanding

1. Genre What kind of text are these two passages? How do you know?

Both are poems, based

on their form and

sensory appeal.

2. Topic Write a topic sentence to tell what each text is mostly about.

"Wild Geese" is about

a response to nature.

"Like You" is about

connections created by

nature.

Reread and Summarize

3. Key Ideas Circle three words or phrases that best express the key ideas in each section. Note why each word or phrase is important in the text.

· Section 1: "Wild Geese"
· Section 2: "Like You"

4. Summary Use your topic sentence and notes from item 3 to write a summary of each selection.

Possible response: "Wild

Geese": Find your place

in the natural world and

be imaginative. "Like

You": If you struggle,

realize that nature and

poetry connect everyone.

Wild Geese

by Mary Oliver

You do not have to be good.
You do not have to walk on your knees
for a hundred miles through the desert, repenting.
You only have to let the soft animal of your body
5   love what it loves.
Tell me about despair, yours, and I will tell you mine.
Meanwhile the world goes on.
Meanwhile the sun and the clear pebbles of the rain
are moving across the landscapes,
10   over the prairies and deep trees,
the mountains and the rivers.
Meanwhile the wild geese, high in the clean blue air,
are heading home again.
Whoever you are, no matter how lonely,
15   the world offers itself to your imagination,
calls to you like the wild geese, harsh and exciting—
over and over announcing your place
in the family of things.

In Other Words
repenting feeling sorry, regretting
despair sadness, hopelessness

Arbol con Luces 1, Judy Paul. Mixed media on birch panel.

Like You

by Roque Dalton
translated by Jack Hirschman

Like you I
love love, life, the sweet smell
of things, the sky-blue
landscape of January days.

5 And my blood boils up
and I laugh through eyes
that have known the buds of tears.

I believe the world is beautiful
and that poetry, like bread, is for everyone.

10 And that my veins don't end in me
but in the unanimous blood
of those who struggle for life,
love,
little things,
15 landscape and bread,
the poetry of everyone.

In Other Words
unanimous shared

Reread and Analyze

5. Style   Reread lines 1–5 in "Wild Geese" and lines 1–8 in "Like You." Highlight words and phrases that help you visualize the poets' ideas. Explain your choices.

Possible response: In "Wild Geese," the poet uses "soft animal of your body" to help reinforce the idea that we are part of the natural world. In "Like You," "life" and "sky-blue landscape" liken life to nature.

6. Style   Find more words and phrases that help you visualize the poets' ideas. What do these words and phrases tell you about how the poets feel about nature?

Answers will vary.

7. Representations in Poetry and Art   Compare the poems to the painting. What ideas do both the poems and the painting convey? What ideas found in the poems are absent in the painting?

Answers will vary.

CLOSE READING "Wild Geese" / "Like You"

Discuss

8. **Synthesize** With the class, revisit these poems. Together, list some of the words and phrases that the poets use to express their ideas. Discuss how these words and phrases help you visualize the poets' ideas. *Answers will vary. Possible responses are shown below.*

Poem	Word or Phrase	Idea That I Visualize
"Wild Geese"	*walk on your knees (line 2)*	*discomfort or pain, connected with praying*
"Like You"	*Like you I / love love, life, . . . (lines 1–2)*	*giving life a big hug*

Then, with the class, discuss how each poet's style helps his audience visualize his ideas. Make notes.

Answers will vary but should include examples of words and phrases with a strong sensory appeal as well

as repeated sounds, words, and phrases. Students may suggest that it is easier to remember ideas that are

expressed in a way that the senses—not just the intellect—can grasp.

9. **Write** Use your notes from question 8 to write about how these two poets use structure and style to express ideas relating to nature. Use the questions below to organize your thoughts.

> · What does Oliver see as the relationship between people and nature? How is Dalton's viewpoint similar or different?
>
> · Which word choices appeal to your senses?
>
> · What pictures form in your mind as you read? What ideas do those pictures express?
>
> · How well do Oliver and Dalton put forward images to make their ideas memorable?

Answers will vary but should show how students have carried forward their thinking from item 8.

_____

_____

_____

_____

_____

_____

_____

Connect with the **EQ**   What Deserves Our Care and Respect?

Consider the things that all people share.

10. **Viewpoint** Do Oliver and Dalton feel that there are people, objects, or ideas that we should take care of and respect? What details in "Wild Geese" and "Like You" lead you to that answer?

Answers will vary. Responses should include evidence from the text to support students' analysis.

11. **Theme** What is each poet's message about what deserves our care and respect?

Answers will vary. Responses should include evidence from the text to support students' analysis.

Unit 7

Key Vocabulary Review

A. Use these words to complete the paragraph.

envious   fractured   infuriate   resolve

feud   impudently   resolution

Jill and I behaved __impudently__ (1) toward each other for years. The way she acted would __infuriate__ (2) me, but in truth I was __envious__ (3) of her. Then one day she came to school with a __fractured__ (4) leg, and she couldn't walk. After that, I found the inner __resolve__ (5) to end our __feud__ (6). My new __resolution__ (7) is to treat everyone with respect.

B. Use your own words to write what each Key Vocabulary word means. Then write a synonym and an antonym for each word. *Answers will vary. Possible responses are shown.*

Key Word	My Definition	Synonym	Antonym
1. dense	crowded or compact	thick	bare
2. destitute	poor, without money	penniless	rich
3. mature	fully developed	grown-up	childish
4. perfection	the state of being the best	excellence	imperfection
5. perish	to die	expire	survive
6. respectably	tolerantly or graciously	courteously	rudely
7. traditional	conventional and established	time-honored	innovative
8. tremulous	fearful and hesitant	timid	confident

Unit 7 Key Vocabulary

• attitude	destitute	feud	infuriate	prophecy	suffice
commercial	endure	fractured	• mature	resolution	• traditional
• compensate	envious	impudently	perfection	• resolve	tremulous
dense	essence	industrial	perish	respectably	

• **Academic Vocabulary**

C. Answer the questions using complete sentences. *Answers will vary. Possible responses are shown.*

1. How would you describe the **essence** of your personality?

   I am free-spirited and generous to the people I care about.

2. Name three items that are produced in **industrial** buildings.

   Cars, airplanes, and refrigerators are produced in industrial buildings.

3. Describe your **attitude** toward athletics.

   Athletics helps teens learn teamwork.

4. What is one thing you think will continue to **endure** for a long time?

   I think the pyramids in Egypt will endure for a long time.

5. Describe a **prophecy** you would be happy to hear.

   I would be happy to hear that cancer would be curable by the year 2020.

6. How much would you **compensate** someone for cleaning your room?

   I would pay someone $5.

7. When you are very hungry, what type of meal will **suffice**?

   A hamburger and fries will suffice.

8. What types of businesses could you find in the **commercial** district of a city?

   You could find clothing stores, real estate agents, and restaurants.

Acknowledgments

Alfred Publishing Co., Inc.: "Strength, Courage and Wisdom," words and music by India Arie © 2006 WB Music Corp. and Gold & Iron Music Publishing. Lyrics recorded by permission of Alfred Publishing Co., Inc. All Rights Reserved.

The Atlanta-Journal Constitution: "Stall Teen Motorists" by Maureen Downey from *The Atlanta Journal-Constitution*, April 24, 2006. Copyright © 2006 by The Atlanta Journal-Constitution. Recorded with permission from The Atlanta Journal-Constitution.

Arte Publico Press: "Mi Madre" by Pat Mora from *Chants*. Copyright © 1985 by Pat Mora. Recorded with permission by Arte Público Press-University of Houston.

Fred Bayles: "Drivers Ed, Not Age, Is Key to Road Safety" by Fred Bayles from *The Boston Globe*, March 30, 2006. Copyright © 2006 by Fred Bayles. Recorded by permission of Fred Bayles.

Jay Bennett: "My Brother's Keeper" by Jay Bennett from *From One Experience to Another*. Copyright © by Jay Bennett. Recorded by permission of the author.

Susan Bergholz Literary Services: "My English" by Julia Alvarez from *Something to Declare*, published by Plume, an imprint of Penguin Group (USA), in 1999 and in hardcover by Algonquin Books of Chapel Hill. Originally published by Brujulla/Compass, fall, 1992. Copyright © 1998 by Julia Alvarez. Recorded by permission of Susan Bergholz Literary Services, New York. All rights reserved.

Black Enterprise Magazine: "My Moment of Truth" by Caroline V. Clarke and Sonja D. Brown, July 2003 issue of Black Enterprise. Reprinted by permission.

George Braziller: "The Hand of Fatima" from *Figs and Fate: Stories about Growing Up in the Arab World Today* by Elsa Marston. Copyright © by Elsa Marston. Recorded by permission of George Braziller.

Caxton Printers: "Say It with Flowers" by Toshio Mori in *Yokohama, California*. Copyright © 1949 by the Caxton Printers, Ltd. Used by permission.

Sandra Dijkstra Agency and Amy Tan: "Two Kinds" by Amy Tan from *The Joy Luck Club*. Copyright © 1989 by Amy Tan. Reprinted by permission of and the Sandra Dijkstra Literary Agency and the author.

Gregory Djanikian: "How I Learned English" from *Falling Deeply Into America* by Gregory Djanikian. Copyright © 1984 by Gregory Djanikian. Recorded by permission of the author.

Mary Duenwald: "The Physiology of...Facial Expressions" by Mary Duenwald from *Discover*, June 2005. Copyright © 2005 by Mary Duenwald. Used by permission of the author.

Fitzhenry & Whiteside Publishers: "Be-ers and Doers" from *The Leaving* by Budge Wilson. Text copyright © 1990 by Budge Wilson. Reprinted by permission of Fitzhenry & Whiteside Publishers.

Grove/Atlantic: "The Journey" from *Dream Work* by Mary Oliver. Copyright © 1986 by Mary Oliver. Reprinted by permission of Grove/Atlantic.

Erin Gruwell Education Project: "The Freedom Writers Diary. Used by permission of Freedom Writers Foundation and Erin Gruwell.

HarperCollins Publishers: Excerpts from *Black Boy* BLACK by Richard Wright. Copyright 1937, 1942, 1944, 1945 by Richard Wright; renewed © 1973 by Ellen Wright. Used by permissions of HarperCollins Publishers.

Hewitt Associates: "Success is a Mind Set" from *Hewitt*, October 2005. Used with permission of Hewitt Associates LLC.

Barbara Kouts Agency: "Skins" by Joseph Bruchac from *Face Relations*. Copyright © 2004 by Joseph Bruchac. Reprinted by permission of Barbara Kouts Literary Agency.

Hal Leonard: "Lean on Me" by Bill Withers. Copyright © 1972, renewed Interior Music Corporation. Used by Permission of the Hal Leonard Corp. All Rights Reserved.

Little, Brown and Co. Inc.: Excerpt from *Long Walk to Freedom* by Nelson Mandela. Copyright © 1994, 1995 by Nelson Rolihlahla Mandela. Used by permission of Little, Brown and Co., Inc.

M. E. Sharpe: "The Woman Who Was Death" by Josepha Sherman from *Mythology for Storytellers*. Copyright © 2003 by M. E. Sharpe. Used by permission of M. E. Sharpe.

Northwestern University Press: "Like You" by Roque Dalton, from *Poetry Like Bread: Poets of the Political Imagination*, edited by Martin Espada, translated by Jack Hirschman. Copyright © 2000, Curbstone Press. Used by permission of Northwestern University Press.

Naomi Shihab Nye: "Remembered" by Naomi Shihab Nye from *Words Under Words*. Copyright © 2006 by Naomi Shihab Nye. Used by permission of the author.

Oxford University Press: Excerpt from *Txting: The GR8 DB8* by David Crystal. Copyright © 2008 by David Crystal. Used by permission of Oxford University Press.

Penguin Group: "Two Kinds," from *The Joy Luck Club* by Amy Tan. Copyright © 1989 by Amy Tan. Used by permission of G.P. Putnam's Sons, a division of Penguin Group (USA) Inc.

Gerald M. Pomper: From "What price loyalty?" by Gerald M. Pomper from the *Star-Ledger*, August 14, 2005. Copyright © 2005 by Gerald M. Pomper. Gerald M. Pomper is Board of Governors Professor of Political Science (Emeritus) at Rutgers University and author of *On Ordinary Heroes and American Democracy*. published by Paradigm Publishers. Used by permission.

Random House: "Breaking the Ice," by Dave Barry from *Dave Barry is Not Making This Up*. Copyright © 1994 by Dave Barry. Used by permission of Crown Publishers, a division of Random House, Inc.

Excerpt from *the Freedom Writers Diary* by the Freedom Writers with Erin Gruwell. Copyright © 1999 by the Tolerance Education Foundation. Used by permission of Freedom Writers Foundation and Erin Gruwell, and by permission of Doubleday, a division of Random House, Inc.

"The Moustache" from *8 Plus 1: Stories by Robert Cormier* by Robert Cormier Copyright ©1980 by Robert Cormier. Used by permission of Random House, Inc.

Excerpt from *My Left Foot* by Christy Brown, published by Secker & Warburg. Reprinted by permission of The Random House Group Ltd.

"Nicole" from *Sugar in the Raw: Voices of Young Black Girls in America* by Rebecca Carroll. Copyright © 1997 by Rebecca Carroll. Used by permission of Clarkson Potter/Publishers, a division of Random House, Inc. and Meredith Bernstein Literary Agency, Inc.

San Francisco Chronicle: "Images of foster life: Teenagers express what it's like to be raised by someone else's parents" by Joshunda Sanders from the *San Francisco Chronicle*, April 18, 2004. Copyright © by the San Francisco Chronicle. Reprinted by permission.

Scholastic: "Can Some People Read Minds?" by Dr. Bruce Perry from *Science World*, September 2000. Copyright © 2000 by Scholastic Inc. By permission of Scholastic Inc.

"Old Ways, New World" by Joseph Berger from the *New York Times Upfront*, January 10, 2005. Copyright © 2005 by Scholastic Inc. and the New York Times. By permission of Scholastic Inc.

"Rules of the Road" by Lynn Lucia from *Scholastic Choices*, September 2001. Copyright © 2001 by Scholastic Inc. By permission of Scholastic Inc.

Tom Seligson: "They Speak for Success" by Tom Seligson. Copyright © 2005 Tom Seligson. Initially published in Parade Magazine. All rights reserved. Reprinted by permission.

Charlotte Sheedy Literary Agency: "Wild Geese" by Mary Oliver, Copyright © 1986 by Mary Oliver. Used by permission of the Charlotte Sheedy Literary Agency.

Simon & Schuster: "There Will Come Soft Rains" reprinted with the permission of Scribner, an imprint of Simon & Schuster Adult Publishing Group from THE COLLECTED POEMS OF SARA TEASDALE by Sara Teasdale. (New York, Macmillan, 1937) and The Estate of Sara Teasdale.

South End Press: "Touching the Earth" by bell hooks from *Sisters of the Yam: Black Women and Self-Recovery*. Copyright © 1993 by Gloria Watkins. Reprinted by permission of South End Press and Between the Lines.

Piri Thomas: "Amigo Brothers" from *Stories from El Barrio* by Piri Thomas. Reprinted by permission of Piri Thomas.

Margaret Tsuda: "Hard Questions" by Margaret Tsuda from *The Living Wilderness*, Autumn 1970. Reprinted by permission of the author.

Universal Press Syndicate: "Doonsbury" by G. B. Trudeau. Copyright © 2002 by G. B. Trudeau. Reprinted with permission of UNIVERSAL PRESS SYNDICATE. All rights reserved.

Sharon Wootton: "Novel Musicians" by Sharon Wootton from the *Daily Herald*, April 18, 2003. Reprinted by permission of Sharon Wootton.

Donald A. Yates: "Just Lather, That's All" by Hernando Tellez from *Great Spanish Short Stories*. Copyright © 1962 by Donald A. Yates. Reprinted by permission of Donald A. Yates.